ALBERT EINSTEIN:
PHILOSOPHER-SCIENTIST

Karsh, Ottawa

A. Einstein.

ALBERT EINSTEIN:

Philosopher-Scientist

VOLUME II

Edited by

PAUL ARTHUR SCHILPP

NORTHWESTERN UNIVERSITY

HARPER TORCHBOOKS / Science Library

HARPER & BROTHERS PUBLISHERS

New York

CONTENTS

PREFACE

THE contents of this volume speak eloquently enough for the inclusion of *Albert Einstein: Philosopher-Scientist* in this series without any superfluous words from the editor.

Almost all of the matters which need to be mentioned here are of the nature of personal privilege.

There is, first of all, the matter of gratitude for help and co-operation. Foremost here stands Professor Einstein himself. Without his consent and willingness to co-operate, this book could never have appeared. But, how to express the editor's thanks and appreciation to him—in the coldness of mere words —this is something I know not how to do. Perhaps he will understand if I state simply that my obligation and gratitude to him are beyond the possibility of verbal expression.

Among the twenty-five other contributors to this volume there are no less than six Nobel-Prize winners in science; and essays have come from as many as eleven countries (viz., Australia, Belgium, Canada, Denmark, England, France, Germany, Ireland, Scotland, Switzerland, and the U.S.A.); an essay for this volume had also been promised by a leading scientist of the U.S.S.R. (although it has not yet actually reached the editor). The editor is as deeply and sincerely obligated to these important and busy scholars the world around as he is to Professor Einstein.

It proved impossible to bring out this volume at the time originally planned. It had been hoped to lay it on Professor Einstein's birthday-table on March 14th last, on the occasion of his seventieth birthday. No one regrets this delay in publication more than does the editor.

Other regrets are no less poignant. It was a tragedy of no mean importance that Max Planck was already too seriously ill, at the time of the conception of this volume, for him to

be able to contribute an essay. Nor has the editor recovered
from the sadness caused by Professor Hermann Weyl's inability
to carry out his original promise to write for this book.

Three other scholars (from as many countries) finally failed
to redeem their pledges given to the editor. In the case of
one of these it is at least conceivable that the reason for the
failure of his essay to reach us may not have lain with himself.
In any case, it is regrettable that the *Library of Living Philosophers* is thus deprived from giving those essays to its
interested readers. We can merely assure these readers that no
stone was left unturned to secure the essays.

All these regrets are compensated for, however, by our
being able to present here Professor Einstein's one and only
intellectual autobiography.

Everyone who knows Professor Einstein personally is all
too well aware of his extreme shyness and his honest and
forthright humility. I do not believe that there would have
been one chance in ten thousand that the world would ever
have secured an autobiography from the hand of Professor
Einstein, if the unique nature of the *Library of Living Philosophers* had not finally convinced him of the worth-while-
ness and significance of such an "obituary," as he calls his
autobiography.

Einstein's "Autobiographical Notes" in themselves assure,
therefore, the unique importance of this volume.

In a kindred category stands Professor Niels Bohr's "Discussion with Einstein,"—an essay, not merely delightfully
written but of the utmost and lasting importance in its content.
These recollections of conversations with Einstein on the
epistemological aspects of physical science would never have
come into being, were it not for the peculiar nature of this
series.

One could go on in this fashion. How can one adequately
praise the care, precision, directness, and beauty of Professor
Einstein's "Reply" (or "Remarks," as he calls them) to his
commentators and critics!

There are, however, still other persons whose kindness or
aid have helped to enhance the value or increase the beauty and

correctness of this book. Professor Peter G. Bergmann, of the physics department of Syracuse University, spared neither time nor effort in helping to put Professor von Laue's paper into the same adequate and beautiful form in English as the author himself had used in his original German manuscript. Professor Arnold J. F. Siegert, of the physics department of Northwestern University, carefully checked and corrected—especially the technically scientific aspects of—my own translations of both Einstein essays. Mr. Forrest W. Williams, of Northwestern University, very kindly and ably translated the de Broglie and Bachelard essays.

Mere words of gratitude are also quite inadequate to express the editor's appreciation of the wonderfully careful and exacting work accomplished by the bibliographer of Professor Einstein's published works. Long before the present volume got under way, Miss Margaret C. Shields, at that time Librarian of the Mathematics Library of Princeton University, had been at work gathering the data which have now gone into the Bibliography, which constitutes the important Part IV of the present volume. Her labors have been endless and her efforts almost excruciatingly painstaking. The result speaks for itself. Her exhaustive bibliography of the published work of Einstein will prove to be of inestimable value to scientists and scholars for centuries to come. The abiding knowledge of this fact will be a source of deeper satisfaction to Miss Shields than any words of thanks the editor could offer.

Messrs. Surindar Suri and Kenneth G. Halvorsen saved the editor the arduous and laborious task of providing this volume with its accurate and useful index. A host of other individuals contributed their assistance during various parts of the labor of reading proof and seeing the volume through the press. To all of these the editor says a most sincere and heart-felt, "Thank you."

The order in which the essays appear in Part II was determined, in general, by the order in which Professor Einstein chose to discuss the essays in his replying "Remarks." The only exceptions to this rule are those essays to which Dr. Einstein did not reply or which came in after his "Remarks" had been completed.

In reading and editing the contents of this volume, two possible sub-titles have come to the editor's mind again and again, namely (1) "The Scientific Battle of the Twentieth Century," and (2) "The Future of Physics." Viewed from either point of view, this book has been exciting reading, even to its editor. He may be permitted to express the hope, therefore, that the experience of other readers will be similar.

PAUL ARTHUR SCHILPP

DEPARTMENT OF PHILOSOPHY
NORTHWESTERN UNIVERSITY
EVANSTON, ILLINOIS

October 1, 1949

ACKNOWLEDGMENTS

Grateful Acknowledgment is hereby made to the authors, editors, and publishers of all of Professor Einstein's works as well as of any other books, quotations from which appear in this volume. We are particularly grateful to them for the fact that they have not required us to enumerate these volumes here by author, title, and publisher.

We also wish to express our appreciation to the editors and publishers of the numerous scientific, mathematical, and philosophical journals quoted in these pages, for the privilege of utilizing such source materials therein found relevant to the discussion of Professor Einstein's scientific and philosophical views.

13

Victor F. Lenzen

EINSTEIN'S THEORY OF KNOWLEDGE

13

EINSTEIN'S THEORY OF KNOWLEDGE

I

THEORY of knowledge, or epistemology, is the philosophical discipline that deals with the aims, methods, and achievements of cognition. Subject matter for epistemological analysis is exemplified by the perceptions and opinions of daily life, by the procedures and laws of natural science, by the axioms and deductions of mathematics. Theoretical physics, which is a mathematical scheme for the ordering of certain refined concepts of daily life, provides a fruitful object for epistemological analysis. The science combines the functions of experience and reason in the constitution of knowledge. The impulse to construct a physical theory originates in perception as a mode of experience, but a theory is constructed rationally out of mathematical concepts. In the present essay I shall expound the theory of knowledge which Einstein has formulated in the light of his constructive work in theoretical physics.[1]

Creative advance in exact science historically has provided

[1] In preparing this essay Einstein's theoretical works have been consulted, and in addition the following contributions which are of especial philosophical significance:

1) "Ernst Mach." *Physikalische Zeitschrift*, Vol. 17, 101-104 (1916).
2) "Address in honor of Planck." Quoted by A. Moszkowski, *Einstein*, 67-69 (1921).
3) "Time, Space, and Gravitation." Reprinted from the *London Times*. *Science*, 8-10, January 2 (1920).
4) *Aether und Relativitätstheorie* (1920).
5) *Geometrie und Erfahrung* (1921).
6) *Vier Vorlesungen über Relativitätstheorie* (1922).
7) "Newton's Mechanik und ihr Einfluss auf die Gestaltung der theoretischen Physik." *Die Naturwissenschaften*, Vol. 15, 273-276 (1927).
8) "Maxwell's Influence on the Development of the Conception of Physical Reality." *Essays on James Clerk Maxwell* (1931).

(Continued on next page)

material for new points of view in theory of knowledge. In antiquity the mathematical discoveries of the Pythagoreans gave rise to rationally constructed deductive systems for numbers and geometrical figures. Plato explained the possibility of mathematical knowledge by the theory of ideas, or forms, which were exact, eternal objects of rational insight. In the modern era the creation of classical mechanics and its application by Newton to construct a system of the world provided mathematical knowledge of motion. Kant explained the possibility of a mathematical science of nature by the doctrine that space and time are *a priori* forms of sensibility, and substance and causality are *a priori* categories of the understanding. Since the dawn of the twentieth century new bases for theoretical physics have been created by the theory of relativity and quantum theory. One may expect that new conceptions in theory of knowledge will be required in order to comprehend these new achievements in physical theory. The epistemological analysis of theoretical physics should provide the pathway to a comprehensive theory of knowledge.

Theory of knowledge does not, however, await the completion of a new theoretical physics. There may be invariable principles, so that epistemological analysis is an element in the criticism of prevailing concepts and in the creation of new physical theories. This creative function of epistemology has been acknowledged by Einstein to have been an essential constituent in his own creative work. In an essay on the work of Ernst Mach,

9) "Prologue by Albert Einstein." Max Planck, *Where Is Science Going?* Translated by James Murphy (1932).
10) *The Origins of the General Theory of Relativity* (1933).
11) *On the Method of Theoretical Physics* (1933).
12) A. Einstein, B. Podolsky and N. Rosen, "Can Quantum-Mechanical Description of Physical Reality be Considered Complete?" *Physical Review*, Vol. 47, 777-780 (1935).
13) "Physik und Realität." *Journal of the Franklin Institute*, 313-347 (1936).
14) "Remarks on Bertrand Russell's Theory of Knowledge." *The Philosophy of Bertrand Russell*. Edited by Paul Arthur Schilpp (1944).
The following biographical works also have been consulted:
1) Alexander Moszkowski, *Einstein* (1921).
2) Anton Reiser, *Albert Einstein* (1930).
3) H. Gordon Garbedian, *Albert Einstein* (1939).
4) Marianoff and Wayne, *Einstein* (1944).

Einstein describes the subject matter of *Erkenntnistheorie* as the aims and nature of science, the extent to which its results are true, the discrimination between what is essential and that which rests on accidents of development. He asserts that the truth about these problems must be mastered again and again in conformity to the needs of an era, for reflective insight which is not continually recreated in general becomes lost. Concepts that have proved useful in the constitution of an order of things readily win such an authority over us that we forget their earthly origin and take them to be changeless data. Such concepts then become stamped as necessities of thought, as given *a priori*, so that the path of scientific progress often becomes impassable for a long period. Einstein declared that it is no idle play, therefore, if we engage in analysis of concepts that have been long current and show on what their justification and usefulness depends. The all too great authority of customary concepts is thereby broken: they are set aside, if they can not be justified adequately, corrected if their correlation with given experience was too careless, or replaced by other concepts if it is possible to set up a preferable new system. Einstein has stated that the critical discussions of Hume and Mach influenced him directly and indirectly in the reconstruction of the concepts of space and time for the creation of the theory of relativity. Despite the protests of those philosophers who had placed these concepts in a treasure chest of the absolute, of the *a priori*, critical analysis replaced them by more sharply defined concepts in order to further the development of physical science.

Einstein also has expounded general conclusions concerning the nature of knowledge as exemplified by theoretical physics. His views constitute a contribution to the development of theory of knowledge as a philosophical discipline. As preparation for a preliminary statement of his doctrine I recall the distinction between sensory experience and conceptual description. Empirical knowledge originates in sense-impressions, but its goal is understanding through concepts. The media of scientific knowledge are concepts of properties of things and processes which constitute natural phenomena. A basic problem of theory of knowledge is the relation of concepts to sensory experience; in this question one may distinguish between the rôle of experience in the origin of concepts and the function of concepts in ordering experience. According to empiricism concepts are abstracted from experience. An observer perceives several white things, for example, and abstracts from these particulars the common quality whiteness. The concept of the property whiteness, a universal, thus is explained as derived from experiences that exemplify the universal. The doctrine of empiricism as applied to natural science is that concepts and natural laws are abstracted from experience. It can be claimed that Newton viewed the principles by which he described gravitational phenomena as derived from experience. Einstein has declared that Newton's *"hypotheses non fingo"* can be interpreted only in the sense that Newton held that the concepts of mass, acceleration, and force, and the laws connecting them, were directly borrowed from experience.[2] Although Einstein acknowledges the stimulus which he owes to the empiricists Hume and Mach, he rejects an empirical account of the origin of concepts.

According to Einstein, the concepts which arise in thought and in our linguistic expressions logically are free creations of thought which can not be derived inductively from sensory experiences. Like Plato, Einstein stresses the gap between data of sense and concepts of thought. He contends that there is a gulf, logically unbridgeable, which separates the world of sensory experiences from the realm of concepts and conceptual relations which constitute propositions. The constructive nature of concepts is not easily noticed, Einstein asserts, because we have the habit of combining certain concepts and conceptual relations definitely with certain sensory experiences. In contrast to John Stuart Mill, who held that propositions of mathematics are inductions from experience, Einstein offers the series of integers as obviously an invention of the human mind, a self-created tool which simplifies the ordering of sensory experiences.[3] He asserts that there is no way in which the concept could be made to grow, as it were, directly out of sensory experiences. The concept of number belongs to pre-scientific thought, but its constructive character is still easily recognizable.

In support of Einstein's doctrine of concepts, one can cite

[2] *Method of Theoretical Physics*, 10.
[3] "Remarks on Bertrand Russell's Theory of Knowledge," 286. (cf. 14 in fn. 1).

examples of constructive concepts in physical theory. Although Newton thought of mechanics as derived from experience, its universe of discourse contains conceptual objects, particles and rigid bodies, which are not exactly exemplified in experience. Observation of the results of an experiment involves assignment of physical quantities to a perceptible body. This operation requires a constructive act which may be exemplified by the measurement of distance between two points; in this operation each of the points is brought into coincidence simultaneously with corresponding points on a standard body that is idealized as rigid. Even if a crude concept of distance were held to be abstracted from perceptions of coincidence, the exact concept requires the constructive act of idealization of points and rigid bodies. As Einstein has emphasized, the hypothesis of atomism is based on constructive-speculative concepts. Atoms are conceptual objects, the properties of which are not perceptible but are assigned hypothetically.

Although Einstein recognizes the spontaneity of thought, he agrees with Kant that all thought acquires material content only through its relationship to sensory experiences. Pure logical thinking can give us no knowledge of the world of experience; all knowledge about reality begins with experience and terminates in it. The function of concepts is to order and survey experience, so that a conceptual system is tested by its success in establishing order in the manifold of sense-experiences. Thus reason builds the structure in a system of knowledge. Einstein declares that our experience up to date justifies us in feeling sure that in Nature is actualized the ideal of mathematical simplicity. Accordingly he asserts, "In a certain sense, therefore, I hold it to be true that pure thought is competent to comprehend the real, as the ancients dreamed."[4]

Einstein holds that the truly creative principle in theoretical physics is mathematical construction. It enables us to discover the concepts and laws connecting them which give us the key to the understanding of natural phenomena. Experience may guide us in our choice of mathematical concepts; experience also remains the sole criterion of the serviceability of a mathematical construction for physics; but it cannot possibly be the

[4] *Method of Theoretical Physics*, 12.

source from which a theory is derived. The aim of theory is to reduce the concepts for a field of knowledge to as simple and as few irreducible basic elements as possible. Einstein has further stated, "The basic concepts and laws which are not logically further reducible constitute the indispensable and not rationally deducible part of the theory."[5] The reference to a non-rational element may be explained by a passage from an address in honor of Planck.[6] On this occasion Einstein stated that the development of physics has shown that among all conceivable constructions at a given time, one has proved itself unconditionally superior to all others; that the world of perceptions practically determines the theoretical system, although no logical path leads from perceptions to the principles of the theory, only intuition which rests upon an intimacy with experience. It is appropriate to apply to Einstein his own characterization of Planck: The longing for the vision of the pre-established harmony which was recognized by Leibniz is the source of the inexhaustible patience with which Einstein has been able to devote himself to the general problems of theoretical physics.

II

Einstein has recognized that science is a refinement of the thinking of daily life. Accordingly, he initiates his critical reflections concerning theoretical physics with an analysis of concepts which serve to interpret common experience. The physicist in ordinary activities as well as in science is cognizant of an environment constituted by things that are extended in space and variable in time. Subject matter for physical science is the pattern of basic processes in the spatio-temporal environment. Physical knowledge is expressed by organized sets of propositions which express conceptual relations exemplified in physical processes. The basic concept is that of bodily object by which we interpret the data of perception; a manifold of bodily objects comprises the external world which stands in cognitive relations to observers. As a foundation for the present essay we need to understand the concept of bodily object as set forth,

[5] Ibid., 9.
[6] Moszkowski, Einstein, 69.

for example, in Einstein's monograph "Physik und Realität."

Natural science during the modern era generally has presupposed dualism in theory of knowledge. Data of perception have been acknowledged to be relative to percipient events; objects have been conceived as independent of perception. In dualism a physical object is held to be an independent reality which manifests itself by initiating a chain of processes that act on a sensory mechanism. The resulting perception is interpreted as mediate cognition of an independent object. Einstein has remarked that this dualist conception is an application of physical ways of thinking to the problem of cognition. Dualism was criticized by Berkeley and Hume, but for physical scientists the significant alternative was set forth by Ernst Mach. In his theory the object of perception is a complex of elements, which Mach called sensations but viewed as neutral with respect to the distinction between mental and material. In essays on the philosophy of physics Planck has argued repeatedly against the positivism of Mach, contending that a realist conception of the physical world is necessary for the progress of physical science. Einstein in an essay on Maxwell appears to have accepted the realist doctrine, for he says, "The belief in an external world independent of the percipient subject is the foundation of all science. But since sense-perceptions inform us only indirectly of this external world, of Physical Reality, it is only by speculation that it can become comprehensible to us."[7] In his essay on the method of theoretical physics he expresses the conviction that pure mathematical construction is the method of discovering the concepts and laws for the comprehension of nature. He declares, "Our experience up to date justifies us in feeling sure that in Nature is actualized the ideal of mathematical simplicity."[8] Perhaps it is permissible to conjecture that according to Einstein the relational structure of an independent reality can be cognized by virtue of a pre-established harmony between thought and reality.

The realist language occasionally used by Einstein is exemplified in a discussion of quantum mechanics in collaboration

---

[7] "Maxwell's Influence," 66.
[8] Op. cit., 12.

with B. Podolsky and N. Rosen. It is asserted that any consideration of a physical theory must take into account the distinction between objective reality, which is independent of any theory, and the physical concepts with which the theory operates. These concepts are intended to correspond with the objective reality, and by means of the concepts we picture this reality to ourselves. The following requirement for a complete theory is held to be necessary: every element of the physical reality must have a counterpart in the physical theory. The criterion of reality is: "If, without in any way disturbing a system, we can predict with certainty the value of a physical quantity, then there exists an element of physical reality corresponding to the physical quantity."[9] This criterion is regarded not as necessary but merely as sufficient, and accords with classical as well as quantum mechanical ideas of reality. In my judgment the presupposition of this criterion is that physical reality is conceived to have only those characters that are manifested in observable results of experiments. In so far as physical reality is independent in the sense of a realistic theory of knowledge, its only character which is relevant to physical theory is form as exhibited in the pattern of observable objects.

The realist language of Einstein is further neutralized by his recognition that the significance of concepts depends on sense-impressions. In his systematic discussion in "Physik und Realität" Einstein starts with sensory experiences as would a positivist. He begins his analysis with the observation that upon the stage of our experience there appear in colorful succession sense-impressions, recollections thereof, representations, and feelings. The distinction between sense-impressions, or sensations, and representations is problematic, but Einstein proceeds on the assumption that sense-impressions as such are given and cognizable. The concept of "real external world" of daily life is based upon sense-impressions. Physical science deals with sense-impressions and aims to comprehend the connections between them.

The first step in positing a "real external world" is the con-

[9] "Can Quantum-Mechanical Description of Physical Reality be Considered Complete?" 777.

struction of the concept of bodily object, respectively, bodily objects of different kinds. Certain recurring complexes of sensation are arbitrarily selected by thought out of the fulness of sensations and to them is assigned the concept of bodily object. Einstein holds that, logically considered, the concept of bodily object is not identical with the totality of those sensations, but is a free creation of the human (or animal) spirit. However, the concept of bodily object owes its significance and justification to the totality of sensations to which it is assigned. In positing a "real external world" we attribute "real existence" to the bodily object, and thereby endow the concept with an independent existence. With the help of such concepts and relations which are thought of between them, we are able to find our way in the maze of sensations. The real objects, although free posits of thought, seem more fixed and changeless than individual sense-impressions, whose character in contrast to illusion or hallucination is never completely certified. The world of sense-impressions is comprehensible in the following sense: One fashions general concepts and relations between them, imposes relations between concepts and sense-impressions, and thereby establishes an order between sense-impressions. Einstein declares that it is one of the great discoveries of Immanuel Kant that the positing of a real external world would be meaningless without such comprehensibility. In virtue of the connections between complexes of sense-impressions and concepts, the purely conceptual propositions of science become general assertions about complexes of sense-impressions. The method of forming concepts and connections between them, and the mode of assigning concepts to sense-impressions, is decided only by success in establishing an order of sense-impressions. The rules of correlation can never be definitive, but can claim validity only for a specified region of applicability. Einstein declares that there are no definitive categories in the sense of Kant. He asserts that we must always be ready to alter our conceptions of physical reality, in order to take account of perceptions with the greatest possible logical completeness. The connections between complexes of sense impressions and the elementary concepts of daily life are not comprehensible conceptually and can only be grasped intuitively. Einstein declares that the comprehensibility of the world is the eternally incomprehensible.

Einstein's concept of bodily object may be compared with a theory of Bertrand Russell, according to which a physical object is a collection of sense-data. In his discussion of Russell's theory of knowledge Einstein rejects the conception of a thing as a bundle of qualities which are taken from sensory raw material. He attributes the origin of such a concept of thing to a fear of metaphysics created by Hume. Einstein declares, however, that he can see no "metaphysical danger" in taking the thing (the object in the sense of physics) as an independent concept into the system together with the proper spatio-temporal structure.[10]

In my judgment the minimal significance of the concept of bodily object expresses a matrix to which thought refers sense-impressions. This conception of bodily object as a matrix for the arrangement of sense-impressions can be fashioned so that a decision between idealism and realism is not required for science. Einstein recognizes that the function of the bodily object is to order sense-impressions. Since he rejects the view that the object is only a complex of sensations, his view need not be idealism. He holds that the concept of bodily object is independent, but since the object is not characterized explicitly as the cause of sensations, one extreme of dualism can be avoided. Indeed, since the propositions of physical science are about complexes of sense-impressions, the independent concept of bodily object need not refer to a reality beyond experience. In language occasionally used by Einstein, however, the term bodily object seems to signify an element of an independent reality, whose structure is grasped through the conceptual scheme which orders the manifold of sense-impressions.

III

Einstein's exposition of scientific method starts with the concept of bodily object and then introduces concepts which are fashioned for daily life and refined by science. In the passage from ordinary experience to theories of physics Einstein recog-

[10] "Remarks on Bertrand Russell's Theory of Knowledge," 290.

nizes strata, or levels of knowledge. A primary level has the closest relation to sense-impressions; the primary concepts formed on this level are connected intuitively and directly with typical complexes of sense-impressions. Concepts on deeper levels are significant for experience only to the extent that they can be brought into relation with primary concepts through propositions. Among propositions are definitions of concepts as well as propositions logically deducible from them. Natural laws are propositions which are not deducible from definitions, but which assert relations between primary concepts and thereby between sense-impressions. Einstein states that the distinction between definitions and natural laws depends to a considerable extent on the chosen mode of representation. He remarks that the distinction needs to be carried out actually only if one seeks to investigate to what extent a conceptual system is meaningful from the physical point of view.

On the primary level of natural knowledge the concepts of space and time play a fundamental rôle. The laboratory of experimental physics has a place in space during an epoch of time. Qualitative concepts of these frames of events are used in daily life; in physical science the definitions of these concepts are progressively reformed and sharpened for the investigation of processes in space and time under controlled conditions. The primary concept for the theory of space and time is that of bodily object. According to Einstein the characteristic property assigned to a bodily object is existence independent of subjective time and of sensory perception. We ascribe independence to the object, although we observe changes in qualities and position during time. The term "independence" suggests a realist conception of objects, but in my judgment the term may be applied to a construct of thought which serves to establish order among sense-impressions. The following discussion does not require a decision concerning the ontological status of bodily objects.

Einstein explains the concepts of objective space and objective time in terms of the properties of a specific kind of bodily object, the practically rigid body.[11] Practically rigid bodies are exemplified by solid bodies of common experience. Solid bodies

[11] "Physik u. Realität."

can undergo changes of position which can be reversed by arbitrary motions of an observer's body and are thereby distinguished from changes of state. In a pair of solid bodies each can change its position without change in position of the pair. One thereby attains the concept of relative position and thus the concept of relative position of each body. A special case of relative position is contact of two bodies at a point. Experience shows that if two adjacent bodies are in contact at two points, this contact can be continued during changes of position, and after separation can be restored. By this concept of coincidence of points one describes the properties of a solid body which are expressed by the term "practically rigid body." Two points on a practically rigid body determine a stretch. The stretches on two bodies are called equal to each other if the points of one coincide with the corresponding points of the other. It is postulated that if two stretches determined by points on practically rigid bodies have been found equal, they are always and everywhere equal. This postulate is the basis of equality of stretches at a distance.

A specific body K_0 can be continued by a second body which is in contact with it at three or more points. The quasi-rigid continuation of a body is unlimited. The collection of conceivable quasi-rigid continuations of a body K_0 is the infinite space determined by this body as frame of reference. The concept of space conceptually transforms the manifold of positional relations of bodily objects into the manifold of positions of bodily objects in space. Every proposition about position thereby becomes one about contact. That a point of a bodily object is to be found at the spatial point P signifies that the given point of the object is in contact, or coincides with, the point P on the suitably conceived continuation of the body of reference K_0. In pre-scientific thought the earth's crust plays the rôle of the body of reference K_0 and its continuation. The term geometry for the mathematical theory of the properties of space indicates that for the Greek creators of the science the concept of space was relative to the earthly body of reference. Einstein describes space in general as the totality of possibilities of relative position of practically rigid bodies.

In geometry as a branch of mathematics the practically rigid body is transformed into an ideal rigid body. The axioms of geometry implicitly define the properties of points, lines, planes, and rigid bodies. Euclidean geometry, for example, consists of the totality of propositions for the relative positions of rigid bodies which are independent of time. Its formal simplicity is characterized by the properties of homogeneity, isotropy and existence of similar figures in space. The central significance of Euclidean geometry from the physical point of view lies in the fact that its validity is independent of the qualitative nature of bodies. The description of position by co-ordinates, as in the geometry of Descartes, has been a powerful tool in the quantitative development of the subject. Einstein points out that the content of Euclidean geometry can be based axiomatically on the propositions:

1) Two points on a rigid body determine a stretch.

2) To any point of space one can assign a triplet of co-ordinate numbers so that to a stretch one can assign a positive number, the square of which is the sum of squares of the co-ordinate differences. The positive number is called the length of the stretch, or the distance of the points, and is independent of position of the given body as well as all other bodies.

Einstein declares that the formulation of geometry in terms of co-ordinates clearly exhibits the connection between conceptual constructions and sense-impressions, upon which rests the significance of geometry for physics. The propositions of Euclidean geometry indeed are embodied in an approximate manner in configurations of solid bodies of common experience. In particular, Euclidean geometry is approximately exemplified in apparatus for measuring quantities such as distance, time, and in general the quantities of classical physics. The axiomatic construction of Euclidean geometry has an empirical foundation, and Einstein declares that forgetfulness of this fact was responsible for the fatal error that Euclidean geometry is a necessity of thought which is prior to all experience.

The concept of objective time is introduced through the intermediary of space. Just as the rigid body is a basis for space, so is the clock for time. Einstein introduces time by two independent posits:

1) Objective local time is based on the correlation of the temporal course of experience with the indications of a "clock," i.e., a periodically running isolated system.

2) Objective extended time is based upon synchronization of distant clocks by signals.

The postulate for stretches in space also applies to time. The propagation of light in empty space correlates to every interval of local time a stretch, the corresponding light path. If two immediately adjacent, ideal clocks run at the same rate at any time and at any place, they will run at the same rate whenever and wherever they are compared at the same place.[12] An empirical basis for this postulate is provided by the agreement of the frequencies of light emitted by individual atoms of the same chemical element.

The distinction between time and local time was vague prior to the creation of the special theory of relativity. Simultaneity of sight and simultaneity of occurrence were not distinguished, because the time required for the propagation of light was neglected in science as well as in daily life. The presupposition of classical mechanics that space and time are independent of bodies obscured the unsharpness of the concept of time from the empirical point of view, but it did facilitate the development of mechanics. Einstein has remarked that the hypostatization of concepts may serve a useful purpose in science; there is danger, however, that the origin of concepts in experience may be forgotten and concepts considered changeless. The Kantian doctrine of the fixity of concepts is not a constituent of Einstein's theory of knowledge.

The concepts of space, time, and bodily object are basic concepts in the cognitions of daily life. Physical science in its initial stage of development employs as media of cognition primary concepts which are intuitively correlated with the perceptions of common experience. An example is the concept of water as primary substance in the cosmological theory of Thales. Einstein

[12] *Geometrie u. Erfahrung*, 9.

declares that the scientific mind is not satisfied with such a primary stage of cognition, on account of lack of logical unity among concepts and their relations. Accordingly, a secondary system is invented with fewer concepts and relations, and from it the primary concepts and relations of the first stratum are logically derived. The greater logical unity of the secondary system is achieved at the sacrifice of immediate correlation between its concepts and complexes of sense-impressions. The first and second stages of physical science may be exemplified respectively by descriptions of the perceptible properties of matter and the kinetic-molecular theory of matter. In the kinetic-molecular theory a material like the water of Thales is reduced to an assembly of molecules whose different modes of arrangement furnish the basis of solid, liquid, and gaseous states. Further striving for logical unity leads to the creation of an even more impoverished tertiary system from which the concepts and relations of the secondary system can be derived. The process goes on until one arrives at a system with the greatest conceivable unity and poverty of concepts, and which is consistent with the structure introduced into the manifold of sense-impressions by primary concepts. The strata are not sharply separated. In the present unfinished state of theoretical physics the strata represent stages of partial success. The science as a whole consists of parts in different stages of development, and contains apparently inconsistent constituents. If a definitive, unified system should be created, the intermediate stages would disappear.

Consideration of the construction of a system of theoretical physics raises the question as to how we shall choose concepts and principles so that we may hope for confirmation of their consequences by experience. Einstein offers two guides for construction, one empirical, one rational. The aim of theory is to achieve the most complete conceptual comprehension of sense-impressions. Hence the most favorable results are to be expected from hypotheses which are suggested by experience. Such hypotheses establish what Einstein has called theories of principle.[13] He gives as examples the hypothesis of the non-exist-

[13] "Time, Space, and Gravitation."

ence of a *perpetuum mobile* as a foundation for thermodynamics, and Galileo's law of inertia as a constituent of classical mechanics. The fundamental hypotheses of the special theory of
relativity are similar in nature. The special theory rests upon:

1) The principle of relativity of uniform motion, a proposition which has been confirmed negatively by the failure
   to detect the effects of the earth's motion with respect to
   an ether.

2) The principle of the constancy of the velocity of light, a
   principle which serves to represent the Maxwell-Lorentz
   theory of electromagnetic phenomena in moving bodies.

The union of the two principles requires that the velocity of
light be the same in all inertial frames of reference. The principles of the theory of relativity determine time and space to
be relative to the frame of reference. The four-dimensional
space-time of Minkowski then provides the approximate frame
for events.

The construction of physical theory is also guided by ideals
of reason. Reason demands the greatest possible simplicity
in a physical theory. Simplicity is understood to consist in a
minimum number of fundamental concepts and relations together with a maximum of abstractness. The creative function
of such logical ideals was especially exemplified by the creation
of the general theory of relativity. The general theory was constructed to conform to a general principle of relativity, according to which the equations which express physical laws are covariant under all transformations of co-ordinates. The creative
function of mathematical ideals has been succinctly expressed
by Einstein:

The physical world is represented as a four-dimensional continuum. If
in this I adopt a Riemannian metric, and look for the simplest laws
which such a metric can satisfy, I arrive at the relativistic gravitation
theory of empty space. If I adopt in this space a vector-field, or the
anti-symmetrical tensor-field derived from it, and if I look for the
simplest laws which such a field can satisfy, I arrive at the Maxwell
equations for free space.[14]

[14] *Method of Theoretical Physics*, 13.

The use of rational criteria for the construction of physical theories confirms Einstein's doctrine that concepts are free creations of the mind. The fundamental axioms, he declares, can be chosen freely. To be sure, the freedom is controlled to the extent that consequences of the axioms must be confirmed by experience. The freedom is not that of a novelist, but of the person who solves a cross-word puzzle. Any word can be proposed as a solution, but there is only one that fits the puzzle in all parts. In view of Einstein's distinction between theories of principle, which are suggested by experience, and constructive theories, it might be thought that the creative nature of concepts does not hold for theories of principle. But theories of principle, such as thermodynamics, are formulated in terms of sharply defined concepts of properties that are never exactly exemplified in experience. Again, the synthesis of principles for the special theory of relativity created the concepts of relative space and time and thus provided the basis for space-time. Hence it is justifiable to agree with Einstein that physical concepts in a logical sense are free creations of the human mind.

Einstein states that during the classical period scientists believed that the basic concepts and laws of physics were derivable from experience by abstraction. The great successes of the Newtonian theory of gravitation prevented recognition of the constructive nature of its principles. According to Einstein, it is the general theory of relativity which showed in a convincing manner the incorrectness of the view that concepts are derived from experience. This theory revealed that by using principles quite differently conceived from those of Newton it was possible to comprehend the entire range of the data of experience in a manner even more complete and satisfactory than on Newton's principles. The constructive character of the principles is made obvious by the fact that it is possible to exhibit two essentially different bases, each of which yields consequences in agreement with experience to a large extent. This indicates, Einstein declares, that an attempt to derive logically the concepts and laws of mechanics from the ultimate data of experience is doomed to failure. There is no inductive method that can lead to the fundamental concepts or principles. The truly creative principle of theoretical physics is mathematical construction.

IV

The aim of theoretical physics is the unified conceptual representation of physical reality. This end has been accomplished in large part by the construction of models for physical processes. The pattern of common experience has provided models, such as particles and waves, with which to picture physical reality. Solid bodies perceived in daily life suggest the concept of a bodily object that is relatively small in extent; ripples on water suggest the concept of a wave by which a continuous field is propagated through space. I have already discussed Einstein's conception of theories of principle, and shall now examine his doctrine of constructive theories in physics.

A relatively small solid body provides the empirical basis for the precisely defined concept of the material point as a bodily object concentrated in a point. Classical mechanics is a theory of motion of material points, the positions of which can be described in terms of co-ordinates relative to a space K_o. The law of inertia states that the acceleration of a material point vanishes if it is sufficiently far removed from all other points. The law of motion is that force equals mass times acceleration. As Einstein has remarked, the laws of mechanics constitute a general schema. The laws acquire content through laws of force which express interactions between material points in accordance with the law of action and reaction. Newton's law of gravitation is a law of force which made possible application of classical mechanics to planetary motions. The laws of motion in classical mechanics hold only with respect to bodies of reference K_o with a specific type of motion, and hence such spaces of reference are endowed with a physical property which is foreign to the geometrical concept of space. Einstein has declared that it is a defect of classical mechanics that laws of force can not be won through formal-logical considerations; the choice of such laws is to a great extent arbitrary *a priori*. Newton's law of gravitation is marked out from other conceivable laws of force through its success in prediction. By constrast, Einstein's law of gravitation was found by seeking the simplest covariant law for space-time with a Riemannian metric. Einstein's criticism of Newton's law of gravitation recalls to the student of Plato that philosopher's criticism of the employment of hypotheses in mathematics without rational comprehension obtained by dialectic. The formal-logical considerations which Einstein employed in creating the general theory of relativity accord with the Platonic conception of "episteme."

Einstein declares that classical mechanics leads necessarily to the atomic constitution of matter, a result which demonstrates that the theory of atomism does not arise inductively out of experience. The atomistic point of view, however, is limited by phenomenological physics, which operates with concepts intuitively correlated with experience. Thus the configuration of a rigidly connected system of material points can be described in terms of a number of generalized co-ordinates. Again, a deformable system of material points can be treated approximately as a continuous distribution of matter. Such a fiction, which avoids the explicit introduction of material points, is made the basis of theories of elasticity and hydrodynamics. The program of phenomenological physics also called for the description of heat, electricity, and light in terms of variables in addition to the mechanical ones. The functional dependence of these variables on one another and on the time was to be found empirically. During the latter half of the nineteenth century many scientists, in particular Ernst Mach, envisaged the goal of physical science as the representation of processes through concepts inductively derived from sensory experience. On Einstein's view the consistent application of Newtonian mechanics carried theoretical physics beyond the phenomenological standpoint. The kinetic-molecular theory of gases correlated phenomena which seemed to be independent. Statistical mechanics furnished a mechanical interpretation of the concepts and laws of thermodynamics. This reduction of the phenomenological stratum to an atomistic one required assignment of real structure to material points which thereby became atoms or molecules. Einstein declares that the speculative-constructive character of these particles was obvious; no one could hope to perceive an atom directly. The kinetic-molecular theory of matter was opposed by an empiricism which was represented by Ernst Mach. Mach viewed atoms as auxiliary fictions which were to be discarded after the complete correlation of sensations was achieved. A creative exponent of atomism was Boltzmann, who in his statistical mechanical theory of thermodynamics expressed entropy as proportional to the probability of the state of an assembly of particles. Planck applied Boltzmann's methods to heat radiation, and in the first year of the twentieth century invented the concept of quantum of energy from which he derived a law for black body radiation that agreed with experimental results.

Einstein contributed significantly to the theory of atomism. An early work was a statistical mechanical theory of thermodynamics. He applied statistical methods to the Brownian movement, the irregular thermal motion of colloidal particles suspended in a liquid. Of special significance was his application of Boltzmann's theory of entropy as probability to radiation in order to introduce the concept of discrete quanta of radiant energy. He further extended Planck's theory of the quantized oscillator to atomic motions in a solid and derived the result that the specific heat of a monatomic solid is a function of the temperature. The quantum theory received great impetus when Bohr introduced stationary states determined by quantum conditions into the nuclear model of the atom. The stationary states of atomic hydrogen, for example, were represented as motions of a single electron in quantized orbits about a positive nucleus. In conformity with Einstein's quantum theory of radiation, Bohr also postulated that atoms jump from one stationary state to another with the emission or absorption of a quantum of radiant energy. Einstein then constructed a theory for the emission and absorption of radiation in equilibrium with an assembly of atoms characterized by stationary states and obtained Planck's law of radiation. Later, Bose applied a new kind of statistics to photons in order to derive Planck's law; Einstein then extended the Bose statistics to an ideal gas. One may summarize Einstein's contributions to constructive theories based on atomism: initially he founded his statistical investigations upon classical mechanics and in the course of development applied and extended the concepts of quantum theory to obtain new statistical theories.

The mechanical theory of atomism was applied in Newton's corpuscular theory to explain the phenomena of light. Later, particles that carry electric charges were conceived for the explanation of electric and magnetic phenomena. Wave motion in material media then suggested more suitable models for optical and electromagnetic phenomena. The interference and diffraction of light required explanation in terms of waves. Electric and magnetic forces, which were initially conceived to act at a distance like gravitation, were interpreted to be manifestations of a continuous field which transmits actions by contact. The theory of partial differential equations, which had been developed for the continuous functions of phenomenological mechanics, provided mathematical methods for the theory of the field.

A wave theory of light initially represented the physical basis of visual sensations as wave motion in a mechanical ether. Faraday invented, and Maxwell developed, the concept of field as a region in which electric and magnetic forces are continuous functions of position. According to Einstein, the theory of electromagnetic field constituted a further step in the direction of constructive speculation. For the existence of the field is manifested only if electrically charged bodies are brought into it. Electric charges are regions of non-vanishing divergence of electric force. Maxwell's differential equations correlate the spatial and temporal rates of change of electric and magnetic forces. Light consists of undulatory processes in the electromagnetic field. Maxwell sought to construct mechanical models for the field, but gradually the field acquired a fundamental rôle. Under the influence of Heinrich Hertz the equations of electromagnetism came to be interpreted as representations of fundamental realities. Thus the strictly mechanical view of nature was gradually abandoned. H. A. Lorentz applied the theory of electromagnetism to material media with the aid of the concept of electron. He considered the ether to be the seat of electromagnetic fields within material bodies as well as in empty space. Electrons, that is elementary particles which carry electric charges, enabled Lorentz to account for electromagnetic phenomena in moving bodies. Einstein has remarked that Lorentz took from the ether all its mechanical properties except immobility.[15] The electron theory was a synthesis of the Newtonian mechanics of material points and Maxwell's theory of the electromagnetic field. This dualism of theoretical foundations inspired attempts to explain the electron in terms of the field.

The special theory of relativity was based on the Maxwell-Lorentz theory of the electromagnetic field. According to the special theory, physical phenomena can be described with equal correctness in a multiplicity of inertial frames of reference. If the seat of electromagnetic processes is called an ether, it must be deprived of a definite state of motion. Einstein thus considers that the special theory of relativity completed the work of establishing the electromagnetic field as a fundamental reality. He has said, "This change in the conception of Reality is the most profound and the most fruitful that physics has experienced since the time of Newton; but it must be confessed that the complete realization of the program contained in this idea has so far by no means been attained."[16]

The conception of field as physical reality was further developed by Einstein in the general theory of relativity. According to this theory, the metrical properties of the space-time continuum are dependent upon matter. The formulation of this field theory, however, required the concept of material particle. Einstein has sought to resolve the dualism between field and particle. He declares that in the foundations of a consistent field theory the concept of particle must not occur alongside that of field. The whole theory must be based on partial differential equations and solutions thereof which are free from singularities. Concerning the problem of quanta, Einstein looks for a solution by which the foundations of field physics are united with the facts of quanta. This basis is the only one which

[15] *Aether u. Relativitätstheorie,* 7.
[16] "Maxwell's Influence," 71.

in the light of the present status of mathematical methods fits the postulate of general relativity.[17]

V

As a final topic in this essay on Einstein's theory of knowledge I consider his evaluation of the achievements of theoretical physics in attaining knowledge of reality. For this discussion we need to distinguish between empirical science and pure mathematics.

The universe of discourse for empirical science is the properties of things and processes known through sensory experience. For example, the relation between the lengths of perceptible rods that constitute a triangle is matter of fact for geometry as a branch of experimental physics. The concept of measurement of theoretical physics presupposes that an immediate repetition of a measurement will yield the same result. In actual practice, however, measurements are carried out with instruments made of practically rigid bodies, and results are only approximately reproducible. Thus the properties of bodily objects as found by perception lack complete consistency. A proposition which expresses a relation between sharply defined concepts admits only approximate confirmation by experience. In contrast, the propositions of mathematics have been credited with certainty. Although empiricists like John Stuart Mill have held mathematics to be empirical, there is wide acceptance to-day of the doctrine that mathematics is abstract. Einstein accepts the standpoint of Axiomatics, according to which the formal-logical content of mathematics is neatly separated from the factual or intuitive content. The formal-logical content is the object of pure mathematics, the factual content is a concrete interpretation of applied mathematics.

The axioms of mathematics exemplify Einstein's view that concepts are free creations of the human mind. The construction of a mathematical system occurs when propositions, more precisely propositional functions, are postulated to hold exactly for a set of objects. The objects of the system are realized in thought by postulates for conceptual relations between the objects. In so far as he acknowledges mathematical objects to be constructions, the theory of Einstein reminds one of Kant who held that objects of mathematics were constructed in pure intuition. In Kant, however, the creative activity of mind was limited by *a priori* forms of intuition. Mathematical thought was liberated by the invention of non-Euclidean geometries, and hence it is fitting that Einstein should endow thought with greater freedom for creation than Kant. Einstein is allied to Kant in that he recognizes spontaneity of thinking. In view of his emphasis on the distinction between thought and sense, Einstein's doctrine has elements in common with the Platonic conception of mathematical objects as exact forms that transcend sense. Einstein has said, "In so far as the propositions of mathematics refer to reality they are not certain and in so far as they are certain they do not refer to reality."[18] The certainty of mathematical axioms, more adequately, the precision with which they hold, is founded on the function of creating their objects.

Theoretical physics, when adequately developed for a field of physical processes, can be reduced to a set of principles which express functional relations between variables. The theory based on the principles further includes theorems which are derived by transformation from the principles. The certainty of the theory resides in the mathematical transformations of the deductive system.

Systems of physical theory were based initially on propositions which were refinements of generalizations from experience. For example, propositions which expressed positional relations of practically rigid bodies were taken as precise for Euclidean geometry. The transition from generalizations of empirical science to the principles of a deductive system is also exemplified by the creation of classical mechanics for material points. A principle of stationary action serves as a fundamental principle in this field. The mathematical physicist further may set up principles for any conceivable set of objects and unfold the logical implications of the principles. However, physical theories are constructed for the comprehension of experience,

---

[18] *Geometrie u. Erfahrung*, 3.

and therefore are subject to confirmation or disconfirmation, if only approximately, by experience. The mathematical physicist enjoys freedom to create whatsoever forms he wishes, but if he presumes to represent physical reality, he is subject to the control of experience.

Confirmation of an applied theory by perception is only approximate. The variables in a physical theory are interpreted by results of measurement which are never completely consistent. One reason for the inconsistency of measurements is that the establishment of conditions under which controlled experimentation is carried out requires a method of successive approximation. A standard measuring rod, for example, exemplifies unit distance only under conditions which are specified in terms of quantities that are themselves defined in terms of distance. The concept of distance, as defined to a given approximation, must be used in order to specify conditions under which it is precise to a higher approximation. As Einstein has emphasized, laws of classical physics are limiting cases of laws based on the theory of relativity or the quantum theory. Experimental apparatus is constructed in terms of approximate classical laws. Einstein has stated that Newtonian mechanics would continue to be a basis for physics. Bohr has taught that the interpretation of experiments requires the concepts of classical physics. If there should be created the unified theory for the physical world, which Einstein believes embodies the ideal of mathematical simplicity, this theory could only be confirmed by successive approximation.

Einstein's conception of physical theory is expressed in his criticism of quantum mechanics. This theory has given a relatively adequate account of the extra-nuclear structure of atoms in terms of concepts adapted from the classical mechanics of particles. The interpretation of quantum mechanics as given by Bohr limits the applicability of classical concepts to the elements of physical reality. Heisenberg's principle of indeterminacy expresses the limit of precision to which co-ordinates of position and momentum can be assigned simultaneously to a particle.

The interpretation of the formalism of quantum mechanics is based on the doctrine that in any investigation a line must be drawn between the object of observation and the measuring apparatus of the observer. The apparatus must be presupposed in an operation of measurement, and it falls outside the field of quantum mechanics during a given investigation.[19] If the behaviour of apparatus is considered in order to find the result of a measurement, classical physics is employed. The determination of position is with respect to a space-frame of reference, for example, a screen which is attached to a massive table rigidly attached to the earth. The employment of the screen for the definition of position is illustrated by the passage of an electron through a hole in the screen. During its passage through the hole the electron interacts with the screen and exchanges an uncontrollable quantity of momentum with the screen. The momentum acquired by the screen is absorbed by the frame of reference, presupposed in the experiment, and can not be used to calculate by the conservation law the change in momentum of the electron during the observation. After position is determined, the result is immediately reproducible, and therefore the value of the quantity has physical reality in conformity to the criterion of reality as formulated by Einstein, Podolsky, and Rosen. The result of a measurement of momentum is unpredictable, and therefore this quantity is without reality. The momentum of an electron could be found from its original momentum, and the change resulting from passage through a mobile screen, the momentum of which is determined before and after the passage. But a screen mobile with respect to the space-frame would lose its function for definition of position. Preparation of conditions under which position is defined excludes conditions under which momentum is defined, and vice versa. The experimental arrangements for the determination of conjugate quantities are mutually exclusive, and hence the state of a system is not describable in terms of simultaneous values of classically defined conjugate quantities. The state is represented by a wavefunction which satisfies Schrödinger's equation, whose characteristic values are the possible results of measurement and whose characteristic functions determine the probabilities of obtaining specific results. According to Bohr, the uncontrollable

[19] N. Bohr, *Physical Review*, Vol. 48, 696 (1935).

disturbance of the object by the instrument of observation is responsible for the use of statistical concepts for the description of atomic systems. The finite reaction of the measuring instruments on an object renders it impossible to take into account the momentum exchanged with separate parts of the apparatus and thus prevents us from drawing conclusions regarding the "course" of such processes, for example, to determine through which one of two slits in a diaphragm a particle passes on its way to a photographic plate. Bohr has declared that the essential property of atomic phenomena is the character of individuality which is completely foreign to classical physics. The limitation imposed upon the description of atomic processes is expressed by Dirac who says that the only object of theoretical physics is to calculate results that can be compared with experiment, and that it is quite unnecessary that any satisfying description of the whole course of the phenomena should be given.[20]

Einstein holds that quantum mechanics is limited to a statistical point of view.[21] On his view the wave-function does not describe the state of a single system; it refers rather to an ensemble of systems in the sense of statistical mechanics. If, except for certain special cases, the wave-function furnishes only statistical propositions for measurable quantities, the reason lies not only in the fact that the operation of measuring introduces unknown elements, but that the wave-function does not describe the state of a single system. What happens to a single system remains unclarified by this mode of consideration. Einstein declares that it is contrary to his scientific instinct to refrain from seeking a detailed mode of representation. He demands a theory that will represent the "course" of events, not merely probabilities of results of observation. Quantum mechanics expresses an element of truth, but it can not serve as starting point for a more adequate theory. Quantum mechanics must be derived as a limiting case of some future theory, just as electrostatics is deducible from electrodynamics, and thermodynamics from classical mechanics. Einstein has declared that he continues to believe in the possibility of constructing a model of reality.

[20] P. A. M. Dirac, *Quantum Mechanics*, 7 (1930).
[21] "Physik u. Realität," 341.

The preceding remark may serve to introduce a concluding summary of Einstein's theory of knowledge.

The postulates of a mathematical system implicitly define the conceptual relations of a set of objects which are thereby realized in thought. Theorems are derivable from the postulates by logical deductions which may be viewed as certain. Cognition of reality, however, originates in sensory experience, is tested by sensory experience, and shares the uncertainty of such experience. Cognition of physical reality occurs through the media of concepts which express properties of objects in a spatio-temporal environment. Theoretical physics represents reality by models, such as particles and continuous fields. A model of reality serves to order sense-impressions; the theory based upon it is confirmed by approximate agreement of logical consequences with sense-impressions. The concepts of theoretical physics need to be correlated with sense-impressions, but in the last analysis concepts are created by the spontaneity of thinking. Experience may suggest theories which operate with concepts which are intuitively related to experience, but for deeply lying objects the search for principles is guided by ideas of mathematical simplicity and generality. Methodical, intimate consideration of a problematic situation is the foundation of an intuition which gives insight into the order of reality. That the model of reality represents an order independent of experience is justified by the belief, founded on past successes, that nature embodies an ideal of mathematical simplicity. The pursuit of truth under the guidance of mathematical ideals is founded on the faith that a pre-established harmony between thought and reality will win for the human mind, after patient effort, an intuition of the depths of Reality.

VICTOR F. LENZEN

DEPARTMENT OF PHYSICS
UNIVERSITY OF CALIFORNIA
BERKELEY, CAL.

14

F. S. C. Northrop

EINSTEIN'S CONCEPTION OF SCIENCE

EINSTEIN'S CONCEPTION OF SCIENCE

ALBERT EINSTEIN is as remarkable for his conception of scientific method as he is for his achievements by means of that method. It might be supposed that these two talents would always go together. An examination, however, of statements upon scientific method by truly distinguished scientists indicates that this is far from being the case. Nor is the reason difficult to understand. The scientist who is making new discoveries must have his attention continuously upon the subject matter of his science. His methods are present, but he must have them so incorporated in his habits that he operates according to them without having to give any conscious attention to them. He is like the truly natural athlete, who performs spontaneously, but who often cannot teach others how he does it. Albert Einstein, however, is an exception to this frequently illustrated rule. He has given as much attention consciously and technically to the method of science as he has given to the theoretical foundations of physics to which he has applied scientific method.

Moreover, his analysis of scientific method has taken him beyond empirical logic into epistemology. In fact, his technical epoch-making contributions to theoretical physics owe their discovery and success in considerable part to the more careful attention which he has given, as compared with his predecessors, to the epistemological relation of the scientist as knower to the subject matter of physics as known. It happens, therefore, that to understand Albert Einstein's conception of scientific method is to have a very complete and precisely analyzed epistemological philosophy—an epistemological philosophy, moreover, which, while influenced by positivism on the one hand and ancient Greek and Kantian formal thinking on the other, departs nonetheless rather radically from both and steers a course of its own, checked at every point by actual methodological practices of scientists. The result is an epistemology which has fitted itself to an expert understanding and analysis of scientific method rather than an epistemology, such as Kantianism or positivism, which has come to science with certain epistemological premises and prescriptions and tried to fit scientific procedure to these prescriptions.

In this connection, Albert Einstein himself gives us very important advice. At the very beginning of a paper "On the Method of Theoretical Physics" he writes, "If you want to find out anything from the theoretical physicists about the methods they use, I advise you to stick closely to one principle: don't listen to their words, fix your attention on their deeds."[1] Obviously this is excellent advice, and, as we shall see, Einstein has followed it, illustrating all his statements about scientific method and epistemology by specific illustrations from technical scientific theories and the technical scientific methods which they entail in their formulation, discovery and verification.

Nonetheless, his words as thus stated might easily mislead one who has not read everything which Albert Einstein has written on scientific method. One might suppose that, when he talks about fixing one's attention on the deeds of physicists, he means by "deeds" the denotatively given operations and experiments performed in a laboratory; in other words, one might suppose that he means something identical with P. W. Bridgman's operationalism.

Actually, however, Albert Einstein's meaning is almost the reverse of this, as the very next sentence in the aforementioned paper clearly indicates: "To him who is a discoverer in this field, the products of his imagination appear so necessary and natural that he regards them, and would like to have them regarded by others, not as creations of thought but as given realities."

What Einstein means here is that the full meaning of verified mathematical physics is only given in part empirically in sense awareness or in denotatively given operations or experiments,

[1] P. 30 in a volume of his collected papers, entitled *The World As I See It* (Covici Friede, Publishers, New York, 1934).

and hence involves also meanings which only the imagination can envisage and which only deductively formulated, systematic, mathematical constructions, intellectually conceived rather than merely sensuously immediate, can clearly designate. But because these deductively formulated constructions, as the scientist becomes more at home with them, so capture his imagination as to appear both "necessary and natural," and also because their deductive consequences become empirically confirmed, the tendency of the scientist is to think that they are merely denotative, empirically "given realities," rather than empirically unobservable, purely imaginatively or intellectually known, theoretically designated factors, related in very complicated ways to the purely empirically given.

This counsel by Albert Einstein is something which philosophers especially need to take seriously. If one approaches epistemology by itself, simple answers to epistemological questions often seem very satisfactory. It is obviously much more simple to affirm that all meanings in science come down to purely empirically given, positivistically immediate, denotative particulars than to hold that the source of scientific meanings is much more complicated than this. Consequently, if some philosopher, especially one with a position in a physics department, holds this simple-minded theory and asserts that this is the scientific epistemology, he can fool most philosophers, even those who are experts in epistemology. There is only one cure for this, and this cure is an examination of the technical theories of the physical sciences, their technical concepts, the specific scientific methods used actually by the scientist who introduced the concepts, and the attendant specification of the epistemological relations joining the meanings of the concepts as specified by the deductively formulated theory to meanings denotatively exhibited in empirical experience. Albert Einstein has the competence to construct such an epistemology, and he happens to have directed his attention seriously and technically to this end.

It is valuable also that Albert Einstein is a theoretical rather than an experimental physicist. The experimental physicist's business is to perform denotatively given operations. This tends to cause him to have his attention upon, and consequently to emphasize, the purely empirical, positivistically immediate side of scientific theory. It tends also to cause him to want to reduce all other meanings in science to such purely empirical, positivistically immediate operational meanings. The theoretical physicist, on the other hand, tends to approach science from the standpoint of its basic theoretical problems, as these problems are defined either by the points of difference between major theories in different parts of the science or by points of difference between the deductions from a single systematic scientific theory and propositions incompatible with these deductions, which are nonetheless called for by the experimental evidence. Thus the experimental physicist who writes on the methodology, epistemology and theory of physics tends naturally to reduce imaginatively constructed, systematically and deductively formulated scientific meanings to positivistically immediate, purely denotatively given meanings. The theoretical physicist, on the other hand, tends to see that the problems of physics are only theoretically formulatable, since facts cannot contradict each other; only the theoretically prescribed conceptualizations of the facts can contradict one another.

Albert Einstein has seen that in scientific knowledge there are two components, the one given empirically with positivistic, denotative immediacy, the other given imaginatively and theoretically and of a character quite different from the empirically immediate. In the aforementioned paper Albert Einstein makes this point unequivocally clear. After telling us to watch what physicists do, he writes as follows: "Let us now cast an eye over the development of the theoretical system, paying special attention to the relations between the content of the theory and the totality of empirical fact. We are concerned with the eternal antithesis between the two inseparable components of our knowledge, the empirical and the rational. . . ." Upon this epistemological point Albert Einstein, notwithstanding all his other major departures from Kant, is a Kantian and a Greek empirical rationalist, rather than a Humean British positivistic empiricist. Albert Einstein, at a formative period in his intellectual life, did not study Immanual Kant's *Critique of Pure Reason* to no avail.

Furthermore, in the sentence immediately following the aforementioned quotation Einstein continues:

We reverence ancient Greece as the cradle of western science. Here for the first time the world witnessed the miracle of a logical system which proceeded from step to step with such precision that every one of its deduced propositions was absolutely indubitable—I refer to Euclid's geometry. This admirable triumph of reasoning gave the human intellect the necessary confidence in itself for its subsequent achievements. If Euclid failed to kindle your youthful enthusiasm, then you were not born to be a scientific thinker.[2]

There is, to be sure, the empirical, positivistically immediate, denotatively known component in scientific knowledge also. This Einstein immediately proceeds to designate:

But before mankind could be ripe for a science which takes in the whole of reality, a second fundamental truth was needed, which only became common property among philosophers with the advent of Kepler and Galileo. Pure logical thinking cannot yield us any knowledge of the empirical world; all knowledge of reality starts from experience and ends in it. Propositions arrived at by purely logical means are completely empty as regards reality. Because Galileo saw this, and particularly because he drummed it into the scientific world, he is the father of modern physics—indeed, of modern science altogether.

In short, there must be both the postulationally designated, deductively formulated theoretic component and the inductively given, denotative, empirical component in scientific knowledge.

It might be thought from the last quotation, if nothing more by Einstein were read, that, because "knowledge of reality starts from experience and ends in it," what happens in between, as given theoretically and formulated deductively, reduces to the empirical component and hence adds to the conception of "reality" nothing of its own. The sentence, to the effect that "Propositions arrived at by purely logical means are completely empty as regards reality" might seem to suggest this. The point of the latter statement, however, is that logical implications are always carried through with expressions which contain variables; thus in themselves they designate nothing empirical. But logical deductions proceed from expressions containing variables which are postulates, or what Albert Einstein terms "axioms." And these axioms express a systematic relatedness. Consequently, when one finds empirically, by the method of Galileo, the inductive factors which function as material constants for the variables in the postulates of the deductive system, then to this inductively given material there is contributed a systematic relatedness which pure empiricism and induction alone do not exhibit. Thus the theoretically known systematic factor, between the experience with which scientific method begins and that with which it ends, contributes something of its own to what Einstein terms the scientific "knowledge of reality." Hence, Einstein concludes: "We have thus assigned to pure reason and experience their places in a theoretical system of physics. The structure of the system is the work of reason; the empirical contents and their mutual relations must find their representation in the conclusions of the theory."

Furthermore, Albert Einstein makes it clear that it is the rationalistic, deductively formulated, structural component which is the basic thing in mathematical physics and the empirical component which is derived. This was implicit in the last sentence just quoted, when it affirmed that "the empirical contents and their mutual relations must find their representation in the conclusions of the theory." They do not find their representation in the postulates or axiomatic basis of the deductively formulated theory.

Not only do the basic concepts and postulates of theoretical physics fail to reduce to purely nominalistic, denotatively given meanings, but they cannot be derived from the empirical, or what we have elsewhere[3] termed the aesthetic, component in scientific knowledge by any logical means whatever; neither the logical method of formal implication nor the more Aristotelian or Whiteheadian method of extensive abstraction. Upon these points Einstein is unequivocal.

He tells us that the deductively formulated theoretic component in scientific knowledge is a "free invention(s) of the human intellect. . . ." He adds,

Newton, the first creator of a comprehensive, workable system of theoretical physics, still believed that the basic concepts and laws of his system

[3] Chapters VIII and XII, *The Meeting of East and West* (Macmillan, New York, 1946).

could be derived from experience. This is no doubt the meaning of his saying, *hypotheses non fingo*. . . . the tremendous practical success of his doctrines may well have prevented him and the physicists of the eighteenth and nineteenth centuries from recognising the fictitious character of the foundations of his system. The natural philosophers of those days were, on the contrary, most of them possessed with the idea that the fundamental concepts and postulates of physics were not in the logical sense free inventions of the human mind but could be deduced from experience by 'abstraction'—that is to say by logical means. A clear recognition of the erroneousness of this notion really only came with the general theory of relativity, which showed that one could take account of a wider range of empirical facts, and that too in a more satisfactory and complete manner, on a foundation quite different from the Newtonian. But quite apart from the question of the superiority of one or the other, the fictitious character of fundamental principles is perfectly evident from the fact that we can point to two essentially different principles, both of which correspond with experience to a large extent; this proves at the same time that every attempt at a logical deduction of the basic concepts and postulates of mechanics from elementary experiences is doomed to failure.[4]

He adds that the "axiomatic basis of theoretical physics cannot be abstracted from experience but must be freely invented, . . . Experience may suggest the appropriate mathematical concepts, but they most certainly cannot be deduced from it."[5] In short, the method taking one from empirically given experience to the systematic factor in scientific knowledge designated by the postulates of deductively formulated scientific theory is not that of either extensive abstraction or formal implication.

But neither is it that of any explicitly formulatable scientific method grounded in probability rather than deductive certainty. It is precisely at this point, nothwithstanding his agreement with the positivists' emphasis upon empirical verification, that Albert Einstein, along with Max Planck, becomes so uneasy about positivism. The way from the empirical data to the postulates of deductively formulated physical science is a frightfully difficult one. Here, rather than anywhere else, the scientist's genius

[4] *Loc. cit.*, 35-36.
[5] *Ibid.*, 36.

exhibits itself. The way is so difficult that no methods whatever
must be barred; no sources of meaning whatever, imaginative,
theoretical, of whatever kind, are to be excluded. It appears that
nature covers up her basic secrets; she does not wear her heart
upon her sleeve. Thus only by the freest play of the imagination, both the intuitive imagination and the non-intuitive, formal, theoretical imagination, can the basic concepts and postulates of natural science be discovered. In fact, Einstein writes,
with respect to the discovery of "the principles which are to
serve as the starting point . . ." of the theoretical physicist's deductive system, that "there is no method capable of being learnt
and systematically applied so that it leads to the goal."[6]

In a paper on "The Problem of Space, Ether, and the Field
of Physics," Albert Einstein adds that the "hypotheses with
which it [theoretical physics] starts becomes steadily more abstract and remote from experience,"[7] the greater the number of
empirical facts the logical deduction from the basic postulates
includes. Consequently, the "theoretical scientist is compelled
in an increasing degree to be guided by purely mathematical,
formal considerations in his search for a theory, because the
physical experience of the experimentor cannot lift him into the
regions of highest abstraction. The predominantly inductive
methods appropriate to the youth of science are giving place to
tentative deduction."[8] Consequently, instead of hampering the
theoretical physicist by epistemological prohibitions concerning
the kind of meanings and their source permitted in his basic concepts, Albert Einstein writes that the "theorist who undertakes
such a labour should not be carped at as 'fanciful'; on the
contrary, he should be encouraged to give free reign to his
fancy, for there is no other way to the goal." He adds: "This
plea was needed . . .; it is the line of thought which has led from
the special to the general theory of relativity and thence to its
latest offshoot, the unitary field theory."[9]

But if Einstein's dictum that the "axiomatic basis of theoreti-

[6] *Ibid.*, 25.
[7] *Ibid.*, 91.
[8] *Ibid.*, 91-92.
[9] *Ibid.*, 92.

cal physics cannot be abstracted from experience but must be freely invented" entails the rejection on the one hand of the positivistic, purely empirical, Humean philosophy, which would reduce all scientific meanings to nominalistic particulars, and also, on the other hand, of the Aristotelian and Whiteheadian epistemology, which, while admitting universal or nontemporal invariant meanings, would nonetheless insist upon deriving them from empirical immediacy by the method of extensive abstraction, it equally rejects the Kantian epistemological thesis that the postulated, deductively formulated systematic relatedness of scientific knowledge is a categorical *a priori*. The more systematic relatedness of space and time in scientific knowledge is as tentative, even though not given purely empirically, as is the empirical content which may be observed and correlated with factors within the space-time relatedness. This is what Albert Einstein means when he speaks of the method of theoretical physics as the method of "tentative deduction."

There is, for Albert Einstein, as for Kant, spatio-temporal relatedness in scientific knowledge, which is not to be identified with sensed relatedness. But this systematic relatedness is not a universal and necessary presupposition of any possible empirical experience. It has to be discovered by a free play of the formal, mathematical, intellectual imagination, and it has to be tested by a long sequence of deductive implications, the resultant theorems of which are correlated with observable data. Thus, although the forms of space and time, or, to speak more accurately, the form of space-time, is *a priori* in the sense that it is not given empirically and must be brought to and combined with the local, diverse, contingent, inductive data located within it, nonetheless it is not *a priori* in the Kantian sense of being a universal and necessary form of any possible empirical experience whatever.

Nor is it *a priori* in the Kantian sense that it is brought to the Humean sensuous, contingent data of science by the epistemological knower. Thus Albert Einstein writes that it "cannot be justified . . . by the nature of the intellect. . . ."[10] Instead, it be-

---

[10] *Ibid.*, 33.

longs to and is the public physical relatedness of the public
physical field of nature—in fact, it is that particular relatedness
which exhibits itself as the gravitational field. Thus, in the
epistemology of Albert Einstein, the structure of space-time is
the structure of the scientific object of knowledge; it is not
something which merely seems to belong to the object when its
real basis supposedly is solely in the character of the scientist as
knower.

This ultimate basis of space-time in the public, contingent,
physical object of knowledge, rather than in the necessary constitution of the epistemological knower, follows from the tensor
equation of gravitation in Einstein's general theory of relativity. Its ten potentials defining the gravitational field at the
same time prescribe the metrical structure of space-time. Thus
space-time has all the contingent character that the field
strengths, determined by the contingent distribution of matter
throughout nature, possess. Not even Kant would have referred
these contingently distributed field strengths to the necessary
constitution of the scientist as knower. The verification of the
general theory of relativity indicates that there is no more
justification for finding the basis of space-time in the knower.

Furthermore, this structure remains invariant for all possible
physical objects which are chosen as the reference points for the
empirical measurements of the astronomer or experimental
physicist. Thus space-time escapes all relativity, not merely to
frames of reference, but also to all the millions upon millions of
human observers upon a single frame of reference such as the
earth.

This means that, notwithstanding Albert Einstein's use of the
word "fictitious" to designate the non-empirically given, theoretic component in scientific knowledge, this component is nonetheless not a Kantian or neo-Kantian or semantic logical positivist's subjective construct. The space-time of Einsteinian
physics is the relatedness of the gravitational field of nature.
It is fictitious in the sense that it is not a positivistically immediate, purely denotatively, inductively given datum; it is
fictitious in the sense that it is discovered only by a free play of

the scientist's imagination and not by the inductive method of extensive abstraction from empirical immediacy; it is fictitious also in the sense that it is only known positively by a leap of the imagination, a leap even of the formal, purely intellectual imagination; but it is *not* fictitious in the sense that the sole source of its being is in the knower or subject of knowledge. Instead, it constitutes and is literally the physical relatedness of the physical object of knowledge. It belongs to nature. It has its roots in nature; it is not restricted solely to the mind of man.

The foregoing consideration reminds us of the extent to which the Kantian epistemology is still working surreptitiously in the minds of even the contemporary logical positivists who suppose that they have repudiated Kant. The logical positivistic thesis that anything not given with Humean, inductive, purely empirical immediacy is a mere subjective logical construct is a hangover from the epistemology of Kant, a hangover, more-over, which the contemporary mathematical physics of Einstein has unequivocally repudiated.   .

This is why Albert Einstein is able to make another somewhat startling affirmation. It has been noted that he emphasizes the tentative character of the hypotheses embodied in the deductive-ly formulated, indirectly verified theory of mathematical phy-sics. So great, in fact, is the difference between nature as theo-retically designated in its systematic relatedness by deductively formulated theory and nature as given with positivistic, empiri-cal immediacy that Einstein affirms that neither the formal, logi-cal relation of implication nor any probability or other formula-tion of induction can define the method by which the scientist goes from the empirical data to the basic postulates of scientific theory. The scientist has, by trial and error and the free play of his imagination, to hit upon the basic notions. Moreover, it has been noted that these basic notions receive their verification only through a long chain of deductive proofs of theorems which are correlated with the inductive data.

With time and new empirical information the traditional basic postulates have to be rejected and replaced by new ones.

Thus no theory in mathematical physics can be established as true for all time. Nor can the probability of the truth of any given theory be scientifically formulated. For there is neither an empirical frequency nor a theoretical *a priori* definition of all the possibles with respect to which any particular theory can function as a certain ratio in which the number of all the possibles is the denominator term. This was implicit in Albert Einstein's statement that there is no formulated method taking the scientist from the empirical data to the postulates of his deductively formulated theory.

Nonetheless, Einstein writes as follows: "If, then, it is true that this axiomatic basis of theoretical physics cannot be extracted from experience but must be freely invented, can we ever hope to find the right way? Nay more, has this right way any existence outside our illusions?"[11] There could hardly be a more unequivocal formulation of the query concerning whether the systematic spatio-temporal relatedness of nature, as specified in the postulates of the theory of mathematical physics, is a mere subjective construct.

Einstein's answer is unequivocal; he answers

without hesitation that there is, in my opinion, a right way, and that we are capable of finding it. Our experience hitherto justifies us in believing that nature is the realisation of the simplest conceivable mathematical ideas. I am convinced that we can discover by means of purely mathematical constructions the concepts and the laws connecting them with each other, which furnish the key to the understanding of natural phenomena. Experience may suggest the appropriate mathematical concepts, but they most certainly cannot be deduced from it. Experience remains, of course, the sole criterion of the physical utility of a mathematical construction. But the creative principle resides in mathematics. In a certain sense, therefore, I hold it true that pure thought can grasp reality, as the ancients dreamed.[12]

Nor is this mere faith or conjecture on Albert Einstein's part. For we have noted previously that it is an essential point in his general theory of relativity that the form of space-time is not something having its basis in a necessary form of the intellect

[11] *Ibid.*, 36.
[12] *Ibid.*, 36-37.

of the scientist as knower; instead, it is the relatedness of the gravitational potentials of the gravitational field. Thus it belongs to the object of scientific knowledge, as designated by the postulates of Einstein's general theory of relativity. When these postulates become verified through their deductive consequences, then nature as thus conceived—a gravitational field, with such and such potential distribution and such and such a space-time metric—is thereby confirmed as existing.

Albert Einstein supports this conclusion. For in the paragraph immediately succeeding the sentence last quoted he writes,

In order to justify this confidence ["that pure thought can grasp reality, as the ancients dreamed"], I am compelled to make use of a mathematical conception. The physical world is represented as a four-dimensional continuum. If I assume a Riemannian metric in it and ask what are the simplest laws which such a metric system can satisfy, I arrive at the relativist theory of gravitation in empty space. If in that space I assume a vector-field or an anti-symmetrical tensor-field which can be inferred from it, and ask what are the simplest laws which such a field can satisfy, I arrive at Clerk Maxwell's equations for empty space.[13]

These considerations indicate that if we are going to make scientific theory and scientific method our criterion of the epistemology of science, then the form of space-time belongs to physical nature, not to the knower. Thus Albert Einstein's contention that "pure thought can grasp reality, as the ancients dreamed" is justified.

Moreover, the scientific method by means of which this grasp is possible is evident. It is the method of postulation, with indirect verification by way of deduced consequences. There is nothing whatever in scientific method or in the relation of the scientist as knower to the subject matter he is trying to know which prevents the scientist from formulating postulationally the properties and systematic relatedness of the thing in itself, which is the subject matter. In fact, one of the outstanding accomplishments of the general theory of relativity is its scientific demonstration that, notwithstanding all the relativity of

[13] Ibid., 37.

reference frames and standpoints, inevitable in making specific measurements, science nonetheless arrives at a systematic conception of this subject matter which remains constant through all the relative standpoints.

Considerations such as these make it evident that science is much more than a weapon for utilitarian technology and prediction. It is also an instrument by means of which men are able to obtain systematic, deductively formulated, empirically verified conceptions of reality. Upon this point also Albert Einstein is explicit. He writes:

It is, of course, universally agreed that science has to establish connections between the facts of experience, of such a kind that we can predict further occurrences from those already experienced. Indeed, according to the opinion of many positivists the completest possible accomplishment of this task is the only end of science. I do not believe, however, that so elementary an ideal could do much to kindle the investigator's passion from which really great achievements have arisen. Behind the tireless efforts of the investigator there lurks a stronger, more mysterious drive: it is existence and reality that one wishes to comprehend. . . . When we strip [this] statement of its mystical elements we mean that we are seeking for the simplest possible system of thought which will bind together the observed facts. . . . The special aim which I have constantly kept before me is logical unification in the field of physics.[14]

In this connection it must be kept in mind, as has been previously noted, that this theoretically designated, logical unification is not a mere abstraction from purely empirical, positivistic immediacy, nor can it be logically deduced from this empirical immediacy. The postulated, deductively formulated, theoretically known component in scientific knowledge contributes something of its own. As Albert Einstein writes in his paper on "Clerk Maxwell's Influence on the Evolution of the Idea of Physical Reality," "the axiomatic sub-structure of physics" gives "our conception of the structure of reality. . . ."[15]

It may seem that Albert Einstein's conception of scientific procedure as "tentative deduction," which, because of the fallacy of affirming the consequent involved in its indirect method

[14] Ibid., 137-138.
[15] Ibid., 60.

of verification, prevents the achievement of scientific theories which are timelessly true, enforces the conception of such theory as a mere subjective construct and invalidates his conclusion that such theory designates the character and "the structure of reality." He is fully aware of the indirect method of verification, as a subsequent quotation from him will demonstrate. He knows that the scientifically verified conceptions of this structure change with the discovery of new empirical evidence and the investigations into the theoretical problems of physics by the theoretical physicists. But this means merely that our verified scientific theories give us more and more adequate conceptions of what the character and structure of reality are. It by no means follows from the tentative character of scientific theories that they are mere subjective constructs.

Furthermore, Albert Einstein points out that it is easy to exaggerate this tentativeness. Thus, in a paper entitled "Principles of Research" delivered before the Physical Society in Berlin, he writes:

The supreme task of the physicist is to arrive at those universal elementary laws from which the cosmos can be built up by pure deduction. There is no logical path to these laws; only intuition, resting on sympathetic understanding of experience, can reach them. In this methodological uncertainty, one might suppose that there were any number of possible systems of theoretical physics all with an equal amount to be said for them; and this opinion is no doubt correct, theoretically. But evolution has shown that at any given moment, out of all conceivable constructions, a single one has always proved itself absolutely superior to all the rest. Nobody who has really gone deeply into the matter will deny that in practice the world of phenomena uniquely determines the theoretical system, in spite of the fact that there is no logical bridge between phenomena and their theoretical principles; . . . Physicists often accuse epistemologists of not paying sufficient attention to this fact.[16]

The point here is that while Poincaré is undoubtedly right theoretically in his contention that no one knows all the possible theories of reality, and hence the uniqueness of any present theory can never be established, nevertheless, for all the possible theories which scientists are able to formulate in the light

[16] *Ibid.*, 22-23.

of mathematical and logical investigations into the possibles, it is actually the case that mathematical physicists, using the deductive method with its indirect mode of empirical verification, are able to show that, among the present possible theories, one is unique in its capacity to bring the widest possible range of empirical data under a single minimum set of assumptions. Moreover, it is not any subjective constructive power of the scientist which is the criterion of this uniqueness, but the correlation of the theory with the empirical data of nature. In short, the criterion of uniqueness is grounded in nature rather than in the subjective, constructive capacity of the knower of nature.

The manner in which the postulationally or axiomatically designated structure of nature is connected with the "wild buzzing confusion" of empirically given data, so that nature is found in itself to be a systematic unity, must now concern us. This connection becomes evident when one examines the method of mathematical physics as a whole. No one has stated the epistemological situation within which this method operates and to which it conforms more concisely than has Albert Einstein. In the first paragraph of his previously mentioned paper "On Clerk Maxwell's Influence" he writes:

The belief in an external world independent of the perceiving subject is the basis of all natural science. Since, however, sense perception only gives information of this external world or of 'physical reality' indirectly, we can only grasp the latter by speculative means. It follows from this that our notions of physical reality can never be final. We must always be ready to change these notions—that is to say, the axiomatic substructure of physics—in order to do justice to perceived facts in the most logically perfect way. Actually a glance at the development of physics shows that it has undergone far-reaching changes in the course of time.[17]

It will be worth our while to take up the sentences in the foregoing quotation one by one, bringing out the full content of their significance. The first sentence reads: "The belief in an external world independent of the perceiving subject is the basis of all natural science." The justification for this belief exhibits itself in Einstein's special theory of relativity.

[17] *Ibid.*, 60.

Albert Einstein has emphasized that the key idea in this theory is the thesis that the simultaneity of spatially separated events is not given empirically.[18] It is the case, however, as Alfred North Whitehead has emphasized, that we do immediately apprehend the simultaneity of spatially separated events. An explosion can be sensed beside one at the same time that one sees a distant flash in the sky. Clearly, these two events are separated spatially and they are sensed as occurring simultaneously. Why, then, does Einstein insist that the simultaneity of spatially separated events is not directly observed? The answer to this is that physicists want and require a simultaneity which is the same for all human beings at rest relative to each other on the same frame of reference.[19]

Immediately sensed simultaneity does not have this characteristic. If the observer is equidistant from two events he may sense them as simultaneous. Then any observer not equidistant from the two events will not sense them as simultaneous.

It is the required public simultaneity which is one of the elements going into the notion of the external world. In fact, the concept of the external world is the scientist's terminology for the distinction between publicly valid elements in scientific knowledge and purely private factors varying from one observer to another even on the same frame of reference. Thus Einstein's contention that belief in an external world is at the basis of science is not a dogmatic selection of one epistemological theory of physical science from many possible theories, but is something grounded in distinctions required by scientific evidence itself.

In this connection it may be noted also that Alfred North Whitehead's philosophy of physics, which affirms an immediately sensed meaning for the simultaneity of spatially separated events, is far nearer to positivism than is Albert Einstein's theory. Furthermore, Alfred North Whitehead's theory that all scientific concepts are derived from "the terminus of sense

[18] Albert Einstein, *The Theory of Relativity*, Fourth Edition (Methuen and Co., London, 1921), 21-24.

[19] See my "Whitehead's Philosophy of Science," in *The Philosophy of Alfred North Whitehead*, this *Library*, Vol. III, ch. 3.

awareness" by abstraction is much nearer to positivism than is the
physics of Einstein, in which the theoretical concepts cannot be
abstracted from or deduced from the empirical data.

Consider now Einstein's second sentence in the foregoing
quotation: "Since, however, sense perception only gives information of this external world or of 'physical reality' indirectly,
we can only grasp the latter by speculative means." The basis
for this statement scientifically is in the method of hypothesis
which deductively formulated scientific theory uses. But Albert
Einstein realizes also that it follows epistemologically from
Bishop Berkeley's analysis of the empirically given. Bishop
Berkeley noted that all that is empirically given are sense qualities, that these are relative, private things, varying from person
to person and hence relative to the mind that is apprehending
them. Thus the physicist's concept of a physical object as something three-dimensional, possessing a back side which we do not
sense, with right-angle corners constant through the varying
sensed angles which we sense empirically is not guaranteed by
positivistic, empirical observation. Even the notion of a common-sense object involves an imaginative leap by the method of
hypothesis beyond pure fact. Not merely scientific objects such
as electrons and electromagnetic fields, but also common-sense
objects entail indirectly verified postulation.

Once this is noted, the shift of the logical positivists from
the Berkeleyan sensationalism of Carnap's *Logischer Aufbau* to
"physicalism" is seen to be a departure from positivism. The
reason for this shift confirms the present analysis. The logical
positivists wanted a scientific verification which gave objective,
publicly valid meanings, not Berkeleyan solipsistic, private subjective meanings merely. But such objectivity is not given empirically; it is only given theoretically by postulation indirectly
verified. This is what Einstein means when he says that "since
sense perception only gives information of the external world
or of 'physical reality' indirectly, we can only grasp the latter by
speculative means."

His next sentence reads: "It follows from this that our notions of physical reality can never be final." The basis for this
conclusion is that formal logic in scientific method runs not

from the empirical data to the postulates of the deductively formulated theory but in the converse direction, from the postulates back through the theorems to the data. This means that, in scientific verification, the logic of verification is always committing the fallacy of affirming the consequent of the hypothetical syllogism. This does not entail that a theory thus verified is false. It means merely that it cannot be shown to be necessarily true. The fact that the theory is thus indirectly confirmed justifies its retention. The fact, however, that it is not related to empirical data necessarily forces one to hold it tentatively. But this is an asset rather than a liability; for otherwise we would be at a loss to explain how scientific, or even humanistic religious, theories can be empirically verified and yet shown later, with the advent of further empirical information and further theoretical investigation, to be inadequate and to require replacement by a different theory grounded in different postulates. Hence Albert Einstein's final two statements: "We must always be ready to change these notions—that is to say, the axiomatic sub-structure of physics—in order to do justice to perceived facts in the most logically perfect way. Actually a glance at the development of physics shows that it has undergone far-reaching changes in the course of time."

One additional element, often overlooked in scientific method, which Albert Einstein clearly recognizes, remains to be indicated in order to complete his conception of science. It has been noted that the basic concepts of deductively formulated scientific theory as conceived by him are neither abstracted from nor deduced from empirically given data. Consequently, they do not "reduce" to sentences about sense data, nor can they be derived from such sentences. In short, they are concepts of a kind fundamentally different from the nominalistic particulars which denote data given empirically.

This presents a problem so far as scientific verification is concerned. For, if the primitive concepts, in terms of which the deductively formulated scientific theory is constructed, gain their meanings by postulation, in terms of the formal properties of relations and other such logical constants, then the theorems deduced from the postulates of such theory must be concepts of the same character. An examination of scientific theory such as Maxwell's electromagnetic theory shows also that the concepts in the theorems refer no more to sense data than do the concepts in the postulates. They refer, instead, to numbers for wave lengths, etc. These are not sensuously qualitative things. But if this is the case, how, then, can concepts with such meanings, designating such empirically unobservable scientific structures and entities, be verified? For verification requires the relating of the theoretically designated to the positivistically and empirically immediate. This relation which must exist in scientific method remains, therefore, to be specified.

The foregoing considerations of this paper indicate that this relation, joining the theoretically designated factor in nature to the empirically given component, cannot be that of identity. What then, is the relation? In his paper "Considerations Concerning the Fundaments of Theoretical Physics" (*Science*, May 24, 1940), Albert Einstein answers this question as follows: "Science is the attempt to make the chaotic diversity of our sense experience correspond to a logically uniform system of thought. In this system single experiences must be correlated with the theoretic structure in such a way that the resulting co-ordination is unique and convincing." In other words, the relation between the theoretic component and the empirical component in scientific knowledge is the relation of correlation. Analysis of scientific method shows that this relation is a two-termed relation.[20]

The recognition of the presence of this relation in scientific method is the key to the understanding of Albert Einstein's conception of scientific method and scientific epistemology. Because the empirical component is joined to the theoretic component by correlation, one cannot get the latter from the former by either extensive abstraction or logical implication. For, in the two-termed relation of epistemic correlation, one term does not logically imply the other, nor is the theoretic term a mere ab-

---

[20] See the author's *The Meeting of East and West*, ch. XII, and *The Logic of the Sciences and the Humanities*, chs. VI-VIII (Macmillan, N.Y., 1947); also H. Margenau, in *The Monist*, XLII (1932), *Journal of the Philosophy of Science* (1934); and *Reviews of Modern Physics* (1941).

straction from the empirical term. And because the theoretic term cannot be derived from the empirical term, theoretic physics contributes something of its own to the scientific conception of nature and reality.

This means that the positivistic theory that all theoretical meanings derive from empirical meanings is invalid. Furthermore, the thesis that the theoretically designated knowledge gives us knowledge of the subject matter of science and of reality, rather than merely knowledge of a subjective construct projected by a neo-Kantian kind of knower, confirms the thesis that the thing in itself can be scientifically known and handled by scientific method. Thus ontology is again restored, as well as epistemology, to a genuine scientific and philosophical status.

Hence, although the positivists are wrong in their purely empirical theory of meaning in empirical science, they are right in their contention that philosophically valid propositions are scientifically verifiable propositions. The important thing is not where the meanings of scientific concepts come from, but that they be verified through their deductive consequences and attendant epistemic correlations with empirically given data, before anyone claims that they have philosophical validity as a correct designation of the nature of things.

The foregoing analysis of Einstein's conceptions of science shows that scientific concepts have two sources for their meanings: The one source is empirical. It gives concepts which are particulars, nominalistic in character. The other source is formal, mathematical and theoretical. It gives concepts which are universals, since they derive their meaning by postulation from postulates which are universal propositions.

It should be noted also that for Albert Einstein scientific method entails the validity of the principle of causality, not as conceived by Hume in terms of the hope that present sensed associations of sense data will repeat themselves, but in the sense of the mathematical physicist—the sense, namely, that with the empirical determination of the present state of a system, as defined by theoretical physics, the future state is logically implied. Albert Einstein tells us that he refused to accept certain ideas of his general theory of relativity for over a period of two years, because he thought they were incompatible with this theory of causality.[21] When this compatability did become evident to him, he went on with the investigation and publication of the general theory of relativity. Its type of causality is a theoretically given, indirectly verified causality, not a Humean empirical one. But this point is a special, more technical case of the general thesis that scientific knowledge involves a correlation of an empirically given component with a postulationally prescribed, systematic, theoretically designated component.

F. S. C. NORTHROP

DEPARTMENT OF PHILOSOPHY
YALE UNIVERSITY

[21] *Op. cit.*, 107.

15

E. A. Milne

GRAVITATION WITHOUT GENERAL RELATIVITY

GRAVITATION WITHOUT GENERAL RELATIVITY

GENERAL relativity arose through the supposed impossibility of bringing gravitation within the scope of the Lorentz formulae of what has been called 'Special Relativity.' The Lorentz formulae are the expression of the equivalence of observers in uniform relative motion: an observer O, using Cartesian co-ordinates x, y, z and a time co-ordinate t, is enabled by the Lorentz formulae to infer the description of an event (x', y', z', t') (in his co-ordinates) which would be made by a second observer O' moving with some uniform velocity V relative to O. That is to say, O can calculate the values x', y', z', t' of the co-ordinates which would be attributed to the same event by O'. These formulae were originally obtained by Lorentz as the conditions that Maxwell's equations of the electro-magnetic field should take the same form for O' as for O. They were given a far more general derivation by Einstein, who showed that they could be deduced from the simple postulate that the speed of light was the same to O and O': that they were the linear transformation which made

$$c^2 t^2 - (x^2 + y^2 + z^2)$$

vanish when

$$c^2 t'^2 - (x'^2 + y'^2 + z'^2)$$

vanished. It is a consequence of these formulae that the so-called interval ds defined by

$$ds^2 = c^2 dt^2 - (dx^2 + dy^2 + dz^2)$$

is conserved by the transformation both in value and form, i.e.,

$$ds^2 = ds'^2,$$

where

$$ds'^2 = c^2 dt'^2 - (dx'^2 + dy'^2 + dz'_2).$$

The great success of these transformation-formulae as applied to the phenomena of electromagnetism made it all the more surprising that they appeared incapable of dealing similarly with gravitation. For example, a gravitational potential $\gamma m/r$ did not apparently transform into a gravitational potential $\gamma m/r'$ where r, r' were the distances of a material gravitating particle from O and O'. To remove this difficulty, Einstein abandoned the methods which had been so successful in the relativity of uniform motion. No longer insisting on the operational principle that only such symbols should be introduced into the theory as could be defined in terms of observations which could in principle be carried out, he introduced undefined co-ordinate systems, and required only that the value, but not necessarily the form, of the "interval" should be conserved. He allowed ds^2 to represent non-Euclidean spaces or space-times, and required that laws of nature should be describable in equivalent forms in *all* sets of co-ordinates; that is to say, he made *all* observers equivalent. Gravitation was then considered as the restriction defining the nature of space-time in the neighbourhood of gravitating matter.

But it is open to doubt whether the general principle of relativity, that all sets of co-ordinates will yield the same forms for laws of nature, i.e., that all observers are equivalent, should be expected to hold good in the universe at large. According to the views of Mach, gravitation, in particular, is a consequence of the general distribution of matter in the universe. If that be so, then only those observers who stand in the same relation to the whole distribution of matter in the universe would be expected to be equivalent, i.e., would find similar descriptions of the law of gravitation. Now the matter of the universe appears to be concentrated into galaxies, which are approximately homogeneously distributed and which are apparently receding from one another with velocities proportional to their distances from one another. Observers situated at the nuclei of the galaxies would be similarly related to the large-scale distribution of matter and motion in the universe, and might accordingly be expected to formulate similar accounts of the law of gravitation;

only such observers would be equivalent. If these observers are in fact equivalent observers, they can choose a scale of time so that they all appear to one another as in uniform relative motion. Since the Lorentz formulae are the expression of the equivalence of observers in uniform relative motion, they should, therefore, be applicable to descriptions of gravitation by observers at the nuclei of the external galaxies. The Law of Gravitation should, therefore, be capable of expression in Lorentz-invariant form by this restricted class of observers.

It should be noted that this mode of positing the equivalence of observers is more general, not less general, than the general principle of relativity. If the *general* principle of relativity holds good in the universe, in particular it will hold good for the transformation from the nucleus of one galaxy to the nucleus of any other; but our less restrictive principle could hold good without the general principle of relativity being necessarily true. In fact, the less restrictive principle here stated is scarcely an assumption at all; for in a rational universe, when the relation of one observer to the matter of the universe is identical with the relation of a second observer to the matter of the universe, there is no reason why their descriptions of laws of nature should not be identical.

The present article will describe some of the results of carrying out this programme, and some of the investigations suggested by it. But in executing a programme of this kind, it is desirable to begin as far back in physics as is reasonably possible. We do not, therefore, assume any of the results, or appeal to any of the results, of non-relativistic physics, but attempt to build up a physics from first principles. The intellectual climate of the present investigations is, therefore, different from that of contemporary physics. For example, we do not *assume* the Lorentz formulae, or derive them from a supposed physical principle of the constancy of the velocity of light to all observers in uniform relative motion. Instead, we show that they are essentially epistemological in content, expressing the necessary relations between the optical observations made by equivalent observers, without our assuming any properties of light. We attempt, in fact, to give to all the laws of nature covered by the investigation the character of *theorems*, deduced from the defining axioms.

In particular, we do not make the assumption that the "curvature of space" depends on the matter occupying it. We adopt the view that an observer can choose an arbitrary private space for the description of the phenomena presented to him in nature, together with an arbitrarily graduated clock. This position scarcely needs arguing. The observer merely makes a map of the events occurring in his world-wide *present*, and as he experiences the passage of time he makes a succession of such maps. We shall make little use of the notions of *space-time*, which is just as much an artificial construct as any chosen space, but which often obscures the physical content of the investigations in progress. Each map made by the observer is a mere correlation of the whole or part of the space he adopts, with the point events throughout the universe to which he assigns the same value of the time-co-ordinate t. For the purpose of this correlation, he can adopt Euclidean space if he chooses. The triple infinity of points in the whole or a portion of this Euclidean space can be brought into correlation with the events of any assigned t. Questions which then have to be answered arise as to the correlation between different observers' private spaces. But we attribute no physical properties to space itself.

CONDITIONS OF EQUIVALENCE OF OBSERVERS

A primitive stage in the development of a physics is given when we endow every observer with a single measuring instrument, the clock. Since each observer is conscious of the passage of time at himself, he can correlate the occurrences of events at himself with the real numbers, and by a *clock*, in the first instance, we mean simply some such correlation. The clock is then arbitrarily graduated.

Consider two such observers A and B, each furnished with his own arbitrarily graduated clock, in any arbitrary type of a relative motion. Observer A's primitive type of observation consists in reading B's clock at the same instant as he reads his own. But to read a distant clock requires illumination. Let observer A provide his own illumination by striking a light. He can then note the reading of his clock when he first provides the illumination, say t_1, the reading of his clock (say t_3), when he first sees B's clock, and the reading of B's clock (say t_2') when first illuminated. It is *a priori* possible that t_3 might coincide with t_1, (it cannot precede it). We shall assume that this is not the case, and that t_3 is later than t_1. We can interpret this by saying that light takes a finite time to travel from A to B and back again. With a similar interpretation we can say that B has reflected the light at instant t_2' by B's clock, and that the reflected light has reached A at instant t_3 by A's clock.

Suppose this sequence of operations is repeated indefinitely often. Then A can construct the graph of t_2' as a function of t_1, and the graph of t_3 as a function of t_2'. Then it is possible for A to dictate to B a re-graduation of his (B's) clock so that after re-graduation, the new t_2' is the same function of t_1, as t_3 is of the new t_2'. If the relation of A to B is a symmetrical one, we can now say that A and B are provided with *congruent* clocks. In this way, for any B, it is possible to set up at B a clock congruent to A's arbitrarily graduated clock. All "transport" of clocks from A to a distant B is avoided, and we achieve in this way the setting up of a congruent clock at a distance. This procedure eventually obviates any need for the hypothetical transport of "rigid measuring rods," and so avoids all the difficulties of defining the latter expression. We now say that B is equivalent to A, and write $B \equiv A$.

The same observations, (but without need for B's clock-reading t_2'), permit the attribution by A of *co-ordinates* to B. Observer A assigns to the event of the reflection of light by B the co-ordinates (t, r), where

$$t = \tfrac{1}{2}\,(t_3 + t_1), \qquad\qquad r = \tfrac{1}{2}\,c\,(t_3 - t_1),$$

and c is an arbitrary number chosen by A. It is particularly to be noted that these assignments do not pre-suppose any equality of times of travel of light to and fro, though they lead to the inference of such equality. A can now attribute to B the instantaneous velocity $V = dr/dt$, and he finds also that c is the velocity he assigns to a light-signal—all by A's arbitrary clock

Similarly B can complete his observations of A and assign co-ordinates to any event at A. More generally A and B can similarly assign co-ordinates to any event E in line with A and B.

If the observations of B by A are expressible by the formulae

$$t_2' = \theta_{12}(t_1), \qquad t_3 = \theta_{12}(t_2'), \qquad (1)$$

then simple arguments show that, for any event E in line with A and B to which A, B respectively assign co-ordinates $(t\ r)$, $(t'\ r')$, we have

$$t' - r'/c = \theta_{12}(t - r/c) \qquad t' + r'/c = \theta_{12}^{-1}(t + r/c). \qquad (2)$$

These are generalisations of the Lorentz-Einstein formulae, now made to refer to any relative motion of A and B, and to arbitrary but congruent clocks carried by A and B. They can be shown to reduce to the formulae of Lorentz-Einstein when we take the relative motion of B and A to be defined by

$$\theta_{12}(t) \equiv \alpha_{12}t,$$

in which case it can be shown that

$$\frac{V_{12}}{C} = \frac{\alpha_{12}^2 - 1}{\alpha_{12}^2 + 1}, \qquad \alpha_{12} = \left[\frac{1 + V_{12}/c}{1 - V_{12}/c}\right]^{1/2}, \qquad (3)$$

where α_{12} is any constant and V_{12} is the constant relative velocity of B and A, as defined above.

The content of the Lorentz formulae is thus purely epistemological, and assumes no physics of a quantitative type. They express merely the self-consistency of the observations that A and B can make with arbitrarily-running but congruent clocks. These observations consist of the most elementary sense-data, namely those of visual perception. Moreover, any statement involving the co-ordinates (t, r) or $(t'\ r')$ can be immediately translated back into the observations from which the co-ordinates are assumed deduced. They do not involve the isolation of the concept of 'uniform time.'

To make further progress towards the isolation of the concept of 'uniform time' we consider a third observer C, in line with A and B, and suppose A has dictated to C regraduations of his (C's) clock which make C's clock congruent to A's. Then $B \equiv A$, $C \equiv A$. We require the condition that C's and B's clocks are now congruent, i.e., that $C \equiv B$. This condition is found to be of the nature of a restriction on C's motion relative to A, given B's motion relative to A. When this restriction is satisfied, we can consider a fourth collinear observer D, and find the condition that D is equivalent to A, B and C; and so on. A set of collinear observers who are all equivalent in pairs, i.e., who can be provided with congruent clocks, are said to form an *equivalence*. If, in the previous notation, $\theta_{pq}(t)$ is the *signal-function* connecting the equivalent observers A_p and A_q, so that, for a light-signal leaving A_p at time t by A_p's clock, reaching A_q at time t', by A_q's clock and returning to A_p at time t_3 by A_p's clock, we have

$$t_2' = \theta_{pq}(t_1), \; t_3 = \theta_{pq}(t_2')$$

then the condition that . . . A_p . . . A_q form an equivalence is that the signal functions are given by

$$\theta_{pq}(t) = \psi\alpha_{pq}\psi^{-1}(t), \tag{4}$$

where α_{pq} is a real number characteristic of the pair A_p, A_q and $\psi(t)$ is a monotonic increasing function characteristic of the whole equivalence and known as the generating function of the equivalence. Moreover

$$\alpha_{ps} = \alpha_{pq}\alpha_{qs}, \qquad \alpha_{qp} = \alpha_{pq}^{-1}. \tag{5}$$

These are the analytical conditions expressing the conditions that all the θ's commute in pairs,* $\theta_{pq}\,\theta_{rs}(t) = \theta_{rs}\,\theta_{pq}(t)$. The idea of an equivalence is readily extended to three dimensions; and once this has been done the appropriate generalisations of the transverse Lorentz formulae for any kind of relative motion can be obtained.

The main property of an equivalence is the re-graduation property: if all the clocks of an equivalence are regraduated from reading t to reading T, by a relation of the type $T = \chi(t)$ then the equivalence remains an equivalence. An equivalence is a definite kinematic entity, which has the property that all members of the equivalence can be given clocks which are congruent to one another, i.e., which in a well-defined sense "keep the same time." Essentially there is only one equivalence,

_____

We write $\theta_{pq}^{-1}(t) \equiv \theta_{qp}(t)$.

since any given equivalence may be transformed into any other given equivalence by a suitable regraduation of its clocks. In order, then, to set up a consistent system of time-keeping throughout the universe, we must find in the universe, or construct in the universe, an equivalence. The necessary circumstance that there is essentially only one equivalence corresponds in nature to the fact of the existence of only one universe. It is by no means necessary that there shall be a single "uniform" scale of time, and we shall see later that it is convenient to introduce *two* scales of time.

Another important property of an equivalence is that if ever two members of the equivalence coincide, then all the members of the equivalence coincide at the same instant. This instant I call the *natural origin of time*, for the equivalence. The most important example of an equivalence possessing an instant of coincidence for all its members, and thus a natural origin of time, is the *uniform relative motion* equivalence, in which the members all move with uniform but different relative velocities after parting company all at the same instant. This is given by the generating function $\psi(t) \equiv t$. The most important example of an equivalence not possessing an instant of coincidence is the *relatively stationary* equivalence, all of whose members are at relative rest. This is given by the generating function $\psi(t) \equiv t_0 \log (t/t_0)$. These two equivalences are convertible, in accordance with the general theory: The regraduation which transforms the uniform motion equivalence into the relatively stationary equivalence is

$$\tau = t_0 \log (t/t_0) + t_0, \qquad (6)$$

where t is the reading of any clock in the uniform motion equivalence, τ the reading of the same clock in the relatively stationary equivalence. It will be seen that $t = o$ corresponds to $\tau = -\infty$, so that the epoch corresponding to the event of coincidence in the t-equivalence is never reached however far we push the τ-equivalence backwards.

If consistent time-keeping is to be possible by observers situated at the nuclei of the external galaxies, then these galaxies must form an equivalence. We can then choose for the arbitrary graduations of their clocks that mode of graduation which makes each pair of galaxies in uniform relative motion. More generally, if the external galaxies themselves do not form an equivalence, we can construct a uniform motion equivalence and refer them to it. In either case the members of the equivalence will be referred to as the *fundamental particles* of the equivalence.

The question now arises, can we identify any one of the possible modes of graduation of the clocks of the equivalence with what is ordinarily understood as *physical time?* To solve this problem we need to leave the domain of mere kinematics, and to pass to that of dynamics. The essential step is, if possible, to deduce the equation of motion of an arbitrary free particle and compare it with the equation of motion of a free particle in Newtonian physics. Comparison should lead to the isolation of one mode of graduation of the clocks of an equivalence as that corresponding to Newtonian time.

The concept of a free particle is fundamental in Newtonian physics. By a *free* particle, in Newtonian physics, is meant a particle subject to no "external" force. To realise this freedom from external force, the particle must be thought of as removed to an indefinitely great distance from all gravitating matter. But in the universe as it actually is, it is impossible to consider a particle at an indefinitely great distance from all attracting matter, because we cannot even in imagination remove ourselves to an indefinitely great distance from all the extra-galactic nebulae: there are nebulae or galaxies everywhere, and however far we move from any one galaxy, we merely move into the neighbourhood of others. We must, therefore, modify the Newtonian concept of a free particle, replacing it by the concept of a particle at large in inter-galactic space. We require to calculate the acceleration of a particle moving through an arbitrary point at an arbitrary time with an arbitrary velocity, as reckoned by an observer and his clock situated at any fundamental particle of the system, i.e., situated at the centre of an arbitrary galaxy.

The Substratum

We have identified the motions of the galaxies with those of an equivalence, and we have arranged the graduations of the clocks of the fundamental observers so that these galaxies all appear in uniform relative motion, radially outwards from one another. That is, if O is an arbitrary fundamental observer, $\mathbf{P}$ the position-vector he assigns to an arbitrary galaxy at epoch t as reckoned by his (O's) clock, $\mathbf{V}$ its velocity by the same clock, then

$$\mathbf{P} = \mathbf{V}t \quad \text{or} \quad \mathbf{V} = \mathbf{P}/t, \tag{7}$$

t being reckoned from the natural zero of time for the system. But we have still to arrange the spatial distribution of the galaxies so that the relation of each pair is symmetrical, i.e., that each galaxy stands in the same relation to all the others. This arrangement is achieved by distributing the galaxies with density-distribution n per unit volume at time t, in the reckoning of the arbitrary fundamental observer O, where

$$n\,dx\,dy\,dz = \frac{Bt\,dx\,dy\,dz}{c^3(t^2 - \mathbf{P}^2/c^2)^2}. \tag{8}$$

Here B is an arbitrary multiplicative constant without real significance, and c, the arbitrary constant adopted by all observers in assigning distance co-ordinates, is identified with the velocity of light.

This density-distribution has many remarkable features. It is centrally symmetrical not only about the origin O, but also about any other member O' of itself when transformed by the Lorentz transformation from O to O'. Moreover it takes the same form about any member O' of itself taken as origin; that is to say, if (x',y',z') is the position at time t', in reckoning, of a typical galaxy, then the distribution appearing as (8) to O appears to O' as

$$n'\,dx'\,dy'\,dz' = \frac{Bt'\,dx'\,dy'\,dz'}{c^3(t'^2 - \mathbf{P}'^2/c^2)^2}. \tag{8'}$$

Thus although for any one origin the density increases outwards in all directions, the same holds good for any other particle, a member of the system, taken as origin. Each member, in its own view, is equally the centre of the rest. No member of the system is in a privileged position.

Locally the system is nearly homogeneous, but the density tends to infinity as $|\mathbf{P}| \to ct$. The system is wholly included within the sphere $r = ct$ centred at any arbitrary member of the system, in that member's private Euclidean space. The radius of this sphere is thus expanding with the speed of light. The sphere is itself a locus of singularities, each of which is the counterpart of the singularity of "creation," the initial singularity $t = o$, $r = o$. This sphere effectively prevents any intercourse between the interior of the sphere $r = ct$ and the exterior. No meaning attaches to any question about the space exterior to the sphere, since such space is completely screened from observation by the dense crowding of members of the system towards $r = ct$, in O's description. Nevertheless, if an observer leaves the origin O and cruises in the interior with any speed not exceeding c, he always encounters regions of density smaller than that he left behind at O; he can never avoid the continuous process of density-dilution which accompanies the expansion. However fast he cruises, he is always in regions of local time later than the epoch at which he left O. Thus the singularities in density at the boundary are only apparent singularities.

The epochs of events witnessed by O as occurring on more and more distant nebulae are earlier and earlier in time, partly due to the time of transit of the light from the distant nebula, partly due to the Einstein slowing-down of the clock at the distant nebula occasioned by its rapid recession. Towards the apparent boundary $r = ct$, the local time t' of events now being witnessed by O tends to zero. An observer O' on such a fundamental particle, near $r = ct$ in O's reckoning, would see himself just as much the centre of the whole system as O does. The actual locus $r = ct$ is for ever inaccessible.

It should be mentioned that the density-distribution (8) is preserved by the expansion-law (7) in the sense that the two together satisfy the equation of hydrodynamical continuity.

This model of the expanding universe of galaxies I shall call the *substratum*. It achieves in the private Euclidean space of each fundamental observer the objects for which Einstein developed his closed spherical space. Although it is finite in volume, in the measures of any chosen observer, it has all the properties of infinite space in that its boundary is forever inaccessible and its contents comprise an infinity of members. It is also homogeneous in the sense that each member stands in the same relation to the rest.

This description of the substratum holds good in the scale of time in which the galaxies or fundamental particles are receding from one another with uniform velocities. This choice of the scale of time, combined with the theory of equivalent time-keepers developed above, makes possible the application of the Lorentz formulae to the private Euclidean spaces of the various observers. It thus brings the theory of the expanding universe into line with other branches of physics, which use the Lorentz formulæ and adopt Euclidean private spaces. We see that there is no more need to require a curvature for space itself in the field of cosmology than in any other department of physics. The observer at the origin is fully entitled to select a private Euclidean space in which to describe phenomena, and when he concedes a similar right to every other equivalent observer and imposes the condition of the same world-view of each observer, he is inevitably led to the model of the substratum which we have discussed.

The present value of t, the present epoch reckoned from the natural origin of time, is obtained by applying the formulae $t = |\mathbf{P}|/|\mathbf{V}|$ to Hubble's data on the recession of the galaxies, as derived from the red-shifts in their spectra when interpreted as Doppler effects. The result is about $t = 2 \times 10^9$ years. This then is the age of the universe on the t-scale of time.

The Equation of Motion of a Free Particle

Having found, in the scale of time in which the fundamental particles are in uniform relative motion, a model for the substratum, we can take up again our enquiry as to the relation of this scale of time to that of Newtonian Physics. We require to deduce the equation of motion of a free particle in the presence of the substratum. A particle at position-vector $\mathbf{P}$, at epoch t, is projected with arbitrary velocity $\mathbf{V}$, (as reckoned by an arbitrary fundamental observer O) in the presence of the substratum. We wish to obtain the value of the acceleration vector $d\mathbf{V}/dt$ in terms of $\mathbf{P}, \mathbf{V}, t$.

Comparatively simple arguments based on the theory of the Lorentz transformation show that $d\mathbf{V}/dt$ must be of the form

$$\frac{d\mathbf{V}}{dt} = \frac{Y}{X}(\mathbf{P} - \mathbf{V}t)G(\xi), \qquad (9)$$

where $X = t^2 - \mathbf{P}^2/c^2$, $Y = 1 - \mathbf{V}^2/c^2$, $Z = t - \mathbf{P}.\mathbf{V}/c^2$, $\xi = Z^2/XY$, and $G(\xi)$ is some function of ξ still to be determined. The dimensionless number ξ is an invariant, taking the same value for all fundamental observers. The equation (9) preserves its form under a Lorentz transformation from O to any other fundamental observer.

Before we discuss the determination of $G(\xi)$, an inference of importance can be made from (9). We see that the acceleration of a free particle vanishes when $\mathbf{V} = \mathbf{P}/t$. Thus the fundamental particles, hitherto considered as moving *kinematically* according to this law, may be now considered as *free* particles. The substratum therefore constitutes a *dynamical* system. This could also have been seen from the circumstance that each fundamental particle is central in the field of the remainder, and if it is at local rest at any instant it will remain at local rest.

In order to determine the function $G(\xi)$ we have to introduce the negative consideration that the substratum is of hydrodynamical character, with a unique velocity at every point, and not a gas-like statistical system, with a velocity-distribution in the neighbourhood of every point. Rather complicated analysis, which cannot be reproduced here, results in the evaluation of $G(\xi)$ in the general case of a statistical system and then the interpretation of the expression for $G(\xi)$ as containing a term depending only on the substratum. The arguments consist essentially in determining the general distribution law of a statistical system and then ensuring that the accelerations to which it gives rise are compatible with the relation expressed by Boltzmann's equation. The function $G(\xi)$ for a pure substratum is then found to be

$$G(\xi) \equiv -1. \qquad (10)$$

The equation of motion of a free particle is thus found to be

$$\frac{d\mathbf{V}}{dt} = -\frac{Y}{X}(\mathbf{P} - \mathbf{V}t). \tag{11}$$

This can be shown to be equivalent to the pair of equations

$$\frac{1}{Y^{1/2}}\frac{d}{dt}\left(\frac{\mathbf{V}}{Y^{1/2}}\right) = -\frac{1}{X}\left(\mathbf{P} - \mathbf{V}\frac{Z}{Y}\right), \tag{12}$$

$$\frac{1}{Y^{1/2}}\frac{d}{dt}\left(\frac{c}{Y^{1/2}}\right) = -\frac{1}{X}\left(ct - c\frac{Z}{Y}\right), \tag{12'}$$

whose form, since $(\mathbf{P}, ct)$ and $(\mathbf{V}/Y^{1/2}, c/Y^{1/2})$ are 4-vectors and $Z/Y^{1/2}$ is an invariant, is obviously conserved under a Lorentz transformation from one fundamental observer to any other.

Equation (11) is not of Newtonian form. It will be found to have as an integral

$$\xi^{1/2} = \text{const.} \tag{13}$$

Further, if for a *non-free* particle we define an external force $(\mathbf{F}, F_t)$ by the equations

$$\frac{1}{Y^{1/2}}\frac{d}{dt}\left(m\xi^{1/2}\frac{\mathbf{V}}{Y^{1/2}}\right) = -\frac{m\xi^{1/2}}{X}\left(\mathbf{P} - \mathbf{V}\frac{Z}{Y}\right) + \mathbf{F} \tag{14}$$

$$\frac{1}{Y^{1/2}}\frac{d}{dt}\left(m\xi^{1/2}\frac{c}{Y^{1/2}}\right) = -\frac{m\xi^{1/2}}{X}\left(ct - c\frac{Z}{Y}\right) + F_t, \tag{14'}$$

and define the rate of performance of work by $(\mathbf{F}, F_t)$ in shifting the particle relative to its immediate cosmic environment by the relation

$$\mathbf{F}\cdot\left(\frac{\mathbf{V}}{Y^{1/2}} - \mathbf{P}\frac{Y^{1/2}}{Z}\right) - F_t\left(\frac{c}{Y^{1/2}} - ct\frac{Y^{1/2}}{Z}\right) = \frac{1}{Y^{1/2}}\frac{dW}{dt}, \tag{15}$$

we are led to

$$\frac{dW}{dt} = \frac{d}{dt}(mc^2\xi^{1/2}). \tag{16}$$

These relations result in our identifying $m\xi^{1/2}$ as the *mass M* of a particle of rest mass m, and $mc^2\xi^{1/2}$ as its energy E, whence the relation

$$E = Mc^2, \tag{17}$$

originally due to Einstein. Since the invariant $\xi^{1/2}$ reduces to unity for a particle for which $\mathbf{V} = \mathbf{P}/t$ we see that all fundamental particles have the same mass. Moreover when we take as origin the fundamental observer O in the immediate neighbourhood of the particle in question, we calculate $\xi^{1/2}$ by putting $P = o$, when we get

$$E = \lfloor mc^2 \xi^{1/2} \rfloor_{\mathbf{P}=0} = \frac{mc^2}{(1 - \mathbf{V}^2/c^2)^{1/2}}, \tag{18}$$

also in agreement with Einstein. But now V is the velocity of the particle relative to the fundamental observer it is passing, i.e., its velocity relative to the local standard of rest in the substratum. Moreover the energy E of a moving particle is in this dynamics an invariant, the same for all fundamental observers, and not, as in Einstein's dynamics, the fourth component of a 4-vector. A consequence of this dynamics is that we must not attribute to the distant fast-receding galaxies vast stores of kinetic energy; all have precisely the same energy, $m_o c^2$ where m_o is the rest-mass of a fundamental particle.

INTERPRETATION OF THE EQUATION OF MOTION OF A FREE PARTICLE

The equation of motion (11) gives an acceleration directed inwards to the apparent centre of the substratum $\mathbf{V}t$ in the frame in which the free particle is at rest. We can compare this acceleration with the acceleration calculated on Newtonian principles for a particle in the presence of the substratum. The acceleration near the observer, in the frame in which the particle is momentarily at rest, is by (11)

$$-\frac{r}{t^2} \tag{19}$$

where we have put r temporarily for $|\mathbf{P}|$. Now the particle-density of the substratum near the observer, as given by (8) is $B/c^3 t^3$. Hence if m_o is the mass of a fundamental particle, the mass enclosed in a sphere of radius r is $\frac{4}{3}\pi r^3 m_o B/c^3 t^3$, and the Newtonian gravitational acceleration due to this is

$$- \gamma \frac{\frac{4}{3}\pi r^3 m_0 B}{c^3 t^3} \cdot \frac{1}{r^2} . \qquad (20)$$

Equating (19) and (20), we get

$$\gamma = \frac{c^3 t}{M_0}, \qquad (21)$$

where

$$M_0 = \frac{4}{3}\pi m_0 B = \frac{4}{3}\pi (ct)^3 \frac{m_0 B}{c^3 t^3} . \qquad (22)$$

Thus M_0 is the mass that would just fill the volume of the substratum $\frac{4}{3}\pi (ct)^3$ with matter of density equal to the density at the origin. In the t-scale, then, the Newtonian 'constant' of gravitation varies secularly with the epoch t. Its present value inserted in (21) gives

$$M_0 = \frac{(3 \times 10^{10})^3 \times 2 \times 10^9 \times 3.16 \times 10^8}{6.66 \times 10^{-8}} = 2.6 \times 10^{55} \text{ grams.}$$

We can use (21) also to calculate the mean space-density ϱ_0 near ourselves, for $\varrho_0 = m_0 B/c^3 t^3 = M_0/\pi c^3 t^3$, giving on eliminating M_0,

$$\rho_0 = \frac{1}{\frac{4}{3}\pi \gamma t^2} = 0.9 \times 10^{-27} \text{ gram cm.}^{-3}$$

Quite a different interpretation of (10) is obtained by transforming the scale of time. For distances small compared with the radius ct of the substratum and for velocities small compared with c, the equation of motion (11) may be written

$$\frac{d\mathbf{V}}{dt} = -\frac{\mathbf{P} - \mathbf{V}t}{t^2},$$

or

$$\frac{d}{dt}\left(\mathbf{V} - \frac{\mathbf{P}}{t}\right) = 0. \qquad (23)$$

But $\mathbf{V} - \mathbf{P}/t$ is the velocity of the free particle relative to the fundamental particle in its immediate neighbourhood, which has velocity $\mathbf{P}/t$ relative to O. The last equation accordingly states that the velocity of a free particle relative to its immediate cosmic environment remains constant. This resembles the Newtonian First Law of Motion, which states that the velocity of a particle in free space remains constant, and it suggests that the nuclei of the galaxies, here treated as in motion, are the fundamental inertial frames of Newtonian physics. Einstein and Infeld have pointed out the difficulty of defining an inertial frame, or Galilean frame of reference, in customary physics. Our analysis has at several points suggested that it is the nuclei of the galaxies which define local standards of rest and inertial frames.

We seek to transform (23) into the actual Newtonian equation of motion of a free particle, by re-graduating all the clocks of the equivalence so as to reduce the equivalence to relative rest. It was mentioned earlier that the required re-graduation is

$$\tau = t_0 \log (t/t_0) + t_0, \tag{24}$$

or

$$\frac{d\tau}{t_0} = \frac{dt}{t}. \tag{24'}$$

Co-ordinates r, t of a distant particle in t-measure will now be replaced by co-ordinates λ, τ as determined from the same observations made with clocks reading τ. Thus we have, using the earlier notation,

$$r = \tfrac{1}{2}c(t_3 - t_1), \qquad t = \tfrac{1}{2}(t_3 + t_1)$$
$$\lambda = \tfrac{1}{2}c(\tau_3 - \tau_1), \qquad \tau = \tfrac{1}{2}(\tau_3 + \tau_1)$$

where τ_3, τ_1, being actual clock-readings, are connected with t_3 and t_1 by

$$\tau_3 = t_0 \log (t_3/t_0) + t_0, \qquad \tau_1 = t_0 \log (t_1/t_0 + t_0.$$

Elimination of the signal times t_1, t_3, τ_1, τ_3, then gives

$$t = t_0 e^{(\tau - t_0)/t_0} \cosh (\lambda/ct_0). \tag{25}$$

The velocity-law for a fundamental particle, $dr/dt = r/t$, gives at once

$$r = ct_0 e^{(\tau - t_0)/t_0} \sinh (\lambda/ct_0). \tag{26}$$

so that the fundamental particles now appear at rest. For

near-by events, (25) and (26) yield approximately

$$\frac{d\lambda}{d\tau} = 0$$

so that

$$r = (t/t_0)\lambda,$$

This one can write as

$$V = \frac{dr}{dt} = \frac{\lambda}{t_0} + \frac{t}{t_0}\frac{d\lambda}{dt} = \frac{r}{t} + \frac{d\lambda}{d\tau}.$$

$$\mathbf{v} = \frac{d\lambda}{d\tau} = \mathbf{V} - \frac{\mathbf{P}}{t},$$

and so, in terms of τ-measure, the equation of motion (23) reduces approximately to

$$\frac{d\mathbf{v}}{d\tau} = 0. \tag{27}$$

This is the Newton-Galileo equation of motion of a free particle in empty space. The carrying through of the exact transformation (25), (26), applied to the exact equation of motion (11) shows that the τ-velocity in the now-stationary substratum remains constant.

The conclusion from this investigation is that, in Newtonian physics, the independent time-variable is τ, not t. The epoch co-ordinate τ of any event on the τ-scale can be shown to be independent of the observer measuring it, and so in the τ-scale there is a world-wide simultaneity. There is also a public space, in τ-measure, of hyperbolic character, extending to infinity, and in this space the non-stationary galaxies or fundamental particles are uniformly distributed. Instead of an expanding universe of galaxies, of finite age t and finite volume, distributed with apparently increasing density in all directions, we have a stationary universe, of history extending backwards to $\tau = -\infty$, of infinite volume and strictly homogeneous. There are merely two different descriptions of the same physical entity. The world-wide simultaneity of epochs τ is of course connected with the circumstance that in the τ-description all the fundamental particles are at relative rest.

Since the galaxies show an observed red-shift in their spectra, the frequency of a light-wave must be constant in t-measure. For in t-measure, the members of the substratum are receding, and the red-shift is then the usual Doppler effect. In τ-measure there is no Doppler effect, since the members of the substratum are relatively stationary, but the frequency of the comparison atoms increases secularly with the epoch, and hence the frequency of light emitted by distant nebulae, long ago, is by comparison slower.

THE GRAVITATIONAL POTENTIAL

It was stated earlier that in order to derive the equation of motion of a free particle in the presence of the substratum, we had to introduce the negative consideration that the substratum is not a statistical system but is of hydrodynamical character. A positive result of great value emerges however from the discussion of statistical systems: not only is the function $G(\xi)$ evaluated as identically -1 for a substratum, but also this function is evaluated for a system containing point-singularities, and the term corresponding to a point singularity suggests the Lorentz-invariant form for the elementary gravitational potential; the gravitational mass appears in the form of a constant of integration. The interpretation of the analysis, details of which are here omitted, is that the potential energy X of two point-masses m_1, m_2 located at points of position-vectors $\mathbf{P}_1$ and $\mathbf{P}_2$ with respect to an arbitrary fundamental observer O, a member of the substratum, is given by

$$\chi = -\frac{m_1 m_2 c^2}{M_0}\frac{X_{12}}{[X_{12}{}^2 - X_1 X_2]^{1/2}} \tag{28}$$

where $\qquad X_1 = t_1{}^2 - \mathbf{P}_1{}^2/c^2, \qquad X_2 = t_2{}^2 - \mathbf{P}_2{}^2/c^2,$
$$\mathbf{X}_{12} = t_1 t_2 - \mathbf{P}_1 . \mathbf{P}_2/c^2,$$

and t_1, t_2 refer to epochs at the respective particles. The values of X_1, X_2, X_{12} are invariant, the same for all observers O in the substratum, and the potential energy is therefore invariant for Lorentz transformations from any fundamental observer O to any other fundamental observer O'.

To see the physical meaning of (28), take the observer O to be at the fundamental particle which coincides with one of the particles, say m_2. Then in (28) we must take $P_2 = o$, and accordingly $X_{12} = t_1 t_2$, $X_2 = t_2^2$, $X_{12}^2 - X_1 X_2 = t_2^2 P_1^2/c^2$. Then

$$\chi = - m_1 m_2 \frac{c^3 t_1}{M_0} \frac{1}{|\mathbf{P}_1|} . \qquad (29)$$

But by (21), $c^3 t_1/M_0$ is just γ_1, the value of the Newtonian 'constant' of gravitation at the epoch t_1 at the distant particle m_1. Thus (28) reduces to the elementary Newtonian potential energy of m_1, due to m_2 at the origin, namely $-\gamma_1 m_1 m_2 /|\mathbf{P}_1|$. It is particularly to be noted that it is independent explicitly of the epoch at m_2 when m_2 is taken as origin; and therefore without selecting a convention of simultaneity connecting t_2 and t_1 in (28), the formula for X is adequate to determine the orbit of a particle m_1 in the vicinity of a massive fundamental particle of mass m_2.

It has been shown by the present writer, in work in the course of publication,* that formula (29) introduced into the t-equations of motion of a particle m_1 moving in the vicinity of a massive fundamental particle yields orbits of spiral type, and leads eventually to a theory of the spiral nature of external galaxies. The spiral arms are such a well-marked characteristic of "late-type" galaxies that a gravitational explanation of them is urgently demanded. Though attempts have been made to explain the spiral character on Newtonian lines, it cannot be said that they have had a marked degree of success, and the way is therefore open for such a fundamental revision of the basis of gravitational theory as is implied by our conclusion that the so-called 'constant' of gravitation varies secularly with the epoch. It was to be expected that the present account of gravitation, which takes its origin in the grand phenomenon of the expanding universe of galaxies, should have something to contribute towards the explanation of the spiral character of the resolved galaxies. The

* Since the original writing of this essay published in *Monthly Notices* of the Royal Astronomical Society, 106, 180 (1946) and *ibid.*, 108, 309 (1948); also *Astrophysical Journal*, 106, 137 (1947).

general relativity theory of gravitation, making as it does only minute modifications in the Newtonian law, makes no contribution to this end.

Transformation of the scale of time from t to τ throws further light on the nature of the elementary gravitational potential given in Lorentz-invariant form by (28) or (29). Taking the origin again for simplicity at m_2, and substituting from (25) and (26) for the co-ordinates (t_1, P_1) of the event considered at the particle m_1, the potential energy (29) comes out to be

$$-\frac{m_1 m_2 c^2}{M_0} \frac{1}{\tanh(\lambda/ct_0)}, \qquad (30)$$

which for distances λ not comparable with ct_0 reduces very closely to

$$-\frac{m_1 m_2 \gamma_0}{\lambda}. \qquad (30')$$

γ_0 being the value of the 'constant' of gravitation at the fixed epoch t_0. It will be seen that (30) contains no longer any reference to the epoch τ_1 at m_1; and it is readily shown that the more general formula (28), when transformed to τ-measure, contains no reference to either of the epochs τ_1 or τ_2.

To make the τ- and t-clocks agree at the present moment in rate, t_0 must be taken to be the present value of t, and γ_0 becomes the present value of the 'constant' of gravitation. But this must not be allowed to obscure the fact that the 'constant' of gravitation is secularly increasing, at the rate of one part in 2×10^9 per year, on the present theory of gravitation. Apart from this the τ-equations of motion reduce to the Newtonian equations to a first approximation.

It may be asked whether the present theory of gravitation accounts for those small effects like the motion of perihelion of a planet and the deflection of light by the sun whose experimental verification is claimed as triumphs for the general relativity theory of gravitation. The answer to this question is not yet known, for the sun is not at the nucleus of our galaxy, and the present theory as so far developed does not necessarily apply to the calculation of orbits about a centre of gravitational force which is not a fundamental particle. Tentative recent investigations by A. G. Walker in this direction show that the precise answers to the question of the so-called 'crucial phenomena' depend upon the exact way in which the gravitational potential (28) is introduced into the equation of motion. In Newtonian dynamics, the 'external force' acting on a particle is derived by taking the gradient of the potential; but in our t-dynamics, this gradient requires to be corrected by small terms depending on the variation of mass with velocity. The present writer's calculation of these small terms is not wholly accepted by A. G. Walker, who has proposed in unpublished work modifications which are capable of agreeing with the effects predicted by general relativity. But Walker has found as yet no unique way of fixing these small terms, and the whole question must be considered as *sub judice*.

Nevertheless, the present writer does not attach an importance to these small terms comparable with the importance of describing the main Newtonian phenomena within the scope of the Lorentz formulae and of transformations from one equivalent observer to another. Moreover, the present theory, with its dependence at each stage on the age of the universe reckoned from the natural zero of time can give an account of gravitation over periods of time comparable with the age of the universe which is beyond the scope of Newtonian gravitation.

RECAPITULATION

The present theory of gravitation without general relativity makes its first departure from Einstein's theory by not regarding all systems of co-ordinates, i.e., all observers, as equivalent. Since any observer is conscious of the passage of time at himself, a transformation of co-ordinates involving inter-connections between time and space co-ordinates means really a change of observer, and it is far from clear that all observers in the universe, whatever their motion, should be equivalent as regards the law of gravitation. Instead, the present theory imposes equivalence only on a limited class of observers, namely those associated with the nuclei of the galaxies, or fundamental observers, as they are here called. For only such observers can stand in the same general relation to the distribution of matter and motion in the universe at large, and so be equivalent.

Its second departure from Einstein's theory is that it regards the choice of a space as arbitrary for any observer. He is fully entitled to choose a private Euclidean space for the description and location of phenomena he observes. The object of relativity is then achieved by correlating the spaces and times used by different observers.

Its third departure from Einstein's theory is its denial of any natural measure of time which may be called 'proper time.' Instead, it regards the scale of time as at the observers' choice in the first instance. It then proceeds to find the conditions relating different observers' measures of time in order for them to be consistent with one another, i.e., in order that a meaning can be attached to saying that *congruent* clocks can be constructed at different observers. For simplicity, and because it envolves no *a priori* constants, the different *equivalent* observers then graduate their clocks so as to describe one another as in *uniform relative motion*, this corresponding to the generating function $\psi(t) \equiv t$ of the associated equivalence. This mode of time-keeping is called *kinematic* time t. The Lorentz formulae are then available for correlating the descriptions of events by the different equivalent observers.

These equivalent observers then set about describing one another, and the result is a model of the universe of receding galaxies constructed in the private Euclidean space and kinematic time used by any arbitrary member of the class. This model, though occupying a finite portion of Euclidean space bounded by an expanding sphere, describes an essentially homogeneous universe in expansion, with the same properties, at the same epoch, at every point. It involves a singularity, which one may call creation, at the natural origin of time; but like a Delphic oracle, it refuses to give answers as to the state of affairs at, or before, the epoch of creation. It contains an infinity of members, distributed with finite density at every accessible point, the singularity in density at creation re-appearing at the inaccessible frontier of the expanding sphere. It provides a natural class of frames of reference, or inertial frames, each at local rest, one being associated with each galactic nucleus or fundamental particle. In view of the equivalence of these frames of reference, laws of nature should be described in identical ways by the fundamental observers using them. This finite expanding sphere has many of the properties of infinite space, and it achieves the objects for which Einstein developed his spherical space as a model for the universe. The use of the Lorentz formulae in constructing this model involves no loss of generality. For it is always open to equivalent observers to regard themselves as in uniform relative motion, and for each of them to adopt a private Euclidean space.

In the presence of this model, or *substratum* as it may be called, two principal laws of nature are deduced: the law of motion of a free particle, arbitrarily projected, and the law of gravitational attraction between a pair of massive particles; and an associated dynamics has been constructed. This dynamics has the distinguishing feature that in it, *energy* is an invariant, therefore, the same for all fundamental observers, and not, as in Einstein's dynamics, the time-component of a 4-vector. A consequence is that the receding galaxies are not to be regarded as stores of kinetic energy.

The law of motion of a free particle can be compared with the Newtonian attraction on a free particle near the observer in a locally homogeneous universe; this results in the isolation of a formula for the Newtonian constant of gravitation which represents it as dependent on the velocity of light, the epoch, and a basic mass-constant, the mass of the apparent homogeneous universe. Or it may be compared with the Newtonian equation of a free particle in empty space; this shows that the non-Newtonian t-equation of motion transforms into the Newtonian law of zero acceleration when all clocks previously reading t are regraduated to read τ, which apart from a normalisation constant is substantially the logarithm of t. This transforms the t-dynamics into something akin to classical dynamics, and at the same time transforms the expanding substratum into a relatively stationary, infinitely extending, homogeneous universe devoid of singularity, for which the most convenient space to use is a public hyperbolic space. It must be remembered that the two modes of description, in t- and τ-time respectively, relate to the same entity, the substratum.

The law of gravitational attraction between two point masses is an expression in Lorentz-invariant form of the Newtonian elementary potential, with a Newtonian 'constant' of gravitation varying secularly with epoch. When converted to τ-measure, it yields an elementary potential which reduces to the Newtonian form at distances not comparable with the radius of the universe, and with a 'constant' of gravitation now *constant*, but involving the normalisation constant of the time-scale. This formulation of the law of gravitation is capable, in the writer's opinion, of accounting for the spiral character of resolved galaxies.

That the Newtonian 'constant' of gravitation varies secularly with the epoch is a property not confined to gravitation. Planck's 'constant' h can be shown, by later developments, to depend also secularly on the time.

In conclusion, the theory developed in the present article is believed to carry out the programme suggested by the success of Einstein's so-called 'special relativity' better than his later 'general relativity,' which, in the writer's opinion, is of a nature alien to the main tradition in mathematical physics. The present theory reposes none the less on the genius of Einstein.

E. A. Milne

Wadham College
Oxford University

16

Georges Edward Lemaître

THE COSMOLOGICAL CONSTANT

THE COSMOLOGICAL CONSTANT

1. Matter as Curvature

ACCORDING to the general theory of relativity, matter can be described as a manifestation of the curvature of space-time. Let us recall how this inference is reached.

According to Riemann, curvature is a departure from flatness of a space, or space-time, which is, approximately, flat or Euclidean.

In Euclidean space, the square of the elementary distance of two points is a quadratic form of the differences of the co-ordinates of the points. When these co-ordinates are chosen conveniently, the quadratic form has constant coefficients.

In Riemannian space, it still is a quadratic form of the co-ordinates and these co-ordinates may be so chosen that their coefficients are constant approximately; thus geometry is Euclidean to the same approximation.

Nevertheless, the reduction to a form with constant coefficients cannot be achieved rigorously and, when regions are considered which are not too small, the effect of curvature, or lack of flatness, cannot be completely ignored.

Geodesics, i.e., the straightest lines in Riemannian space, are affected by curvature. In Euclidean analytic geometry, with co-ordinates such that the differential form has constant coefficients, geodesics are represented by linear equations. For space-time of three plus one dimensions, this is interpreted as rectilinear motion with constant velocity.

When curvature of space-time does not vanish, geodesics can no more be represented by linear equations and the corresponding motion is accelerated.

Planets are supposed to describe geodesics of space-time,

and their curvilinear motion is a manifestation of curvature.

Therefore curvature occurs in interplanetary space where there is no matter present. Matter is represented by curvature, but not every curvature does represent matter; there may be curvature "*in vacuo.*" Mathematically, curvature is described by an array of quantities, collectively called a tensor: the Riemannian tensor which contains twenty independent components. If matter is described as curvature, it must be described, not by the whole Riemannian tensor, but by some combination of its components. Otherwise gravitation would not be effective outside matter and Newtonian attraction would not act at a distance. The combination of the whole Riemannian tensor which really describes matter must be carried out according to definite rules, the rules of tensor-calculus, which ensure the essential freedom of changing coordinates which characterises relativity. In short, matter will be described by some contracted tensor extracted from the complete Riemannian tensor.

This is not the whole story. If any values of the contracted Riemannian tensor could be a possible representation of matter, its actual distribution at some instant could be completely independent of its distribution in the past. Clearly matter does not behave in that way; matter varies, but not in a completely arbitrary way; matter is conserved; the possibilities of its evolution and therefore of the combination of the Riemannian tensor which is able to represent matter is essentially restricted by some tensorial relation, involving the variations in space and time of the components: some differential identity must be satisfied.

These requirements can be fulfilled, and when too complicated solutions, which would involve derivatives of a high order, are excluded, it is found that matter is represented by a two-indices-tensor $T_{\mu\nu}$ which can be written

$$T_{\mu\nu} = a(R_{\mu\nu} - \tfrac{1}{2}Rg_{\mu\nu}) + bg_{\mu\nu} \qquad (1)$$

In this equation $g_{\mu\nu}$ are the coefficients of the differential form which describes the interval of space-time. They are ten independent quantities which are called, collectively, the metrical or fundamental tensor. $R_{\mu\nu}$ and R are called the contracted Riemannian tensor and the totally contracted Riemannian tensor, respectively. They are definite expressions of the $g_{\mu\nu}$ and their derivatives up to the second order. They must occur in the actual combination in order that $T_{\mu\nu}$ should be restricted by some differential identity.

a and b are two constants which are not determined by the foregoing discussion. Their values depend on the comparison of the theory with observation only.

This comparison may be simplified, by introducing some assumptions which are legitimate in astronomical applications and may be called the "Newtonian approximation."

First of all, in the actual world, departures from Euclidean geometry are not very conspicuous and, therefore, space can be described by Cartesian rectangular co-ordinates, in the usual way, with a rather high approximation. Similarly Newtonian time can be introduced and the simple Galilean expression can represent the interval of space-time as in special relativity. Of course, this expression is not taken as an exact one, and the acceleration of the geodesics is a manifestation of small departures from the Galilean values. For moderate velocities these accelerations are expressed by equations similar to those of classical mechanics such as

$$\frac{d^2x}{dt^2} = \frac{\partial U}{\partial x}$$

where the "Newtonian potential" U arises from the coefficient g_{44} of dt^2 in the quadratic form according to

$$g_{44} = c^2 - 2\,U,$$

c being the velocity of light, which is equal to unity when distances are measured by the light-time.

The leading component of the material tensor is T_{44}. It is the density ϱ of matter, or rather the corresponding density of energy ϱc^2. Other components are small, astronomical velocities being small compared with the velocity of light.

Within this Newtonian approximation, the equation of gravitation reduces to

$$- \tfrac{1}{2}\Delta g_{44} = - \frac{\mu}{2} T_{44} + \lambda g_{44}$$

where μ and λ are two constants which can replace a and b. ($\mu = - 1/a$, $\lambda = - b/a$). Δ is the Laplacian operator.

Writing

$$\lambda = \frac{\mu}{2} \rho_0 \qquad (2)$$

the equation becomes

$$\Delta U = - \frac{\mu}{2} c^2 (\rho - \rho_0) \qquad (3)$$

and is very similar to the Poisson equation

$$\Delta U = - 4\pi G \rho \qquad (4)$$

(G is the gravitational constant) which is equivalent to the Newtonian law of attraction.

The theory is therefore in agreement with observation if the constant μ (or a) is related to the gravitational constant in some obvious way and if ρ_0, which depends on the other constant b or λ, is small enough to produce only insensible perturbations in the motion of the planets. Within the limits imposed by the precision of planetary observations ρ_0 or λ is completely unknown.

When approximation higher than the Newtonian approximation is considered, the theory predicts small departures from the Newtonian law. They constitute the three astronomical tests of the theory: the gravitational red-shift, the deflection of light, double of the Newtonian expectation, and the advance of the perihelion of the planets. But even within the Newtonian approximation, theory provides for an unknown correction to gravitational attraction which can be represented by the so-called *cosmological constant* lambda or the corresponding *cosmical density* ρ_0.

The logical convenience of the second constant λ or ρ_0 was not realised at the early stages of the elaboration of the theory. It is rather by a happy accident that, in 1917, Einstein put the final touch to the equations of gravitation by introducing in it the cosmological constant lambda.

"Its original reason was not very convincing and for some years the cosmical term was looked on as a fancy addition rather than an integrated part of the theory."[1]

Even if the introduction of the cosmological constant "has lost its sole original justification, that of leading to a natural solution of the cosmological problem,"[2] it remains true that Einstein has shown that the structure of his equations quite naturally allows for the presence of a second constant besides the gravitational one. This raises a problem and opens possibilities which deserve careful discussion. The history of science provides many instances of discoveries which have been made for reasons which are no longer considered satisfactory. It may be that the discovery of the cosmological constant is such a case.

2. ENERGY AND GRAVITATIONAL MASS

Before investigating whether there are other empirical reasons to maintain lambda, besides Einstein's original one, I should like to insist on the logical convenience or even the theoretical necessity of its introduction.

Newtonian gravitation depends on the mass (through the density ϱ) and it produces on the planets a definite acceleration proportional to the attractive mass. Mass is but a form of energy and any form of energy has to be counted as mass. Energy essentially contains an arbitrary constant; it can be counted from a zero-level which can be chosen arbitrarily. Therefore, if gravitational mass, which has a definite effect, viz., the Newtonian attraction, must be identified with energy, which is defined but for an additive arbitrary constant, it is necessary that the theory should provide some possibility of adjustment when the zero-level from which energy is counted is changed arbitrarily.

Poisson's equation in its original form does not meet this requirement; but in the modified equation the density comes out as $\varrho - \varrho_0$ only. The arbitrary change of ϱ, arising from the change of zero-level, can then be compensated by an

[1] A. S. Eddington, *The Expanding Universe*, 24 (1932).
[2] A. Einstein, *The Meaning of Relativity*, 121 (1946).

equivalent change in the unknown constant ϱ_0 or in lambda. In this way no modification results in the gravitational attraction.

In other words, to suppose that lambda is exactly zero would mean that the conventional level, from which physicists are used to count energy, is more fundamental than any other they could have chosen just as well.

3. TIME-SCALE

In order to investigate the possibilities which are opened by the cosmological term, in questions connected with the evolution of the expanding universe, we must consider, in detail, the consequences of the introduction of this term into the gravitational equation.

The consequences of importance are connected with the equilibrium which might arise between the gravitational attraction and a new force which results from lambda, and also from the unstable character of this equilibrium.

Since this happens when the sign of λ or ϱ_0 is positive, we shall limit our discussion to that case.

Within the Newtonian approximation, and assuming spherical symmetry around some point, the equation of motion along the radius r is

$$\frac{d^2r}{dt^2} = -\frac{Gm}{r^2} + \frac{\lambda}{3}r.$$

This acceleration is the net result of two conflicting forces, the gravitational attraction and the cosmical repulsion arising from λ which is proportional to the distance r.

In this equation, m is the mass contained inside the sphere of radius r: $m = (4\pi/3)\,\varrho r^3$.

When $\varrho = \varrho_0$ the two forces balance one another, and, if the actual value of the velocities is zero, the system may remain in equilibrium.

If we do not make use of the Newtonian approximation, but assume, at least as an approximation, not only spherical symmetry but complete equivalence of each point and each direction, i.e., homogeniety and isotropy, so that spherical symmetry exists around any point, then the behaviour of the universe is completely described by the successive values taken by the variable radius of space R. The application of the gravitational equation gives in this case Friedmann's equation

$$\left(\frac{dR}{dt}\right)^2 = -1 + \frac{2M}{R} + \frac{\lambda}{3} R^2 \qquad (6)$$

with

$$M = \frac{4\pi}{3} \rho R^3.$$

When the values of M and λ are such that this equation can be written

$$\left(\frac{dR}{dt}\right)^2 = (R - R_E)^2 \frac{R + 2R_E}{R}, \qquad (7)$$

then $R = R_E$ is a possible solution. It is the case of equilibrium (static solution) originally found by Einstein.

This equilibrium is, on the grand scale, the same equilibrium we have just discussed within the Newtonian approximation.

The opposite case, where the density ϱ is very small in comparison with ϱ_0, has been considered by de Sitter.

In that case, radial motion occurs according to the equation

$$\frac{d^2r}{dt^2} = \frac{\lambda}{3} r$$

from which results

$$\left(\frac{dr}{dt}\right)^2 = \frac{\lambda}{3} r^2 + \text{constant.}$$

Comparison with Friedmann's equation shows that the constant is very small in the homogeneous case. Dropping the constant, we have

$$\frac{v}{r} = \frac{1}{T_H} = \sqrt{\frac{\lambda}{3}}. \qquad (8)$$

Velocities of recession are proportional to the distance and this constant ratio depends on the cosmological constant through the above equation.

The astronomic observations are given in kilometers per second per mega-parsecs, which is the inverse of the time T_H.

As an example of the conversion of one kind of units into the other, we may quote from Eddington: that a velocity ratio of 572 kilometer per mega-parsecs corresponds to a T_H of $1.72 \cdot 10^9$ years. The observed value given by Hubble in the *Realm of Nebulæ:* 530, is not very different.

T_H fixes the scale of time for the description of the expanding universe. Geometrically, it is the sub-tangent to the curve obtained by plotting r as ordinate against t as abcissa, or the radius R as a function of t. This meaning of Hubble's ratio is quite general and is independent of any hypothesis on the relative values of ϱ and ϱ_o. If ϱ_o would vanish or be negative, then the acceleration should be negative and the curve would lie below its tangent; the time available for the evolution of the universe would be smaller than T_H.

If we are not ready to accept that the evolution of the universe did not last more than T_H, (which is the duration of the geological ages, known from the lead-content of radio-active minerals), then it is unavoidable to introduce the cosmological constant (with a positive sign).

Let us return to the hypothesis of de Sitter, $\varrho \ll \varrho_o$, in order to see if this hypothesis is consistent with observation.

The value of T_H quoted above corresponds to a definite value of the cosmical density ϱ_o. This value is $1.23 \cdot 10^{-27}$ gr. per cm³. If de Sitter's hypothesis is tenable this must be much greater than the density of matter ϱ.

The value of this density is known with some precision. There are, in the mean, twelve nebulae per cubic- mega-parsecs.[3]

On the other hand, the masses of a few nebulae can be estimated from the observation of their spectroscopic rotation. The observations are difficult and in some instances corrections have been published even to the extent of reversing the

[3] This takes account of a statistical correction given by A. Fletcher, *Monthly Notices R.A.S.* 106 (1946), 123.

sign of the rotation. If the real masses were much greater, the observation would be comparatively easy.

The three available observations give a mean of $35 \cdot 10^9$ times the mass of the sun. They refer to exceptionally bright nebulae; the average nebula must be less massive. Assuming that the ratio of mass to luminosity is essentially the same for all nebulae, the mean mass is found as $2 \cdot 10^9$ times the mass of the sun.

This gives a density $\varrho = 1.6 \cdot 10^{-30}$, much smaller than ϱ_0.

From these figures, we may infer that actual distances are about ten times greater than at the time of equilibrium.

Therefore, astronomical observation definitely favours de Sitter's hypothesis that the actual value of the density is negligible; matter is, by no means, in equilibrium and the cosmical repulsion prevails on gravitation.

Of course conditions may have been very different in the past.

Equation (7) can be satisfied by other solutions than $R = R_E$. These solutions are expressed by elementary functions. R may start with initial values not much greater than R_E and slowly increase until finally it approaches the de Sitter case.

This special solution of Friedmann's equation, which had been emphasized by the author in 1927, has been described by Eddington as showing the instability of Einstein's equilibrium and giving instances of the rupture of this unstable equilibrium towards expansion.

If the relation between M and T, which reduces Friedmann's integral to elementary functions, is satisfied approximately only, i.e., if

$$(9) \qquad 3^{3/2} M/T = I + \eta$$

where η is small, then the process of evolution will not take an infinite time.

If η is negative, the actual expansion would have been preceded by a similar contraction, the minimum radius being a little greater than the equilibrium value.

In the more interesting case, where η is positive, the value of the radius has been initially smaller than the equilibrium value, and, theoretically at least, started from zero. In the early stages of the evolution the cosmological constant was therefore quite negligible. When the value of the radius reached the equilibrium value, the velocity of expansion, though small, did not vanish, and the radius was able to go beyond the equilibrium value; then cosmical repulsion began to dominate and expansion started again with resumed vigour until the de Sitter condition, $\varrho \ll \varrho_0$ should be realised.

This ever-expanding type of expansion was called by Friedmann the monotonic universe.

It is possible to compute the time elapsed from the instant where the radius started from zero to the one where its value amounts to about ten times the equilibrium value. This depends on the small value of η and, if we write this quantity:

$$(10) \qquad \eta = 10^{-n},$$

the duration of evolution just defined is given by the approximate expression

$$1.3 \, (n + 2) \, T_{\mathrm{H}}.$$

How far exceedingly small values of η may retain physical significance is a matter of judgment. One more zero before the significant figures increases the available time by $2.7 \, 10^9$ years only. We may conclude that evolution during 15 to 20 10^9 years is within the realm of possibility. The other type of motion would lead to essentially the same figures.

This definitely steers clear of the dangerous limit fixed by the known duration of the geological ages; but the margin so gained is not very large. Here again, the way out of the difficulty comes out of the instability of the equilibrium.

4. INSTABILITY

In order to discuss the effect of instability on matter going through equilibrium, we must make some assumption about the state of matter at that time. It would be meaningless to suppose that matter was already arranged into stars and extra-galactic nebulae, since we, precisely, intend to explain the formation of stars and nebulae; but we must consider some simpler state of matter from which, as an effect of instability, stars and nebulae would result.

We shall suppose that, at that time, matter was arranged into gaseous clouds, similar to the actual diffuse nebulae, and that these clouds had large relative velocities. The question of the origin of these clouds must, of course, be postponed; presently we shall investigate if they could account, in the moderate time available, for the actual universe, formed of galaxies of stars and diffuse nebulae.

The state of matter we postulate may be compared to a gas; it is a kind of super-gas, the molecules of which are the individual clouds. Nevertheless this comparison cannot be stressed too far. Although collisions between "molecules" would occur sometimes, they would, unlike collisions in a gas, not be elastic, and they would not bring about any statistical equilibrium or anything like Maxwell's law of distribution of velocities.

We may even suppose that collisions are rare. Then each cloud behaves independently of the others under the effect of the common gravitational field, or rather under the effect of the fluctuations of this gravitational field, because the main effect is neutralised by the cosmic repulsion.

Under these circumstances, we could understand that some cloud, or some accidental arrangement of clouds, moving with nearly equal velocities, may act as an attractive center, which would retain under its dominating influence other clouds which approach this attractive center with moderate relative velocities.

A larger condensation will result which will move along with the velocity of the initial attractive center and which will not disperse when the universe resumes expansion.

The net result is that, after passage through the unstable equilibrium, the universe will be formed of local condensations which remain condensed, while their mutual distances increase.

This would look like the actual universe formed of condensed structures, the extragalactic nebulae, arranged in an expanding assembly. It would help us to understand how these nebulae have a rather large dispersion of their proper velocities (i.e., departure from the mean velocity which constitutes the expansion). This velocity is given as 200 KM/sec. for field nebulae and is much greater in the big clusters of nebulae.

As long as collisions are neglected, the agglomeration of

clouds would arrange themselves with some concentration at the center and correspondingly with greater velocities. In the central region, the higher density and the greater velocity will give more chance to collision. These collisions would occur with velocities of the order of 300 kilometer sec. and such collisions would not be elastic collisions. The colliding clouds would merge one into the other and the kinetic energy would be dissipated into radiation. Further central condensation with an increase of density and of speed will result and therefore more collisions. The colliding clouds would finally turn into stars and the system of stars and remaining clouds (the diffuse nebulae) would gain a strong degree of central condensation. It is clear, that, at least in a preliminary qualitative way, we reach here the essential features of our actual universe. It would not be wise to go into more minute details at this point, but it is clear that this whole process could be accomplished in time of a few T_H. Thus the difficulty arising from the shortness of the time-scale can be avoided.

Let us summarize our argument in favour of the cosmological constant; we have shown that the introduction of this term into the equations of gravitation was necessary to make acceptable the short scale of time which is imposed by the value of the red-shift of the nebulae. This is achieved in two ways: first, by providing a positive acceleration, it enlarges the scale and makes it definitely greater than the duration of geologic ages; possibility ten times greater; secondly, by the mechanism of the instability of the equilibrium between Newtonian attraction and cosmical repulsion it produces, within the short time available, great differentiations in the distribution of matter as an effect of small accidental fluctuations in the original distribution, and thus might account for the formation of stars and nebulae.

5. Beginnings

We have postponed the question of the origin of the clouds from which stars and nebulae have been formed. Our discussion would not be complete unless we inquire if it is possible to derive these clouds, by a natural process of evolution, from some simpler original state of matter.

The gaseous clouds are not the only thing which we have to explain; we must realise that it is also necessary to include the cosmic rays in the discussion.

It is not likely that these rays are actually formed in the galaxy. All presumptions point to a far more remote origin; therefore we can assume that they uniformly fill up the whole space between the galaxies.

Their energy can be estimated from the number of ions they are able to produce, not only in their passage through the atmosphere, but down to the bottom of the lakes or even at extreme depths in coal mines where their presence can still be detected. The whole energy thus found is given as $3 \cdot 10^{-3}$ erg per cm^2. These figures can be turned into a density of energy by being divided by their velocity, which is nearly the velocity of light c. Finally, for the purpose of comparison with the density of matter: $1.6 \cdot 10^{-30}$ gr. per cm^3, resulting from the estimation of the masses of the nebulae and of their mean distances, they have to be turned into density of mass by being divided again by c^2. In that way, the energy of the cosmic rays is found to be $1.1 \cdot 10^{-34}$ gr. per cm^3. This energy amounts to one ten thousandth of the energy of matter.

Cosmic rays must, therefore, be looked upon as essential constituents of matter and their existence must be explained, as well as that of the gaseous clouds, by great velocities which are needed at the time of equilibrium.

At that time the energy of the cosmic rays was even greater than now, because this energy has been reduced as an effect of the expansion.

In the same way, the dispersion of the velocities of the nebulae, or rather of the centers of condensations which have caused their formations, was ten times greater than now. Judging from the actual dispersions of velocities of the field-nebulae, 200 km per sec., it was 2000 km per sec. at the time of equilibrium.

The cosmic rays amounted to one thousandth of the total (nuclear) energy of matter. Of course, if they did originate when the radius of space was much smaller, or if they have been appreciably absorbed, their original energy was even nearer the amount of energy of matter.

It is not easy to conceive any simple arrangement of matter which could give rise to cosmic rays and to the gaseous clouds with great relative velocities. One might think of adapting the hypothesis of a primaeval nebula to the expansion of space. When the radius was small, the whole of matter existed as a unique mass of gas with exceedingly high temperature and pressure. Under such conditions radiation similar to cosmic rays could have been produced inside this mass.

It is difficult to explain how this continuous mass could have split into separated clouds, and how the original cosmic rays, formed within the mass, have managed to go through the distended gases without being transformed or absorbed in a way similar to what happens when they enter the earth's atmosphere.

Furthermore, even if the clouds could separate, how did they acquire these great relative velocities? Some separation could, of course, be achieved by going through an unstable equilibrium; but that process can not have happened twice, and we need it for the formation of stars and nebulae.

The requirements of the cosmical problem can be met by the primaeval atom hypothesis.

The idea of this hypothesis arose when it was noticed that natural radioactivity is a physical process which disappears gradually and which can, therefore, be expected to have been more important in earlier times. If it were not for a few elements of average lifetimes comparable to T_H, natural radioactivity would be completely extinct now. It might be thought, therefore, that radioactive elements did exist which are actually completely transformed into stable elements.

Furthermore, artificial disintegration shows that, besides the stable elements, there are a great number of radioactive elements of short mean life so that any stable element may be the product of disintegration of some radioactive one. We know these new radioactive elements in the vicinity of Mendelyeev's line of stable elements only; but there is no indication that they are limited to this vicinity, and when more powerful means shall be available, it may be expected that they will be found farther away from the Mendelyeev line as well.

The hypothesis that all the actually existing elements have resulted from the disintegration of heavier elements now extinct finds some support, therefore, in nuclear physics. This support was not available, however, when the hypothesis was first proposed.[*]

Elements are described by two numbers: their atomic number and their atomic weight. We do not suggest that elements existed with much greater atomic numbers, but that elements, which were isotopes of the actual stable elements or of the neutron, existed temporarily with much higher atomic weight.

In its extreme form the hypothesis suggests, as the simplest conceivable origin of the universe, a unique atom, isotope of the neutron which had an atomic weight equal to the total mass of the universe. From the successive disintegrations of this atom and of the smaller atoms resulting of its fragmentation, all actual stable atoms have been formed.

Let us discuss this hypothesis in its broad outlines and see if it meets the requirements of the cosmical problem.

It is not very profitable to insist on [the precise nature of] the extreme physical conditions which arose at the very beginning. Strictly speaking, if matter existed as a single atomic nucleus, it makes no sense to speak of space and time in connection with this atom. Space and time are statistical notions which apply to an assembly of a great number of individual elements; they were meaningless notions, therefore, at the instant of the first disintegration of the primaeval atom.

When the individual fragments became numerous enough space and time progressively acquired definite meaning. Then it is possible to think of space as spherical space with a small radius, the value of which was increasing very rapidly.

If some rays, which were emitted in the splitting process, have been able to reach us, they have been reduced enormously, in the ratio of the increase of the radius; they cannot form any significant part of the cosmic rays.

Radioactive process must have continued when the radius was getting larger, say one hundredth of the actual value. If the greater part of the observed rays come out of this epoch, their original energy was about one per cent of the nuclear energy.

Further progress in nuclear physics must be awaited before some definite analysis of the production of the rays in that way can be attempted. Nuclear fragments with extremely high kinetic energy may have existed, and collisions between these fragments may have produced many kinds of rays.

We must content ourselves to notice that this process would make understandable not only the extremely high individual energy of the rays, but also their total intensity, which is a notable part of the remaining energy of matter.

It is easy to understand how some important part of the rays, produced in this way, have escaped, being absorbed by gaseous matter. Actually they separated when gaseous matter was not yet formed.

The formation of gaseoeus matter is somewhat difficult to understand. Originally the atomic fragments must have had enormous kinetic energy (recoil energy), and then elastic collision could not have happened. But these relative velocities are attenuated by the expansion process. After a while collisions with moderate relative velocities might have arisen. If these collisions were mild enough to be elastic collisions, then the process of uniformization of the velocities which leads to Maxwell's distribution and to the statistical equilibrium, which characterises a gas, could have worked progressively.

It is clear that such a progress depends on chance encounters and that the enormous original velocities must result in large velocities of the individual clouds which have been formed in that way.

6. Velocities

The reduction of the proper velocities as a consequence of the expansion has played an essential part in the theory, not only in order to explain the formation of the clouds, but also in the red-shift of light and the attenuation of the energy of the cosmic rays. I should like to make some remarks which might help to shed some light upon the theory of this essential phenomenon, and also to discuss its importance in relation to the clustering of the nebulae.

There are two ways of discussing this phenomenon, each of which emphasizes some different aspect of the question.

The most rigorous way is to consider the trajectories of individual particles as geodesics of the universe of variable radius, defined by the quadratic form:

$$ds^2 = -R^2 d\sigma + dt^2$$

Strictly speaking, σ is three-dimensional, it is the angular distance in an elliptic space of radius one; but this circumstance can be ignored in the actual question.

If it were not for the minus sign, which emphasises the essential difference between space and time, this quadratic form would be the line element on a surface of revolution (the t axis being the axis of symmetry).

A well known theorem of Clairaut states that, for geodesics on a surface of revolution, the sine of the angle made by the geodesics with the meridian plane varies as the inverse of the distance from the axis.

Computation of the geodesics, essentially as in the demonstration of Clairaut's theorem, shows that for the geodesic the relation $(R\, d\sigma/dt = C\tau/R)$ is satisfied.

The velocity, or more strictly the momentum (because the denominator is ds and not dt, so that the variation of mass with velocity is taken into account) is reduced in proportion to the ratio of the expansion.

This extends the theory of the red-shift, so that it can be applied to material particles of any velocity.

There is another way of presenting the theory in a more elementary manner. Instead of using angular space with co-ordinates which follow the mean motion of matter, we may resort to Galilean local co-ordinates, around some point taken as a center of the description.

Then, the mean motion is a radial motion away from the center, with velocities proportional to distance. This defines the mean velocity or, let us say, the normal velocity.

The proper velocity of a material particle shows as a difference between the motion of this particle and the normal velocity at the place where the particle happens to be.

Now, it is easy to see, that a particle with abnormal velocity has a tendency to reach places where its velocity is not so abnormal.

Consider, for definiteness, an abnormal positive velocity along the radius drawn from the center of the representation. The particle travels quicker than the normal particles (which have the normal velocity), and therefore it outruns normal particles which have greater and greater velocities. The difference between its own velocity (assumed to be constant) and the normal velocity at the place it has reached has therefore diminished. That is its proper velocity, and we see that it is reduced as an effect of the expansion. The magnitude of this effect can be computed as a courier problem and gives the same result as the more rigorous proof given above.

A further application of this effect is shown in the correlation which is found between the fluctuations in the distribution of the densities and the fluctuations in the distribution of the velocities. In the great clusters of the nebulae, which have failed to expand as the field nebulae and have retained a density not very different from the cosmical density ϱ_0, the proper velocities are much greater than for the field nebulae.

Actually the velocities in the clusters are only three times greater than for field nebulae, whereas a velocity ten times greater might have been expected from the value of the density. It is difficult to decide if the discrepancy is to be ascribed to uncertainty of the observational data or to some aspect not yet understood in the theory of the clusters of nebulae.

G. Lemaître

Bruxelles, Belgium

17

Karl Menger

THE THEORY OF RELATIVITY AND GEOMETRY

THE THEORY OF RELATIVITY AND GEOMETRY

I. A Brief History of Geometry

A FUTURE historian of geometry, if pressed for space, might devote to the period between Euclid and Einstein a passage somewhat like the following four paragraphs:

(1) The Greeks began the systematic study of objects such as points, lines, planes, polygons, conic sections, and spheres. They discovered how to draw, from a very few assumptions about these objects, an astonishing number of conclusions. Euclid's assumptions (some of which he never stated explicitly) about points, lines, and planes involved a two-fold idealization of the relations between small dots, rigid rods, and flat boards. First, he neglected the extension of the dots as well as the thickness of the rods and boards. Secondly, he assumed the length of the rods to exceed any finite bound. The Greeks also included in their studies a few curves and surfaces more complicated than the conic sections and the sphere. These turned up in the course of their pursuit of certain geometric hobbies, such as the trisection of angles. Archimedes discovered methods for computing the areas bounded by some curves as well as the slopes of their tangents. But it was not until the eighties of the nineteenth century that the foundation of this postulational or "synthetic" geometry was completed. Pasch was the first to formulate explicitly all the assumptions on which a particular branch of geometry is based, and in addition to list all the concepts involved. On these as a foundation he built up the whole theory by purely logical reasoning. Since then, it has become common knowledge that a deductive theory (such as synthetic geometry) is necessarily based on concepts which, within the theory, remain undefined, and on propositions which, within the theory, remain unproved.

(2) In the seventeenth century, after navigators had char-

acterized the points on the surface of the earth by latitude and longitude, Descartes and Fermat introduced analogous methods into theoretical geometry. To do this, they chose as a frame of reference three mutually perpendicular planes. Each point in space they characterized by three numbers, called the co-ordinates of the point in question. These numbers are the perpendicular distances from the three planes of reference to the point. According to this scheme, each of the simple geometrical objects studied by the Greeks is characterized by a simple numerical relation between the co-ordinates (x, y, z) of its constituent points. For example, the sphere of radius 1 with its center at $(0, 0, 0)$ is characterized by the relation $x^2 + y^2 + z^2 = 1$. Conversely, every simple relation between three numbers x, y, and z characterizes an object treated in the Greek geometry. For example, the relation $y = 3x$ characterizes the points of a particular plane. To every assumption and every theorem of the Greek geometry, there corresponds an algebraic theorem about triples of numbers. There was no reason to confine this new method to simple numerical relations; consequently Descartes included within the realm of geometry objects corresponding to numerical relations more complicated than those which characterized the objects of Greek geometry. An example is the equality $y = x^3$. In fact, Descartes began the systematic study of all curves and surfaces defined by numerical relations. In the course of this study, it appeared that the few rather complicated objects known to the Greeks were merely very special individuals in the now immensely increased geometric population. The application of differential and integral calculus to co-ordinate (also called "analytic") geometry resulted in the systematic description of the local properties of curves, such as their slopes, radii of curvature, etc. This so-called "differential" geometry, a broad generalization of Archimedes' results, was later extended by Euler, Monge, and Gauss to surfaces. But differential geometry, by its very nature, is restricted to objects accessible by the methods of calculus—that is, to smooth objects which at all points have tangent lines or planes, curvatures, etc. (A triangle at its vertices has neither curvature nor tangent.) About 1900, Study gave a sound foundation to analytic geometry by developing it as a theory in which (in contrast to synthetic geometry) the objects are explicitly defined: points by pairs or triples of numbers; lines by linear equations, etc. These arithmetically defined objects are then treated by the methods of algebra and calculus.

(3) During the nineteenth century, the very concept of space was profoundly generalized. It was found that assumptions incompatible with those of Euclid can be used as the foundations for consistent deductive geometries. These systems (particularly the first one, developed by Bolyai and Lobachewsky) were called non-Euclidean geometries. In analytic geometry, pairs and triples of complex numbers (of the form $a + b \sqrt{-1}$) were admitted as points, and were treated just as the pairs and triples of real numbers had previously been treated in the analytic geometry of the Euclidean plane and space. Quadruples and quintuples, etc., of numbers were called points in four and five etc. dimensional spaces. Gauss studied surfaces intrinsically— that is, without reference to the space in which they are embedded. He regarded them as generalizations of the plane. Riemann developed n-dimensional spaces which had the same generality and variety as the smooth objects embedded in them. An Italian school studied the effects which a transformation of the frame of reference has on the description of an object— effects similar to those produced by a transformation of the object without change in the frame of reference. An earlier French school had created projective geometry, that is, the geometry dealing with those properties which an object retains when it is projected on another object. For instance, the straightness of a line is left unchanged by a projective transformation, its length, in general, is not. Lie developed a profound theory dealing with groups of transformations. Klein's classification of geometrical properties according to the groups of transformations under which they are invariant, was in fashion for some decades about 1900.

Among the most fundamental characteristics of an object are its so-called topological properties. These properties are the ones which an object retains when it undergoes such an irregular transformation as a diagram undergoes if it be drawn on a rubber sheet, and the sheet then stretched, compressed or distorted in any way which does not result in tearing the fabric apart or cementing it together. Such a transformation may not only alter the length of a curve but may change a straight line into a curved one. Any object which can be obtained from a straight segment (between the points p and q) by a topological transformation is called an "arc." By an "interior" point of an arc is meant any point which is the transform of any point other than p or q of the straight segment. (Interior points can also be defined intrinsically, that is, without reference to the original straight segment and the transformation.) Every arc has the characteristic property that, by the omission of any one of its interior points, it is decomposed into exactly two connected parts. Y-shaped objects and circles (into which a straight segment cannot topologically be transformed) cannot be thus decomposed. If a plane contains two triples of points, and if each point of one triple is connected by an arc with each point of the other triple, then at least two of the nine arcs have at least one interior point in common. This fact is a topological property of the plane, since it remains true no matter how the plane is topologically transformed. On the surface of an anchor ring (a surface into which a plane cannot be topologically transformed) two triples of points can be connected by nine arcs, no two of which have an interior point in common.

(4) During the nineteenth century, the concept of a numerical relation as a basis for the definition of geometric objects was slowly but steadily generalized. The curve represented by $y = x^3$ had already been admitted to the realm of plane curves at a time when some Renaissance geometers denied that $y = 3^x$ represented a legitimate geometric object. Even after such smooth "transcendental" curves had been admitted, conservatives still made smoothness a *sine qua non*. But Cauchy pointed out that a V-shaped curve (which has no tangent at its lowest point) corresponds to the equation $y = + \sqrt{x^2}$, and Weierstrass showed that even curves which have no tangent at any point correspond to generally recognized numerical expressions. The same is true of some objects which defy all graphic representation. Take for example the set consisting of all those points on the line $y = o$ which have an irrational abscissa together with

all those points on the line $y = 1$ which have a rational abscissa. Dirichlet noticed that this set could be defined by the equation

$$y = \lim_{n \to \infty} \lim_{m \to \infty} \cos^{2m}(n!\pi x)$$

an expression essentially of the same nature as the equations customarily used in the Fourier analysis of periodic phenomena.

It was Cantor who, about 1880, took the final step in this program of liberalization by opening the domain of geometry to all sets of points, not only those defined by numerical relations, but those defined in any other way—say, by the joining or intersecting of simpler sets; by omitting parts; by selecting one point from each of a family of sets and uniting the selected points into one set; etc. The new objects introduced into geometry by this point set theory were so vast in number that they dwarfed the additions introduced by analytic geometry during the Renaissance. Some of these new objects exhibited such unexpected properties and deviated so radically from traditional patterns that they were said to defy intuition. But the tremendous new world disclosed by set theory was soon found to be governed by general laws: partly extensions and generalizations of classic results obtained by analytic geometry; partly new laws of the most unexpected kind dealing with radically new patterns, where smoothness, instead of being the general rule, turned out to be a rare and not very important exception.

As a parallel to the extension just described, the very notion of space was broadened until it attained the same generality and variety as the spatial objects contemplated by set-theoretical geometry. According to Fréchet, a general metric space is any set which fulfills the following requirements. With every pair of elements there is associated a number, called the distance between them. This number is positive whenever the elements are distinct, and zero when they are identical. Of the three distances defined by three distinct points, no one is greater than the sum of the other two. (This last stipulation generalizes the theorem that in a Euclidean triangle the length of any one side cannot exceed the sum of the lengths of the other two sides.) There have been formulated conditions under which the elements of such a general metric space can be described by coordinates, and still stronger conditions under which these elements behave in every respect like the points of Euclidean space.

II. The Theory of Relativity and Classical Geometry

One of Einstein's most fundamental contributions to scientific thought was his introduction of non-Euclidean geometry into the foundations of physics. Poincaré had discussed the possibility of describing Nature by some non-Euclidean system; but he offered this suggestion only to dismiss it, for he believed that Euclidean geometry had an inherent simplicity which no other geometry possessed. In direct contradiction to this idea, Einstein greatly simplified the description of Nature by assuming a non-Euclidean space.[1] But, as he and others have emphasized, this assumption is not of a geometric nature. For geometry, in its synthetic aspect, deals with undefined objects (called points, lines, planes, etc., cf. I, 1) and, in its analytic aspect, with arithmetically defined objects (triples of numbers, linear equations, etc., cf. I, 2). Einstein's assumption, on the other hand, deals with physical objects such as cross-hairs in telescopes and the light rays observed by astronomers, etc. It amounts, in fact, to the hypothesis that certain physical objects behave like points and lines of a non-Euclidean rather than a Euclidean space. However, in formulating his hypothesis about the physical world, Einstein employed a geometric terminology. Indeed, his fundamental idea may be split into two parts: (1) That a light ray always follows the shortest path; and (2) that these shortest paths have the properties of lines in a non-Euclidean space. In this sense he geometrized certain basic parts of physics, particularly the theory of gravitation.

[1] The recent development of hyperbolic geometry indicates that Euclidean geometry lacks even the distinction of logical simplicity. For in Euclidean geometry "congruent" and "perpendicular" cannot be defined in terms of intersectional constructions, and hence these (or similarly complicated) relations must be incorporated in the list of undefined concepts on which Euclidean geometry is based. Even "between," while capable of an intersectional definition, cannot be proved to enjoy the properties of linear order except on the basis of complicated assumptions. The only geometry which indeed is simple in the indicated sense is (as has been shown in the Reports of a Mathematical Colloquium, 2nd series) the hyperbolic geometry initiated by Bolyai and Lobachewsky. Hyperbolic geometry is the only one which can be developed from a few simple assumptions concerning "joining," "intersecting," and "continuity" alone.

Einstein, in carrying out his program, went so far as—and essentially no farther than—to assume that the space-time of the physical world is a four-dimensional Riemann space (cf. I, 3). For the quantitative (metric) description of the objects in this space, each observer of the physical world carries with him his own particular frame of reference. Furthermore, Einstein made extensive use of the Italian theorems concerning the transformations of frames of reference (cf. I, 3).

A simple, non-relativistic example may illustrate how physical facts may suggest assumptions even about the qualitative topological properties of a space. Imagine a world the structure of which resembles that of a very thin but infinitely extended sheet of paper. And imagine this world to be inhabited by intelligent beings who are not aware that their world has any thickness at all. They use plane geometry, although their geometers have defined the concept, to them unpicturable, of a three-dimensional space. They have developed chemistry to the structural stage. Their chemists have devised plane diagrams for many simple molecules without finding any two valence bonds with an interior point in common. At last they run across a compound P_3N_3 in which each of three atoms of nitrogen is joined by one valence bond to each of three atoms of phosphorus. For the molecules of this substance the chemists cannot draw a diagram of the usual sort because, in a plane, it is impossible to join each of three points to each of three other points by nine arcs no two of which have an interior point in common (cf. I, 3). But a two-dimensional Einstein living in this paper plane might explain everything by suggesting that the world in question was one of the three-dimensional continua developed by his mathematical colleagues, and that the nitrogen and phosphorus atoms composing any molecule of P_3N_3 were arranged on the surface of a little anchor ring in this continuum. So long as terrestrial chemists confine themselves to one-dimensional valence bonds (valence arcs) they are not forced to assume that their space is a thin slice of a four-dimensional continuum, because, according to a basic theorem of dimension theory, every object composed of arcs can be depicted in three-dimensional space—that is to say, it can be topologically transformed into an object contained in three-dimensional space. The situation might be different if chemists were to find it necessary to use surfaces as bonds. Suppose, for instance, there were two kinds of ozone of different stability, and suppose it were decided to represent one of these by three oxygen atoms joined by the three sides of a triangle, and the other by three oxygen atoms situated at the corners of a triangular surface. The extension of such a system might cause difficulties, because not every object composed of triangular surfaces can be depicted in three-dimensional space. In fact, Flores discovered some which cannot be transformed topologically into any object of a space of less than five dimensions.

III. Some Trends in Modern Geometry

The close relation between modern differential geometry (the work of Levi-Cività, Cartan, Weyl, Schouten) and the theory of relativity is generally known and will undoubtedly be treated elsewhere in this volume. Here I shall discuss certain trends of modern geometry which are less commonly known.

(A). Undoubtedly the most striking feature in the development of geometry during the last 2000 years is the continued expansion of the concept "geometric object." This concept began by comprising only the few curves and surfaces of Greek synthetic geometry; it was stretched, during the Renaissance, to cover the wide domain of those objects defined by analytic geometry; more recently, it has been extended to cover the boundless universe treated by point-set theory. The tree planted by Descartes still continues to bloom, and its admirers have indeed repeatedly tried to exterminate the somewhat bizarre shoots which have sprung from the seed sown by Cantor—growths which, in the natural course of events, seem destined to surround and cover the venerable tree. But although the trend, particularly in the last decade, has been against point-set theory,[2] I do not believe that its antagonists will, in the long run, stunt its growth, any more than their intellectual ancestors, at the time of the Renaissance, harmed analytic geometry by denying

[2] It is a curious fact that some opponents of set theory introduce set theory into the foundation of other branches of mathematics, such as projective geometry, and into parts of analysis which can be developed in a purely algebraic way.

that the equation $y = 3^x$ represents a legitimate geometric object (cf. I, 4). The exponential and logarithmic curves, once denounced as ungeometric, have emerged unscathed from the struggle. Those who claim that Euclid and Descartes would not recognize most point-sets as legitimate objects for geometric treatment are undoubtedly right. But it is equally likely that neither Pythagoras nor Palestrina would recognize a modern symphonic tone poem as music.

(B). Another important modern trend is the transition from the quantitative to the qualitative point of view. Projective geometry began by ignoring length; then came the general theory of order which neglects distances and concentrates attention on mere arrangement. These movements, however, are but steps along the road to topology. In this connection, it is worth noting that even modern algebra, by devoting itself principally to the study of groups, rings and fields, has largely abandoned the quantitative point of view.

(C). A third modern tendency is the one away from co-ordinates. It was by way of co-ordinates that quantity, in the seventeenth century, invaded geometry. But objections to co-ordinates may be raised even by a geometer interested in quantitative results, for every set of co-ordinates refers to just one frame of reference, and it is fair to ask "Why this particular frame?" Indeed, in tensor calculus the co-ordinates of an object are computed with respect to every frame, if the co-ordinates of that object with respect to any one frame are known; and in the theory of invariants, geometers and algebraists have systematically studied properties and relations which are valid no matter what frame is chosen. Why then introduce any frame at all? Unfortunately, in analytic geometry, many relations which are independent of any frame must be expressed with reference to some particular frame. It is therefore preferable to devise new methods—methods which lead directly to intrinsic properties without any mention of co-ordinates. The development of topology of general spaces and of the objects which occur in them, as well as the development of the geometry of general metric spaces (cf. I, 4) are steps in this direction.

(D). The last modern trend which we shall mention is the

one away from assumptions of differentiability. There is no valid reason to restrict numerical relations by such assumptions, even if attention is confined to points defined by co-ordinates, and to objects introduced by equations. In other words, there is no valid reason why only smooth objects should be studied. The motives which prompt so many mathematicians and physicists to limit themselves to the consideration of such objects are, in origin, historical and psychological. The concepts of calculus first opened the field of local geometric properties (e.g., tangents, curvatures, cusps, points of inflection, etc.) to investigation; and the methods of calculus have suggested to geometers problems which have kept them busy for 250 years. The training of mathematicians, and particularly of physicists, begins with calculus, and the spirit of the calculus permeates their later studies. Whatever is customary appears natural and simple. Students, when their mathematical training is finished, handle higher partial derivatives as easily as they handle common fractions; and they are thereby misled into the belief that such derivatives represent natural and simple concepts. In my opinion, the concepts so represented are neither geometrically as natural nor logically as simple as many of the concepts of general topology or general metric geometry, which appear complicated to some mathematicians and abstruse to most physicists. Assumptions of smoothness should be eliminated except where they are really indispensable. For instance, the length of a curve and many related quantities (which in calculus are expressed as integrals involving derivatives) have actually nothing to do with the smoothness of the curve in question. In fact, the concept of length, applied to a polygon, is clearer than the same concept applied to a circle, although the polygon is not smooth and the circle is. Moreover, many general theorems do not hold within the restricted field of smooth curves. Goldschmidt showed that some curves which minimize certain simple and important expressions, have corners, and Hahn discovered that some of these minimizing (!) curves are even of infinite length. Consequently, an *a priori* limitation to smooth curves of finite length often eliminates the very solutions of the minimum problems under consideration. It is only by reason of historical inertia that, even where smoothness has no bearing on either the problem or its solution, differentiability is postulated in order that the traditional methods of the calculus may be applied.

IV. Modern Trends in Geometry and the Theory of Einstein

A geometer who attempts to connect the trends just mentioned with the work of Einstein finds himself in an unenviable position. On the one hand, he realizes that the theory of relativity, one of the greatest achievements of the human intellect, is based entirely on a form of geometry which today deserves to be called classic. On the other hand, he is forced to admit that, no matter how much significance he may attach to the recent progress just indicated, he has only a few suggestions and no substantial results to offer to the physicist. Even so, if he is convinced of the importance of the recent developments in his own field, he cannot help feeling that some day the new geometry must be of use to physicists, particularly in the field of relativity. And since it was Einstein who introduced into physics geometric ideas which, before his day, had been regarded as mere mathematical speculations, an essay on relativity and geometry seems to be the appropriate place for a geometer to air his opinions and his hopes.

Historically, the first attempt to apply modern geometry to physics was not auspicious. The speculations about Nature in which the founder of set theory briefly indulged were not on a par with his profound mathematical ideas. He attempted to connect heat and electricity with denumerability and indenumerability, two quantitative properties of infinite sets. Today, despite the greatly increased knowledge about the regularities and irregularities of point-sets (cf. III, A), it is difficult to imagine how general sets could be applied to physics. Take, for example, only one of the most astonishing conclusions which Banach and Tarski deduced from a discovery made by Hausdorff. It is possible to divide a large sphere (say, of the size of the sun) into a finite number of mutually disjoint parts which together exhaust the volume of the large sphere, and to move each one of these parts (without changing its size or shape) into a small sphere (say, of the size of a pea) in such a way that the moved parts remain mutually disjoint and together exhaust the volume of the small sphere. This statement means that, if a man could only break up the large sphere in the proper clever way, he could put the whole of it into his pocket. Admirable as this result is mathematically, to attempt to apply its method to physics would be hopeless. For, although the theory clearly defines the parts into which the large sphere is to be broken, and precisely describes the motion of each one of these parts into the small sphere, such a construction, since it involves an infinite number of operations, cannot be applied to any physical object. Indeed the same difficulty crops up, though in a milder form, whenever the attempt is made to apply to the physical world the concept of an irrational number. The only conclusion which might be drawn from theorems such as the one just mentioned is an argument in favor of the atomistic structure of matter—or at least in favor of the theory that matter is composed of lumps, each of which is again composed of lumps and so on perhaps *ad infinitum*, but that at every stage of this structure there is empty space between the lumps. A philosopher of nature, trained in logic, might find it worth his while to formulate assumptions on the basis of which this argument and others like it (some of which were anticipated by the scholastic philosophers) might be transformed into rigorous proofs. At present, however, it seems unlikely that the theory of complicated sets can contribute much to the theory of relativity or to physics in general.

Between the sets of set-theoretical geometry and the smooth world lines of the Riemann space with which the theory of relativity deals, there are, however, many intermediate stages. But before these are discussed, a word should be devoted to the qualitative and quantitative concepts (cf. III, B) in mechanics. The antithesis between these concepts is roughly parallel to the antithesis between the synthetic and the analytic points of view in this branch of physics.

Philosophers of science may be interested to know that, considered as synthetic theories, some branches of biology and economics have attained a degree of perfection higher than that hitherto attained by mechanics—the science which, in its analytic phase, is the most highly perfected form of applied mathematics. Indeed, some of the so-called axiomatizations of mechanics are reminiscent of Spinoza's *Ethics* rather than the geometric work of Pasch, Pieri, Hilbert, or Veblen. They have the form of a postulational theory without exhibiting the spirit of rigorous reasoning which is so splendidly displayed in analytic mechanics. Postulational geometry begins with qualitative assumptions about undefined objects. Von Staudt and Hilbert developed this theory to the stage where systems of numbers may be associated (in many different ways) with the undefined objects considered. These systems of numbers are the co-ordinates relative to various frames of reference. There is no reason why a similar postulational mechanics (in the sense of either Newton or Einstein) should be impossible. Such a theory would begin with qualitative assumptions about undefined concepts and would culminate by associating systems of numbers (in many different ways) with the undefined objects. These systems of numbers would be the quantitative co-ordinates of analytical mechanics.

Einstein's theory of relativity looks for smooth lines of minimal length in Riemann spaces which are far more general than the Euclidean space. But in spaces which are still more general, lines of minimal length need not be smooth (cf. III, D). Indeed, Riemann spaces and their immediate generalizations are by no means the last word in generality, even if attention is confined to homogeneous spaces devoid of set-theoretical singularities (cf. I, 4). The day may well come when physicists will take advantage of the wide generality and enormous variety provided by the concepts of modern geometry. The points of general metric spaces are not indeed defined by co-ordinates, but the disadvantages inherent in the use of co-ordinates have already been mentioned (cf. III, C). The relativity theory of the future may seek to formulate intrinsic relations between the lines of general metric spaces, without reference to any arbitrarily chosen frame.

In connection with this prophecy, I venture to elaborate Minkowski's dictum that the laws of nature may find their most perfect expression in the statement of relations between world-lines. It might be suggested to the physicists that they try to express qualitative physical laws by statements about intrinsic topological relations between world-lines in some fairly general continuum. These statements should not mention co-ordinates but should be capable of being expressed with quantitative precision in regard to any particular frame of reference.

V. Future Tasks for Geometers

The further geometrization of physics is bound to raise new problems for geometers—problems other than that of preparing the ground for some generalization of the theory of relativity such as the one outlined in the preceding section.

Postulational non-Euclidean geometries and the analytic geometries of smooth Riemann spaces modify Euclid's idealization of the properties of a rod as its length increases beyond any finite bound (cf. I, 1). This statement is not contradicted by the fact that the geometry used in the present theory of relativity is a differential geometry of the type which, in the eighteenth century, used to be called "the geometry of the infinitely small;" for, paradoxically, this differential geometry has been applied to the macrocosmos, in fact, to astronomical distances. Euclid's other idealization, his neglect of the thickness of rods and planes (cf. I, 1), has not yet been profoundly changed. In fact, a specific geometry of the microcosmos has not yet been well developed. I venture the conjecture that, for the geometrization of physics, especially the physics of the microcosm, idealizations very different from those of Euclid might prove more adequate than his.

One such alternative is a geometry where points are not primary entities. What is here contemplated is a geometry of lumps—that is, a theory in which lumps are undefined concepts, whereas points appear as the results of limiting or intersectional processes applied to these lumps. The reader interested in the details of this idea is referred to the exposition of it which appeared in the Rice Institute Pamphlets of 1940. As a conclusion for the present paper, another possibility is here indicated,— namely, the introduction of probability into the foundations of geometry.

Poincaré, in several of his famous essays on the philosophy of science, characterized the difference between mathematics and physics as follows: In mathematics, if the quantity A is equal to the quantity B, and B is equal to C, then A is equal to C; that is, in modern terminology: mathematical equality is a transitive relation. But in the observable physical continuum "equal" means indistinguishable; and in this continuum, if A is equal to B, and B is equal to C, it by no means follows that A is equal to C. In the terminology of the psychologists Weber and Fechner, A may lie within the threshold of B, and B within the threshold of C, even though A does not lie within the threshold of C. "The raw result of experience," says Poincaré, "may be expressed by the relation

$$A = B,\ B = C,\ A < C,$$

which may be regarded as the formula for the physical continuum." That is to say, physical equality is not a transitive relation.

Is this reasoning cogent? It is indeed easy to devise experiments which prove that the question whether two physical quantities are distinguishable cannot always be answered by a simple Yes or No. The same observer may regard the same two objects sometimes as identical and sometimes as distinguishable. A blindfolded man may consider the simultaneous irritation of the same two spots on his skin sometimes as one, and sometimes as two tactile sensations. Of two constant lights, he may regard the first sometimes as weaker than, sometimes as equal to, and sometimes as stronger than the second. All that can be done in this situation is to count the percentage number of instances in which he makes any one of these two or three observations. In the observation of physical continua, situations like the one just described seem to be the rule rather than the exception.

Instead of distinguishing between a transitive mathematical and an intransitive physical relation of equality, it thus seems much more hopeful to retain the transitive relation in mathematics and to introduce for the distinction of physical and physiological quantities a probability, that is, a number lying between 0 and 1.

Elaboration of this idea leads to the concept of a space in

which a distribution function rather than a definite number is associated with every pair of elements. The number associated with two points of a metric space is called the distance between the two points. The distribution function associated with two elements of a statistical metric space might be said to give, for every x, the probability that the distance between the two points in question does not exceed x. Such a statistical generalization of metric spaces appears to be well adapted for the investigation of physical quantities and physiological thresholds. The idealization of the local behavior of rods and boards, implied by this statistical approach, differs radically from that of Euclid. In spite of this fact, or perhaps just because of it, the statistical approach may provide a useful means for geometrizing the physics of the microcosm.

Perhaps the most promising way to attack local geometric problems would be with a combination of the two ideas outlined in this section, the statistical approach and a geometry of lumps.

KARL MENGER

ILLINOIS INSTITUTE OF TECHNOLOGY
CHICAGO

18

Leopold Infeld

ON THE STRUCTURE OF OUR UNIVERSE

ON THE STRUCTURE OF OUR UNIVERSE

I

SPECULATIONS about the Universe in which men live are as old as human thought and as art; as old as the view of shining stars on a clear night. Yet it was the general relativity theory which, only thirty years ago, shifted cosmological problems from poetry or speculative philosophy into physics. We can even fix the year in which modern cosmology was born. It was in 1917 when Einstein's paper appeared in the Prussian Academy of Science under the title "Cosmological Considerations in General Relativity Theory."[1]

Although it is difficult to exaggerate the importance of this paper, and although it created a flood of other papers and speculations, Einstein's original ideas, as viewed from the perspective of our present day, are antiquated if not even wrong. I believe Einstein would be the first to admit this.

Yet the appearance of this paper is of great importance in the history of theoretical physics. Indeed, it is one more instance showing how a wrong solution of a fundamental problem may be incomparably more important than a correct solution of a trivial, uninteresting problem.

Why is Einstein's paper so important? Because it formulates an entirely new problem, that of the structure of our universe; because it shows that the general theory of relativity can throw new light upon this problem.

The classical physicists thought about our physical space as a three-dimensional Euclidean continuum, our physical time as a one-dimensional continuum common to all observers, whether in

[1] A. Einstein, "Kosmologische Betrachtungen zur allgemeinen Relativitäts-theorie," *S. B. Preuss. Akad. Wiss.* (1917), 142-152.

relative motion or not. These concepts were changed completely when Einstein, in 1905, formulated the special theory of relativity. The physicist learned that, in ordering physical events, it is much more convenient and simple to consider a four-dimensional pseudo-Euclidean time-space continuum as the background for these events. Then, in 1914, he had to learn again that, in order to understand the phenomena of gravitation, he must generalize his concepts once more. In the general theory of relativity, the universe is represented by a four-dimensional manifold, its metric shaped by masses, their motion and radiation; far from masses and sources of energy, this Riemannian space-time continuum more and more closely approaches the pseudo-Euclidean space-time continuum of the special theory of relativity.

In theoretical physics new ideas are born by the genius and imagination of men who can look upon an old problem from an entirely new and unexpected point of view. This is how the special and the general theories of relativity were born; this is how quantum theory entered into physics. In Einstein's paper on cosmology we see the same ability to look upon old problems in a new way. Yet, as we know today, there is an essential difference. Whereas the special and general theories of relativity stand in our present day almost as fresh and complete as in the days when they were formulated, whereas in the last thirty years nothing of fundamental importance has been added to Einstein's structure, the problem of cosmology looks very different today from the way it did in the days when Einstein wrote his celebrated paper.

To consider our universe as a whole means to do something similar to what a child does when he looks at the globe of our earth. He becomes familiar with the general shape of our earth, by ignoring the mountains and valleys, houses and towns, by considering the earth as a smooth surface, by forming a highly idealized picture, useless if he wants to find his way through his back-yard, but useful if he wishes to understand the path of an aeroplane journey around the world. Similarly, in cosmological problems, when we consider our universe as a whole, we must form a highly idealized picture, ignoring small disturbances and local concentrations of masses, smoothing out irregularities and considering the geometry of our universe taken as a whole. Thus, according to Einstein, in such a simplified picture of our universe, matter should be at rest in a suitably chosen co-ordinate system and the proper distances of nebulae from the observer should not change with time.

Experiments later on showed that such a postulate contradicts the law of red-shift, which was discovered some years after Einstein's paper appeared. It is ironical that Einstein wished to form a general picture of our universe in which matter does not run away; yet the famous experiments on the red-shift of nebulae convince us that matter behaves as though it were running away! Thus the fundamental Einstein assumption seems to be too narrow to fit the facts as they were observed later.

The next assumptions which Einstein made were those of *isotropy* and *homogeneity*. Unlike the first assumption, these two (formulated rather implicitly) have survived up to now, although it is not at all sure whether future observations made with new, more powerful, telescopes, will not force us to change them. Yet, mostly because of their simplicity, these two assumptions form the basis of all modern cosmologies.

What is the meaning of these assumptions?

Isotropy means simply that in a proper co-ordinate system an observer looking in different directions will never notice that any of them are preferred. In a suitably chosen co-ordinate system the smoothed out, idealized universe appears the same in all directions, or, as we say, it is *isotropic*.

The assumption of *homogeneity* means that observers placed at different points of the universe, describing its history in different, but properly chosen co-ordinate systems will find these histories identical in their contents; that it is impossible in this way to distinguish one place in the universe from another. Similarly, the two-dimensional inhabitants of a perfect sphere or plane could not distinguish one point of their surface from another.

Thus the two postulates, that of isotropy and homogeneity are implicitly contained in Einstein's work.

These two assumptions survived beyond Einstein's first attempt to formulate a cosmological theory. They are present (explicitly or implicitly) in all modern cosmologies.

We could ask: Is our universe really isotropic? Is our universe really homogeneous? These questions mean: can we formulate a theory consistent with the observed facts by assuming homogeneity and isotropy? At the present time our observations can penetrate only a small corner of our universe. It is possible that future observation may force us to retreat from these simple assumptions. Yet these assumptions are the most obvious ones and we shall change them only under the impact of new discoveries.

Besides isotropy and homogeneity Einstein assumed, as we said before, that in a proper co-ordinate system, the masses at large, which form the universe, are at rest and that the average density of matter ϱ_0 is constant.

Are these assumptions consistent? Let us recall that in the general theory of relativity, Einstein formulated new gravitational equations which must be satisfied by every gravitational field. Is it possible, we ask, to satisfy the postulates of isotropy, homogeneity, and that of constant density of resting masses? A straightforward investigation provides the answer: No! These three postulates together contradict Einstein's original gravitational equations. Thus something must be changed to make the general theory of relativity consistent with Einstein's cosmological considerations. In his paper, Einstein proposed to make the scheme consistent by changing the gravitational equations of the general relativity theory. The change is small, characterized by the appearance of an additional small cosmological term. Whenever in the past the general theory of relativity was confirmed by experiment, it will be confirmed again, if we add this small cosmological term. Its appearance matters little, if we consider the phenomena in our solar system or even in our galaxy. But this cosmological term becomes important, if we consider our universe as a whole. It is this term which makes it possible to satisfy Einstein's cosmological postulates in the now generalized frame of relativity theory. ·

One could argue that the additional introduction of a new term, which we shall call the *cosmological term*, is artificial;

that a satisfactory theory must not introduce new constants, leaving their numerical determination to experiment. There is no doubt that such objections are valid; that the introduction of a cosmological constant—without theoretical specification of its numerical value—does have the character of an *"ad hoc"* hypothesis. Yet, in spite of all that, Einstein's paper, because of the originality of its ideas, because of its imaginative formulation of a new problem, from a new point of view, played a fundamental rôle in the development of our knowledge about the structure of the universe.

Let us add to our discussion a sketch of its mathematical formulation. The so-called Einstein universe is characterized by the following metrical form:

$$ds^2 = R^2 \left[d\tau^2 - d\varrho^2 \, sin^2\varrho (d\theta^2 + sin^2 \theta \, d\varphi^2) \right] \qquad (I, 1)$$

Here τ is the time co-ordinate, ϱ, φ, θ are the space co-ordinates, and c, the velocity of light, is taken to be one. R is a constant called "the Radius of the Einstein universe." If ϱ is very small we can by introducing

$$\varrho = r/R$$
$$\tau = ct/R; \; (c = \text{velocity of light})$$

write the above equation in the following form:

$$ds^2 = c^2 \, dt^2 - dr^2 - r^2 \, (d\theta^2 + sin^2\theta \, d\varphi^2) \qquad (I, 2)$$

This is the ordinary form of the Minkowski or pseudo-Euclidean space-time continuum where the space part is written in a polar co-ordinate system.

The space part in $(I, 1)$ represents an isotropic and homogeneous three-dimensional manifold, the geometry of which is a generalization of the geometry of a two-dimensional sphere. Much can be deduced from the quadratic form $(I, 1)$ without going into the dynamical equations of the general theory of relativity. Let us discuss now the possible *topologies* of a manifold represented by $(I, 1)$, a point to which little attention was paid when Einstein formulated his cosmological theory, and a point, which, I believe, is of great importance for the understanding of cosmological problems.

The angles φ and θ which have the same meaning as in a polar co-ordinate-system also have the same range:

$$0 \leq \varphi < 2\pi$$
$$0 \leq \theta \leq \pi$$

What about the angle ϱ? Take any point characterized by $\varrho = 0$, φ, θ, then, any point characterized by $\varrho = \pi$, φ, θ. The line element ds^2 will have the same form and the same value at these two points for neighbouring events with the same $d\tau$, $d\varrho$, $d\varphi$, $d\theta$. How will the observer distinguish between the two pairs of neighbouring events? The metrical form is the same. If we solve a physical problem on such a geometrical background (e.g., the behaviour of the electromagnetic field) we usually see that the physical events are also identical in two such points. Thus we are faced with two possibilities:

1. The universe is a *mirror* universe. To every event O there corresponds an identical event O' at its antipodal point. In such a universe ϱ ranges from 0 to π, but events at $\varrho = \pi$ mirror those at $\varrho = 0$. It is easy to make jokes about such a universe in which someone like you is reading a treatise on cosmology at this moment. But in our cosmological, idealized and smoothed-out universe, the individuals and even the stars are of little importance.

Such a *mirror* universe is called a *spherical* universe.

2. Another, less paradoxical interpretation assumes: O and O' are *identical* points and the events in them are *identical* events. The points with the co-ordinates $\varrho = 0$ and $\varrho = \pi$ are *the same* points. Such a universe is called an *elliptical* universe.

Both universes, the spherical and elliptical, have the same metric but a different topology, or connectivity. Cut out a piece of paper and form a cylinder from it and you will get a surface with the same metric as on the plane but with a different topology. The edges of the paper regarded as different points are now identified in the case of a cylinder.

It is almost obvious that, faced with a choice between these two interpretations, we should rather choose the second one than populate our universe with ghost-events.

Let us return to our quadratic form (I, 1) and draw from it some simple conclusions:

1. At any point in space, in a co-ordinate system character-ized by (I, 1), we can imagine a particle at rest, not changing its position with time. Rest of a free particle *is* consistent with the Einstein universe and with the relativistic law of motion, accord-ing to which every free particle moves along a geodetic line.

2. A light ray sent out from a point returns to it after a time interval either 2π or π, depending on whether we con-sider the Einstein universe as a spherical or elliptical one. The small and simple number 2π or π is not astonishing. It is due to our choice of the time unit as given by (I, 1). Indeed we could say that our unit of time as used in (I, 1) is tremendously great. In ordinary units the period after which light returns would be

$$T = 2\pi\, R/c \text{ in a spherical universe}$$
$$T = \pi\, R/c \text{ in an elliptic universe.}$$

As R is of the order 10^{28}cm (for reasons to be explained later), we see that the period which light takes to travel around our universe is of the order of 10^{18} second or 10^{11} years!

Other conclusions can be drawn if we assume, besides the metrical form (I, 1), Einstein's dynamical equations general-ized by the appearance of the cosmological constant. These equations are:

$$G_{kl} + \Lambda\, g_{kl} = -k\, T_{kl} \qquad (I, 3)$$

Let us discuss these equations briefly without going into the details of their mathematical structure.

These are 10 equations, or one tensorial equation. The indices k, l take any of the values 0, 1, 2, 3, and all tensorial expres-sions with indices are symmetric, that is $g_{kl} = g_{lk}$; $G_{kl} = G_{lk}$; $T_{kl} = T_{lk}$. The symmetric tensor g_{kl} is the metric tensor. It is completely known in our case, because the metrical form (I, 1) is given. The symmetric Einstein tensor G_{kl}, depending on g_{kl} and its derivatives can be calculated explicitly if the g_{kl} are known, that is when the metrical form (I, 1) is given. Now the expression $\Lambda\, g_{kl}$ is *the* additional cosmological expression which appeared for the first time in Einstein's paper in 1917. Put $\Lambda = 0$ and you will have the old gravitational equations.

The constant k appearing on the right-hand side of (I, 3) is known, and depends in a simple manner on the gravitational constant of Newton's theory and the velocity of light. Thus our equation determines T_{kl}, if the metric form is given and if Λ is known. T_{kl} are the components of the so-called energy-momentum tensor characterizing masses, their motion and radiation energy. If the geometry of our universe is known (that is the g_{kl} tensor), if Λ is known, then the physics of our universe (that is the energy-momentum tensor) is known too.

In Einstein's universe, as we saw before, masses at large are at rest. This, translated into the language of tensors, means that the only surviving component of the T_{kl} tensor will be the T_{oo} component. It is this component which represents the density ϱ_o of matter. Only if we introduce a proper cosmological constant can we achieve the vanishing of all components of T_{kl} with the exception of T_{oo}. The T_{oo} component will then be constant and represent the density of matter in the world.

From Einstein's dynamical equations we can draw two new conclusions:

1. The radius R is known if ϱ_o is known. The oo equation (I, 3) gives us a simple connection between ϱ_o and R. From Hubble's nebuli counts we can at least estimate roughly the mean density of matter. Its order of magnitude seems to be 10^{-30} gram per cubic centimeter. From that we can deduce the order of magnitude of R. This is how the value $R \sim 10^{28}$ cm, quoted before, was obtained. Also, the cosmological constant can be calculated if we know R. We have $\Lambda = 1/R^2 \sim 10^{-57}$ cm^{-2}. Indeed, the additional cosmological term is very small!

2. The total mass of the universe is finite. This is so, because the density of the mass is finite and the volume of the universe is finite. Knowing (or rather assuming we know) the mean density of matter in our universe, and having deduced from it the radius of the universe, we can now calculate its total mass. But again we have to distinguish between a spherical and elliptic space. The total mass in a spherical universe is twice as great as that in an elliptic one.

Thus Einstein's work presents us for the first time with a mathematical model of our universe. The three dimensional parts of our metrical form (I, 1) (if we put $d\tau = 0$) is a generalization to three dimensions of the ordinary two-dimensional sphere or the one-dimensional circle. The universe (I, 1) is sometimes called the "Einstein cylindrical universe." The circle of the ordinary two-dimensional cylinder may be said to correspond in this picture to our three-dimensional sphere; the height to the time dimension. In such a universe free particles may retain their proper distances in space, and light circumvents such a universe in finite time.

We shall have to abandon this picture because it is inconsistent with observation. Yet it was this picture which formed a basis for all further work on cosmology.

II

We shall now sketch briefly the story of fifteen years of development, covering the period 1917-1931, which ends with the appearance of Einstein's two papers on cosmology.

Since Einstein wrote his paper in 1917 great observational progress has been achieved. The human eye has penetrated far beyond the Milky Way, far beyond our galaxy.

As far as we can reach with our most powerful telescopes, we find matter agglomerated into a large number of separate aggregates, the *nebulae.*

Observation on these nebulae has revealed to us the following characteristic features of our universe:

On a tremendous scale, large compared with the distances between nebulae, the distribution of nebulae is *isotropic* and *homogeneous.* This important result is deduced from two facts. First: A comparison of nebular counts to great depths in different portions of the sky shows that the nebulae have an isotropic distribution. Secondly: The number N of nebulae to within a certain distance d (in cm.), is, for sufficiently large d, given by

$$N = 4 \times 10^{-71} \, d^3.$$

Since the nebular masses are of the same order of magnitude (10^{41} grams per nebula) a mean density of luminous matter can be calculated:

$$\varrho_0 = 10^{-30} \, gr \, cm^{-3}.$$

Hubble estimates that the mean density of matter may actually be one thousand times greater because of dust, gas, or unobservable moving particles in intergalactic space.

A further very important result of observational cosmology was the discovery of the *red-shift*. The spectra of nebulae, when compared with the corresponding terrestrial spectra, are shifted towards the red in an overwhelming majority of cases. For any individual nebula the displacement $\Delta\lambda$ of the wave-length λ of any line of the nebulae spectrum is proportional to λ. Thus we may measure the red-shift of the nebulae by $(\Delta\lambda)/\lambda$. The obvious interpretation is to imagine that these nebulae run away from us and the red-shift is due to the Doppler effect. However, the velocities calculated in this way are so tremendous that we may fear that such an obvious interpretation is too obvious to be the correct one. And, besides, what is the reason for such a rapid motion?

This red-shift, as given by observation, appears to depend on the remoteness of the distance of the nebulae. The farther away the nebulae are, the greater the red-shift, the greater seems their velocity. As far as our telescopes penetrate, the relationship between red-shift and distance is approximately linear. We have

$$(\Delta\lambda)/\lambda = kd + \text{departure of higher order and}$$
$$k = 5.68 \times 10^{-28} \, cm^{-1}.$$

Thus, if we look back upon the Einstein universe, we see that the idea of isotropy and homogeneity seems to be confirmed by observation. But there is no place for the red-shift in the Einstein universe! Einstein's model seems to prevent the nebulae from running away. Ironically enough it was invented to do just that. But the nebulae do seem to run away! Thus Einstein's model will not do, and has to be replaced by another. Once, however, the problem was raised by Einstein, it was comparatively easy to look for different models to retain some of Einstein's ideas and to reject others. It was again Einstein's genius which opened a new path into the unknown.

Before we discuss further generalizations, let us return once more to the principles of isotropy and homogeneity. Obviously, in our search for a generalization of our cosmological model, we would like to stick to these assumptions. If for no other reasons than because these assumptions *are* the simplest possible and they are not contradicted by experiment. But does not the phenomenon of the red-shift contradict these assumptions? How is it possible that in a homogeneous universe the nebulae seem to run away from *our* galaxy? The answer to this question is obvious. If we wish to save the principle of homogeneity we must not assume that *our* galaxy is distinguished in any way; that nebulae show their aversion by running away from our galaxy; that this aversion increases with the distance of the nebulae. On the contrary! We must form a model in which the red-shift can be observed from *any* nebula. The history of our universe and its description must be such that it won't matter from what point in space we describe our universe. Putting it more mathematically; the laws of our universe viewed at large must be invariant in form and content with respect to a proper transformation connecting the arbitrary points in space.

Let us now form a very simplified and highly idealized picture of our universe. In it, all local irregularities due to the agglomeration of matter into nebulae or even nebular clusters are neglected; so are all random motions. In such a smoothed-out, idealized model we assume a very dense and uniform distribution of particles. One such particle in our model corresponds to a nebula. We can imagine its presence whenever we wish and we shall call this dense collection of particles—*fundamental particles*. With each such particle we imagine an observer and we shall call him the *fundamental observer*. The law of red-shift seems to indicate that nebulae move with great velocities. Thus in our model we shall assume a vector field, the vector at each point of space indicating the velocity of the fundamental particle and, therefore, representing the motion of a nebula.

Thus we have a picture similar to that we use in hydromechanics: a fluid composed of fundamental particles, their motion prescribed by the vector field.

The law of red-shift broadened our vision of the universe. It cannot be the static Einstein universe.

Can we reconcile the postulates of homogeneity and isotropy

with the observed red-shift and still remain on the ground of the general relativity theory?

Shortly after Einstein's paper appeared, de Sitter[2] proposed a new model of our universe, which reconciles the principles of isotropy and homogeneity on the one hand with the observed facts of red-shift on the other. As a matter of fact, de Sitter formulated his paper before the law of red-shift was discovered. It forms a very beautiful instance of theory predicting experimental results.

The de Sitter universe is mathematically more attractive than Einstein's universe. Whereas the Einstein universe is—vaguely speaking—like a three-dimensional sphere the de Sitter universe is—equally vaguely speaking—like a four-dimensional sphere immersed in a five-dimensional space. Yet, just because it can be represented as a sphere, the demands of isotropy and homogeneity are automatically fulfilled.

We have already mentioned the importance of fundamental particles and their motion. We could ask now: what is the motion of such fundamental particles in the de Sitter universe? Unfortunaely, it is not easy to answer this question for two reasons. First: the description will depend on the choice of our co-ordinate system. Second: there are not one, but three possible de Sitter universes with different kinds of motions. What we shall do now is to pick out *one* of these universes, ignoring the other two. We shall discuss it in a co-ordinate system which unfortunately does not reveal the four-dimensional symmetry of this universe but has other redeeming features which will make our discussion simple.

A universe with the quadratic form

$$ds^2 = \frac{\tau_0{}^2}{\tau^2} (d\tau^2 - dx^2 - dy^2 - dz^2) \qquad \text{(II, 1)}$$

is the de Sitter universe. Here τ_0 is a constant, τ is time and x, y, z the space co-ordinates.

We see that in our co-ordinate system, in which the de Sitter

[2] W. de Sitter, "On the Relativity of Inertia." Remarks concerning Einstein's latest Hypothesis. *Proc. Arad. Wetensch*, Amsterdam (Vol. 19, 1917), 1217-1225. "On Einstein's Theory of Gravitation, and Its Astronomical Consequences: III." *Monthly Not. Roy. Astron. Soc.* (Vol. 78, 1917), 3-28.

universe is represented by (II, 1), the laws of light-geometry will be the same as in a Minkowski (or pseudo-Euclidean), universe. Indeed, the only difference between the de Sitter universe, as represented by (II, 1), and the Minkowski universe, is the presence of the factor τ_0^2/τ^2 in (II, 1). But the presence of this factor means nothing for light-rays, which are zero-geodetic lines. For them we always have $ds^2 = 0$.

The next remark concerns the fundamental particles. For the kind of de Sitter universe *we* have chosen, for the kind of co-ordinate system we have chosen, the fundamental particles are at rest. (There are two other de Sitter universes possible, with the same quadratic form and with the fundamental particles moving in a well defined way, prescribed by the conditions of isotropy and homogeneity.)

We could ask: how is a red-shift possible if the particles are at rest? The red-shift is due partially to the motion of fundamental particles, but partially to the gravitational field. How we divide the total effect into these two components (gravitaional and Doppler-effect) will depend upon the co-ordinate system. The total effect will, of course, be independent of the choice of the co-ordinate system. In the de Sitter universe, which we consider, the total effect is due only to the gravitational field.

Let us now derive the important law of red-shift from our quadratic form and from our knowledge of relativity theory.

Imagine that a nebula at a distance r sends to us radiation received *here* ($r = 0$) and *now* ($\tau = \tau_0$). The radiation was sent at the time $\tau_0 - r$, (where $r^2 = x^2 + y^2 + z^2$), because the laws of light propagation are the same as in Minkowski's space and because the velocity of light was assumed to equal "one." Now, according to relativity theory, an atom keeps its rhythm in the *proper* time. Thus if $_{(s)}\nu$ is the proper frequency and δs is the period of one oscillation, if $_{(\tau)}\nu$ is the period in τ time, and $\delta\tau$ the frequency in τ time, we have because of the form (II, 1):

$$\delta s = \frac{1}{_{(s)}\nu} = \frac{\tau_0 \delta\tau}{\tau_0 - r} = \frac{\tau_0}{(\tau_0 - r)_{(\tau)}\nu}. \qquad \text{(II, 2)}$$

Through its journey in space the radiation preserves its rhythm in τ time because the laws of radiation have nothing to do with the factor $(\tau_0/\tau)^2$ in (II, 1) and are the same in the Minkowski world as in the de Sitter world. Thus, on our earth we can compare the unchanging rhythm of our atomic clock *here*, that is its $_{(s)}\nu$ with the frequency $_{(\tau)}\nu$ sent to us from a distant nebula. We find, from (II, 2):

$$\frac{_{(\tau)}\nu}{_{(s)}\nu} = \frac{\tau_0}{(\tau_0 - r)} = \frac{1}{1 - \dfrac{r}{\tau_0}}.$$

Here and *now* on our earth where $r = 0$, the τ and s frequency coincide. Introducing two wave lengths $_{(s)}\lambda = 1/_{(s)}\nu$ and $_{(\tau)}\lambda = 1/_{(\tau)}\nu$ we have:

$$\frac{_{(s)}\lambda}{_{(\tau)}\lambda} = 1 - \frac{r}{\tau_0}$$

and therefore

$$\frac{_{(\tau)}\lambda - _{(s)}\lambda}{_{(\tau)}\lambda} = \frac{\Delta\lambda}{\lambda} = \frac{\tau}{\tau_0},$$

which gives the famous law of the red-shift. Thus the red-shift is proportional to the "distance" of the source of light. (The quotation marks around the word "distance" indicate that it is an open question whether r as defined above deserves to be called "distance.") We see that the de Sitter universe as considered here gives us the law of red-shift and from its experimental determination we can find the present cosmological τ_0. We see also that a similar consideration repeated for the static Einstein universe would not give us the law of red-shift.

Yet in spite of the mathematical beauty of the de Sitter universe, in spite of the fact that it gives us the law of red-shift, two grave objections can be raised against this mathematical model.

The first objection is common to both the de Sitter and Einstein universes. They both require the change in dynamical equations of relativity theory, they both satisfy the gravitational equations for the gravitational field only if we introduce into them the cosmological constant Λ. But we are also faced with another difficulty peculiar to the de Sitter universe.

If we introduce the metrical form (II, 1), into the gravitational equations (I, 3), then we can calculate the average density of matter. True, the fundamental particles are at rest, but we would expect them to have some density as they had in the case of the Einstein universe. But here the density turns out to be zero! The de Sitter universe is empty! Thus the presence of elementary particles with which we must populate our universe in order to represent the nebulae and their motion, contradicts the dynamical equations of the general theory of relativity. Of course, it is an open question whether we should stick to the equations of dynamics in our cosmological approach. We have violated them, in any case, by adding the cosmological expression. We could violate them further by changing the dynamical equations, so that the density of matter defined in a new way would turn out to be different from zero. But such a procedure would be ugly, and it is doubtful whether a logically consistent theory could be built in this way. Einstein's work is characterized by a rare search for logical simplicity, beauty and clarity. Within the framework of the relativity theory there is no place for *ad hoc* assumptions and artificial hypotheses. They would spoil not only the beauty but also the self-consistency of the general theory of relativity.

The first theoretical recognition that the law of red-shift does follow from de Sitter's model of our universe is due to Weyl. We have here one of the instances where theory predicted events later confirmed by experiment. Indeed, Weyl's theoretical paper appeared in 1923,[3] whereas experimental evidence of red-shift became known only in 1929,[4] when Hubble published his results on red-shift measurement of 46 nebulae, and established experimentally the linear relation between $(\Delta\lambda)/\lambda$ and distance.

The further development of theoretical cosmology is mostly connected with three names: Friedmann (1922),[5] Lemaître

[3] Hermann Weyl, "Zur allgemeinen Relativitätstheorie," *Phys. Zeitschr.* (Vol. 24, 1923), 230-232.

[4] E. P. Hubble, "A Relation between Distance and Radial Velocity among Extra-Galactic Nebulae," *Proc. Nat. Acad. Sci.* (Vol. 15, 1929), 168-173.

[5] A. Friedmann, "Über die Krümmung des Raumes," *Zeitschr. f. Physik* (Vol. 10, 1922), 377-386.

(1927),[6] and Robertson (1929).[7] Each of them dealt with the same problem: to find a more general model of our universe, to go beyond that of Einstein and de Sitter. Indeed, it turned out that both the Einstein and de Sitter universes form, so to speak, two limiting cases of a universe either full of matter or of a universe empty of matter. Between these two limiting cases there is an infinite variety of possible universes.

From the philosophical point of view the most satisfactory discussion of the cosmological problem was given by Robertson. It is general, based on very few assumptions, and kinematical in its character, that is, it ignores the dynamical equations of the general theory of relativity altogether.

In its essence Robertson's problem can be stated as follows: Our universe, taken as a whole, is characterized by a metrical four-dimensional form. What, we ask, is the most general quadratic form that would describe an isotropic and homogeneous universe in a co-ordinate system in which the fundamental particles are at rest. Here is Robertson's answer to this question: Imagine a three-dimensional space with constant curvature. Without loss of generality we may assume that the Riemannian curvature k has the values

$$+1, \ 0, \ -1.$$

(Indeed the curvature can be positive, zero, or negative; therefore it can be made $1, 0, -1$, by a proper change of units). Such a three-dimensional space with constant curvature is both isotropic and homogeneous. Mathematically, the three metrical forms can be written in the following ways:

(A) $d\sigma^2 = d\varrho^2 + sin^2 \varrho \ (d\theta^2 + sin^2 \theta \ d\varphi^2)$ for $k = +1$.

(B) $d\sigma^2 = d\varrho^2 + \varrho^2 \ (d\theta^2 + sin^2 \theta \ d\varphi^2)$ for k $= 0$.   (II, 3)

(C) $d\sigma^2 = d\varrho^2 + sinh^2 \varrho \ (d\theta^2 + sin^2 \theta \ d\varphi^2)$ for $k = -1$.

In relativity theory our universe is represented as a four-dimensional space-time manifold. The demand for isotropy and

[6] G. Lemaître, "Un Univers Homogène de Masse Constante et de Rayon Croissant, Rendant Compte de la Vitesse Radiale de Nébuleuses Extra-galactiques," *Ann. Soc. Sci.* (Bruxelles, Vol. 47A, 1927), 49-59.

[7] H. P. Robertson, "On the Foundations of Relativistic Cosmology," *Proc. Nat. Acad. Sci.*, (Vol. 15, 1929), 822-829.

homogeneity will be preserved, that is, all fundamental observers will describe our universe in the same way, if its metrical form is:

$$ds^2 = R^2(\tau)(d\tau^2 - d\sigma^2),$$

where $d\sigma^2$, is one of the three forms written out before in (II, 3). Thus we have now the most general form for all universes satisfying the conditions of isotropy and homogeneity.

Indeed, take $R = R_o =$ constant and $d\sigma^2$ of the form (A) and you will have the Einstein universe. Take $R(\tau) = \tau_o/\tau$ and $d\sigma^2$ of the form (B) and you will have the de Sitter universe.

Thus we see that we are faced with a tremendous number of possible cosmological models. True, there are only *three* possibilities for $d\sigma^2$, but an infinite number of possibilities for $R^2(\tau)$, and therefore for ds^2. Many of these models will give us the red-shift. Some of them may give us a violet shift and will, therefore, have to be rejected. Some of them may give us a negative mass or density, or violate some other reasonable dynamic requirements. Yet many possibilities remain. Such a situation is not encouraging. We expect a good theory to lead us to definite conclusions, to a model that can be accepted or rejected by experiment. This is not true in this case. There are too many possibilities!

III

In 1931 Einstein[8] indicated a way of restricting the many cosmological possibilities. He suggested the dropping of the cosmological constant which he had introduced in 1917. We remember how the introduction of Λ generalized Einstein's dynamic equations, so that they could be satisfied by the metric of the Einstein universe. Yet we have learned since then that Einstein's universe is only *one* of the many possible; that, besides, it is inconsistent with the law of red-shift. Thus it would

[8] A. Einstein, "Zum kosmologischen Problem der allgemeinen Relativitätstheorie," *S. B. Preuss. Akad. Wiss.* (1931), 235-237.

A. Einstein and W. de Sitter, "On the Relation between the Expansion and the Mean Density of the Universe," *Proc. Nat. Acad. Sci.* (Vol. 18, 1932), 213 f.

seem proper to retreat to the old position held by relativity theory before 1917 and abandon the cosmological constant Λ. In this way the possibilities will become more restricted. The two universes which we considered here in greater detail, the Einstein and de Sitter universes, will not be among those admitted, because they both satisfy only the *generalized* dynamic equations.

In his first paper on this subject, Einstein investigated a cosmological model with $k = 1$ and $R(\tau)$ so chosen that the metric form was consistent with the original dynamic equations, that is those with $\Lambda = 0$. Thus the model which Einstein suggested was a generalization of the previous Einstein universe. But, the fact that $R(\tau)$ was no longer constant made red-shift possible.

In the following year Einstein and de Sitter jointly investigated an especially simple universe. Indeed, in some respects it is the simplest universe yet investigated (of course, with the exception of Minkowski's universe).

The metrical form of this *Einstein-de Sitter* universe, as we shall call it, is:

$$ds^2 = \left(\frac{\tau}{\tau_0}\right)^4 (d\tau^2 - d\sigma^2) \qquad \text{(III, 1)}$$

where $d\sigma^2$ is of the form (B), that is the Euclidean three-dimensional space. A straightforward calculation shows that the metrical form of such a universe is consistent with the original dynamic equations of relativity theory. There is one important conclusion which follows for the absence of the constant Λ and which we shall try to explain now.

Before, we could have argued roughly in the following way: The metrical form introduced a constant, like the constant R_0 in the Einstein universe, or the constant τ_0 in the de Sitter universe. The dynamic equations introduce another constant Λ. Now, generally, such constants as τ_0 can be determined from the observational data on the red-shift. Such constants as Λ can be determined from Hubble's data on nebulae count, that is, from the average density of matter. This is certainly not a satisfactory situation: two constants both determined by measurements.

From the philosophical point of view the Einstein-de Sitter universe appears more satisfactory. Here we have only *one* arbitrary constant, that is τ_0. Its value can be determined from the observation of the red-shift. But if τ_0 is determined, then the value of the density of matter can be *calculated* from it. Thus the theory passes its first test if it gives us reasonable data for the density. In the case of the Einstein-de Sitter universe these data are fairly reasonable.

The density is $6 \times 10^{-28} \, cm^{-3}$, consistent with the upper limit of Hubble's estimation.

Is our universe of such a simple type?

Again we can raise objections both of a practical and of a philosophical nature.

In the first approximation the red-shift is linearly dependent upon the distance. Such a dependence can be explained by many models through a proper choice of a constant (like τ_0) in the metric form. But a more thorough experimental examination shows that the red-shift depends on expressions of *higher* order too. As experimental evidence accumulates, as we are able to reach further and further into our universe, the demands on a theory of our universe will become more and more stringent. A good theory will have to explain the *total* red-shift and not only the approximate red-shift as represented by the linear term. But even now, with our imperfect knowledge of the red-shift effects of the higher order, we know that the Einstein-de Sitter universe is not in close agreement with the experimental results.

The next difficulty is shared both by the Einstein-de Sitter universe and many other models too. We have seen that the red-shift effect allows us to find τ_0, the *"now"* of our universe. Thus we can easily calculate how long—in proper time—the universe has existed until the present moment. The result is 10^9 years, a period which seems too small to squeeze the complicated history of our universe into it. It seems almost too short for even only the geological history of one insignificant member of our universe, the earth.

There is one more argument against the Einstein-de Sitter universe though much more difficult to explain, because it is of a rather philosophical and mathematical character.

Our universe can be either *open* or *closed*. We call our universe closed, if a light-ray sent from a point o ultimately returns to it; the universe is open, if a light-ray does not return to its point of departure. If a co-ordinate system is such that all fundamental particles are at rest in it, then, in an isotropic homogeneous universe, the quadratic form must be of the form (II, 3). The universe is open, if the quadratic form in such a co-ordinate-system is (B) or (C). The universe is closed if it is of the form (A).

Thus among the universes that we have considered until now, the Einstein universe is closed, but the de Sitter universe and the Einstein-de Sitter universes are open. (We may remark in passing that one of the three possible de Sitter universes—not considered here—*is* closed.)

Before we decide the question: what is the particular quadratic form of our universe, we would like to decide a more fundamental question: is our universe *open* or *closed?* This question is more general and more important than the specialized question regarding the metric of our universe, that is, the choice of the function $R(\tau)$. We do not know the answer to this question. Yet every mathematician—if given the choice—would rather see our universe closed than open. There is mathematical beauty in such a universe which reveals itself when we consider any mathematical problem on such a cosmological background. In such a closed universe we have simple boundary conditions and do not need to worry about infinities in time and space. Compared with the closed universe the open one of Einstein-de Sitter appears to be dull and uninspired.

The Einstein universe can be regarded as a prototype of a closed universe. Yet, we remember, there are two possible Einstein universes. An Einstein universe can be either *spherical* or *elliptical*. In the quadratic form (I, 1) we identify the points $\varrho = 0$ and $\varrho = \pi$, if the universe is elliptic. We have mirror events in a spherical universe. They become identical events in an elliptic universe.

This difference between a spherical and elliptic universe appears in every *closed* universe. There is no such distinction in the case of an open universe. Thus if our universe is closed we would have to answer an additional question. Is it spherical with mirror events, or is it elliptic? Scant attention was paid to this question, because it is of little importance if we explore only the neighbourhood of our galaxy. But the description of some phenomena may be very different on two such backgrounds. Indeed, the solution of Dirac's quantum mechanical equation, for example, depends very essentially on the spherical or elliptical character of our universe.[9]

IV

In the last thirty years the centre of investigation has shifted from relativity theory to quantum theory. Yet this statement may be misleading, because it is too much simplified. It ignores the tremendously important rôle played by relativity theory in the development of quantum mechanics. I would like to indicate only one instance: the great progress achieved by Dirac's equations is due to his success in reconciling relativity theory and quantum mechanics. But even the problem of cosmology became connected with the problem of the atom. We ask: are the laws governing our universe independent of the quantum mechanical laws governing the atom? Different theoretical physicists answer this question differently. Some of them believe that there is a connection between the structure of the universe and the structure of the atom. The most outstanding representative of this school of thought is Sir Arthur Eddington, who devoted many years to the difficult task of constructing a conceptual bridge between quantum theory and relativity theory. His work, undoubtedly very audacious and imaginative, is admired by some physicists, but regarded as too speculative and formal by others. Some physicists (Dirac, Schroedinger) believed that Eddington was at least on the right track. Others reject the idea that there is any connection between the fine structure constant, the ratio of proton to electron mass on the one hand and constants characterizing our universe on the other.

[9] L. Infeld and A. Schild, "A New Approach to Kinematic Cosmology," *Phys. Rev.* (Vol. 68, 1945), 250-272, and (Vol. 70, 1946), 410-425.

It is not up to me to say what Einstein's views on this question are. His recent paper[10] would indicate that at present he does not believe in the connection between the structure of the universe and the atom. In it he has shown that local problems like that of a particle or that of our solar system are not affected by the structure of our universe considered as a whole.

Yet I believe that there may be some connection between the description of local phenomena and the structure of our universe, though it may be less spectacular than that searched for by Eddington, and lie in an entirely different direction. Let us take as an example Maxwell's equations and try to find their solution on a cosmological background. If we assume our universe to be an *open* one, then there is no difference between a solution in such a universe and that in a Minkowski world. In other words, the structure of our universe does not reveal itself in Maxwell's equations if the universe is open. But the situation changes radically if we solve the same Maxwell equations in a *closed* universe. It does not change because of the metric, but because of the identification of points $\varrho = 0$ and $\varrho = \pi$. Such an identification changes our problem into a boundary value problem, and we obtain characteristic values for frequencies. In a closed universe the frequency of radiation has its *lowest* value, the spectrum, on its red side, can not reach the frequency zero. It does not matter whether the problem is solved in an Einstein space or in any other closed space; the solution is always the same. Thus, not the *metric* but the *topology* of the universe influences the character of Maxwell's solutions.

A similar situation prevails if we consider Dirac's equations upon a cosmological background. Again the solutions in an open universe are those of the Minkowski space, whereas the solutions in a closed universe are different, not because of the metric, but because of the topology of our universe.

We have tried to sketch briefly the scientists' efforts to grasp the architecture of our universe. These efforts, though linked with observation, are essentially of a speculative character. In

[10] A. Einstein and E. G. Straus, "Influence on the Expansion of Space on the Gravitation Fields Surrounding the Individual Stars," *Rev. of Mod. Physics* (Vol. 17, 1945), 120-125.

the last thirty years we have succeeded in formulating a new problem and in viewing some of the possible solutions; but our answers are neither decisive nor final. Indeed, *there are no final and decisive answers in science.* Yet all our cosmological speculations, though they have gone far from Einstein's original paper, grew from the ideas of the theory of relativity. In the history of human thought they represent one of the many paths emanating from a common source: relativity theory, the creation of one man of genius.[11]

LEOPOLD INFELD

UNIVERSITY OF TORONTO
TORONTO, CANADA

[11] For a fuller quotation of literature and for a more technical exposition of the cosmological problem, the reader is referred to the following sources: H. P. Robertson, "Relativistic Cosmology," in *Review of Modern Physics* (1935), 62-90. R. C. Tolman, *Relativity, Thermodynamics and Cosmology* (Oxford, At the Clarendon Press, 1934). A. Schild, "A New Approach to Kinematic Cosmology" (University of Toronto thesis, 1946).

19

Max von Laue

INERTIA AND ENERGY

INERTIA AND ENERGY

I. Introduction

IN MODERN physics the laws of conservation are of fundamental importance. Essentially, there are three of them: The principle of inertia, which states the conservation of linear momentum; the energy principle, which asserts the conservation of energy; and the law of the conservation of the quantity of electricity. There are two more conservation laws, dealing with the conservation of the angular momentum and of the inert mass. The first of these two, however, is a necessary consequence of the law of conservation of linear momentum, and the latter, as far as we still acknowledge it to be correct, has become identical with the law of the conservation of energy. Finally the laws of conservation of linear momentum and of energy fuse into one for modern relativistic considerations. The discussion that follows is concerned with these unifications of originally distinct laws.

Let us first consider the conservation of the quantity of electricity. The history of this law is soon told, though it extends over a century or more. Under the tremendous impact of Newton's law of gravitational attraction, this law was hypothetically postulated for the electrical attraction and repulsion in the early 18th century. The conservation of mass in which one believed with good reason, was transferred to the electric "Fluida," with the only modification that positive and negative charges cancel each other. Several investigators deduced the inverse proportionality to the square of the distance a long time before Coulomb from the screening effect of electrically conducting enclosures. Coulomb himself cites this effect in a paper on his famous experiment with the torsion balance as a second proof of this law. Only a few persons, however, understood this argu-

ment at the time; thus it was forgotten. The proportionality
between forces and charges was accepted implicitly by all scientists of that time. They could not have proved it, if for no other
reason than that they did not posses a well-defined quantitative
measure of the charge. The idea of defining the quantity of
electricity from Coulomb's law itself was originated by Carl
Friedrich Gauss (about 1840). And the experimental proof of
charge conservation was first given by the ice-bucket experiment
of Michael Faraday in 1843.

The apparatus consisted of a metal vessel with a relatively
small opening, the ice-bucket. This vessel was connected to an
electrometer, but was otherwise insulated. Faraday lowered an
electrically charged body into it, suspended by an insulating
string; immediately the electrometer showed a deflection proportional to the charge. And this deflection remained unchanged, no matter what was done with the charge inside the
ice-bucket, e.g., whether it was transferred to the wall, or
whether it was added to other charges present before the start
of the experiment, which might perhaps compensate for the
new charge. Perhaps this proof is not too accurate. As an in-
tegrating component of Maxwell's theory of electricity, however, the law of conservation of charge is supported by the
numerous and exact experimental confirmations of this theory.
Nowadays nobody doubts it.

This fundamental result has never caused even approximately the same sensation as the law of the conservation of
energy, which was proved at nearly the same time. History
makes us understand this difference. Generations of scientists
have striven for it, but the conservation of the quantity of charge
corresponded to the "*communis opinio*" already a hundred years
before Faraday.

In what follows we shall relate the much more eventful
story of the two other conservation laws and their interrelation-
ship.

II. The Law of Momentum in Newton's Mechanics

The laws of conservation of momentum and energy are results of modern times. The law of momentum is probably the

earlier of the two, because it was clearly formulated, and its significance recognized, sooner than the law of energy, even when we think only of the law of energy in mechanics. It is true, antiquity has left us permanently valuable knowledge for statics, the science of mechanical equilibrium. But influenced by the doctrines of Aristotle, it had advocated a proposition diametrically opposed to the principle of inertia, namely, that a permanent action from without is necessary for maintaining any motion. It was not until the time of Galileo Galilei (1564-1642), that this brilliant originator of the theory of motion, dynamics, in his long life of research, realized that the motion of a body free of outside interaction does not stop, but continues for all time with constant velocity. It is significant that the consideration which led him to this result is based on energy considerations in the modern sense.

It runs as follows: a body on the surface of the earth which falls from a certain altitude, be it directly, on an inclined plane, on the circular path of a pendulum, or otherwise, must obtain precisely that velocity which it requires to return to its former level. For any deviation from this law would furnish a method for making the body ascend by means of its own gravity, perhaps through the inversion of the process of motion which is always possible; and Galileo thinks that this is impossible. Moreover, he confirms his conviction by means of certain experiments. Now let a body ascend again on an inclined plane after it has fallen downwards a certain distance. The lower the inclination toward the horizontal, the longer the path which it requires to obtain its former level on the inclined plane. And if the plane is horizontal, then the body will keep on flying (on it) to infinity with undiminished velocity.

This transition to the limit is not stated explicitly in Galileo's papers, because this rigorous empiricist knew that a plane is not a level surface, because of the spherical shape of the earth, and he avoided intentionally any hypothesis concerning conditions as they might be encountered somewhere away from the earth. But the reader of his *Discorsi* on the mechanics (1638) could not help drawing this conclusion himself. Thus the simplest form of the law of inertia, that the velocity of each force-free body is maintained with respect to direction and magnitude, has become the common property of all scientists since Galileo.

It was soon observed, however, that a more general law was hidden in the law of inertia, when the interaction of two bodies was considered. Collisions were then considered to be the simplest kind of interaction; thus even before Newton a whole series of collision theories had arisen. Few of them were based on exact experiments, but all of them were in agreement that the masses of the colliding bodies were important, their masses simply being identified with the weights. As weighing never showed changes in the weight of a body, the mass, too, was considered to be constant. This important step was taken apparently without misgiving, as a matter of course. Incidentally, these earliest collision theories considered only the central impact of two balls, where all motions take place on a straight line (the connecting line of the mid-points).

From the mass m and the velocity q René Descartes (1596-1650) already formed the *quantity of motion* mq and asserted the conservation of the sum of the quantities of motion of all bodies, and in particular of two colliding bodies, on the basis of philosophic-theological speculations which to us appear strange. But he understood the velocity merely as a number, as a scalar quantity in our terminology, without considering its direction, i.e., its vector properties. Thus his considerations naturally did not lead to successful results.

In 1668 the Royal Society in London made the theory of collisions the topic for a contest. Three papers were submitted. The first candidate, John Wallis (1616-1703), well-known in mathematics by the "Wallis formula," observed, indeed, that opposite velocities had to be provided with opposite signs when the above-mentioned quantity of motion is formed. Otherwise he retained the Cartesian idea of the constancy of the quantity of motion; but of course he could not determine the two momenta after an impact (considered by him as in-elastic) from the initial velocities with the help of this single requirement only; he, therefore, introduces additional assumptions which, being incorrect, vitiate his result.

Christian Huygens (1629-1695) first submitted to the Royal

Society his results only, but he gave the proofs later in a paper (*De motu corporum ex percussione*) published in his *Opuscula posthuma* in 1703. He realized correctly that not only the sum (formed with the correct signs) of the quantities of motion $m \cdot q$ has the same value before and after a perfectly elastic collision, but also the sum of the products of the respective masses m by the squares of the associated velocities, $m \cdot q^2$. These two statements are in fact sufficient to solve the problem. Here we encounter the first application of the principle of mechanical energy, though without any realization of its comprehensive significance. By the way, Christopher Wren (1632-1723), the third candidate, used the principle in the same manner. It is very interesting, however, that Huygens used in his paper the principle of relativity, of course only the one which corresponds to the mechanics of his time and which we call today the Galilean principle of relativity to distinguish it from that of Einstein. In order to generalize the law that two equal elastic balls with equal velocities and opposite signs simply exchange their velocities on impact, Huygens assumes that the impact occurs on a moving ship, and he observes it from shore. Thus he transforms, as we should call it today, from one system of reference to another.

But all these investigations became dated when Isaac Newton (1642-1727) published his *"Principia"* (*Philosophiæ Naturalis Principia Mathematica*) in 1687. In this treatise we find the two pronouncements that the rate of change of (linear) momentum of a mass point per unit time equals the force acting on it, and that the forces between two mass points are equal and opposite (equality of action and reaction). It follows immediately that the interaction of an arbitrary number of mass points never changes their total momentum, but that this total momentum is constant for any system not subject to external forces. Newton calculates the total momentum as a vector quantity, by adding vectorially the individual momenta. His formulation of the first law above appears almost prophetic: He equates the force not to the product of mass and acceleration, but to the rate of change of momentum, even though both formulations are equivalent if the momentum is assumed to be the product $m\,q$. Newton's formulation, however, is consistent with present-day relativity, whereas the other formulation has been disproved by the experiments on the deflection of fast electrons.

Newton's mechanics obtained its principal empirical confirmation from astronomical experience, because he could derive mathematically the planetary motions from its laws and from his law of gravitational attraction. But all the other great ideas of his work, the theory of tides, the calculation of the flattening of the earth and other planets, the derivation of the velocity of sound, etc., lent credence to the law of momentum, once they were verified by experience, because they are all based on it. In the following centuries, the thousandfold empirical verifications of Newton's mechanics produced an almost unlimited confidence in the law of momentum. In the minds of many scientists this law assumed the quality of a mathematical truth—which it is not.

The conservation of the angular momentum is one of the most important mathematical consequences of the law of linear momentum; the angular momentum is a directed quantity (a vector), which is determined by the momentum of a mass point and the radius vector assumed to be drawn to it from a fixed point in space. The angular momentum is perpendicular to these two vectors; its amount is obtained by multiplying the momentum component normal to the radius vector by the length of the latter. The earliest examples for the conservation of angular momentum are the two laws of Kepler, which state that the path of a planet is plane and that the radius vector drawn from the sun to the planet covers equal areas in equal times. Later on, the angular momentum law achieved prominence when, in 1765, Leonhard Euler (1707-1783), with analytical methods, developed the theory of the rotation of a rigid body about a fixed point; then, somewhat later (1834), Louis Poinsot (1777-1859) solved the same problem with the help of synthetic-geometrical methods. All that is needed in this case is the application and mathematical interpretation of the law of angular momentum. The top provides the most obvious example of the types of motion that can be treated with its help. When no point of the rigid body is held fixed, then the translatory motion of its center of mass is controlled by the law of linear momentum alone, and the rotation about this point by the law of angular momentum alone.

As a *physical* problem mechanics was completely solved by Newton. The mathematicians, however, worked on it for another century and a half. They erected a structure with an architectural beauty which Newton, himself, had never divined. The fact, however, that the architects were mathematicians and that they required no new experiment or new observations proves that the foundation laid by Newton was fully sufficient to support this structure. And, since the scientists of that time proposed to reduce all of physics to mechanics, they thought that it would also suffice to support the far greater building of physics. This belief inspired physical research till the end of the nineteenth century. Only then new ideas gained hold in mechanics as well as throughout the other branches of physics.

Newton's mechanics assumed action at a distance between the different bodies. His law of gravitational attraction shows this very distinctly. It is beside the point whether Newton himself had considered this law to be more than an approximation, to be replaced eventually by a law incorporating a finite velocity of propagation. The notion of the rigid body, where each force attacking one part affects the entire body instantaneously, also is based on the idea of action at a distance. More fundamentally, the axiom of the equality of action and reaction shows the importance of action at a distance in Newton's theory: in case body *A* is the source of an action which changes its momentum and which *only later* reaches a body *B*, where it produces an equal and opposite change of momentum, the sum of the momenta of both bodies is evidently not the same during the interval of transfer as before and after. In a later section we are going to show how physics has been able to maintain the law of conservation of momentum by expanding the momentum concept.

We shall conclude this section with a remark concerning the invariability of mass. As mentioned above, this invariability was taken for granted because repeated weighings had never

indicated any change in the weight of a body. After the revolutionary chemical discoveries of the eighteenth and nineteenth
centuries, the question arose whether the chemical reactions left
the total weight of the matter unchanged. Hans Landolt (1831-
1914) achieved the highest accuracy for the necessary weight
determinations for fifteen different reactions in a long series of
tests which lasted from 1893 to 1909. He was able to exclude
relative variations in weight greater than 10^{-6}. In a few cases
he obtained even higher accuracy.

III. The Law of Energy

In mechanics, the beginnings of the knowledge of the law of
energy coincide with those of the law of momentum, as shown
by the aforementioned energy considerations of Galileo and
Huygens. Newton's theory of planetary motion naturally includes the fact that the planet always possesses the same velocity
when it returns to the same distance from the sun. For Newton,
however, this was only one of the many conclusions from the
law of momentum. Gottfried Wilhelm Leibniz (1646-1716)
was the first to devote his attention to the product of mass and
squared velocity, $m\,q^2$. In 1695 he called this expression "*Vis
viva*," and this term was used until the middle of the nineteenth
century. Following Gustave Gaspard Coriolis (1792-1843), it
was applied to one-half of $m\,q^2$, the value of $(m/2)\,q^2$. Johannes Bernoulli (1667-1748) gave us the expression "*energy*,"
but this name did not gain the upper hand until later. We use
"energy" today in a broader sense and denote the "*vis viva*"
as *kinetic energy*. The kinetic energy first came to public attention through the well-known, endless quarrel between the
Cartesians on the one hand and Leibniz and his disciples on
the other, whether $m \cdot q$ or $m \cdot q^2$ represents the correct measure
of force. Actually both quantities play important but different
rôles in mechanics; the whole dispute concerned a fictitious
problem, caused by the then ambiguous meaning of the word
"force" (*vis*). In the eighteenth century, however, the force
concept was still so overgrown with mysticism that profound
thinkers were seriously concerned with the dispute.

A further step in the interpretation of the law of energy was taken by the above-mentioned Swiss mathematicians Johannes Bernoulli and Leonhard Euler. They emphasized that the change in kinetic energy in a closed mechanical system did not at all result in a reduction in its "capacity of action" (*Facultas agendi*), but only in its transition to other forms. In 1826 Jean Victor Poncelet (1788-1867) first introduced the term "work" for that product of a force by the path of its point of application, measured in the direction of the force, which in mechanics equals the change in energy. The kinetic energy is again of great importance in the papers on collision by Thomas Young (1773-1829), which were published in 1807. As one of the results of mechanics it was established by the end of the eighteenth century that it was impossible to construct with mechanical components a *perpetuum mobile*, a machine that would permanently create mechanical work from nothing. That this result had a more general significance was probably suspected even then; at least the Academy of Paris decided in 1775 not to accept any further supposed solutions of the problem of the *perpetuum mobile*, on the grounds that it had already wasted too much of its time examining these schemes. That these negative results could lead to important positive conclusions remained unrecognized at that time.

The stimulus for a generalization of the mechanical to a universal conservation law was furnished by the experience of long standing that kinetic energy or mechanical work could be lost while the temperature of the bodies involved was increased, as through friction, and also by the much more recently observed fact, on the steam engine, that one might gain work from thermic processes. It was with the steam engine that Sadi Carnot (1796-1832) concerned himself in 1824 in a very remarkable paper, which led to the basic result that the production of work was contingent on the transition of heat from the high temperature of the boiler to the lower temperature of the surroundings. His work was marred, however, by the erroneous belief, then current, that heat is an indestructible substance. His successor, Bénoit Clapeyron (1799-1864), still retained the same error in a paper in 1843. But even before, in the first decades of the nineteenth century, there had been voices which asserted the existence of a uniform "force," which was to account equally for the phenomena of heat, light, electricity, magnetism, chemical affinity, etc. Added to these were discussions of the metabolism of food in the body as the source of animal heat as well as their capacity to do work. A discovery was in the air, and several scientists independently made important contributions in its direction.

The first was Julius Robert Mayer (1814-1878), a physician, who (according to M. Planck's 1885 paper on the conservation of energy) "preferred, in his whole mental attitude, to generalize in the manner of a philosopher rather than build piecemeal and by experimental methods." In his brief paper of May, 1842, he operated with the principles *"Ex nihilo nihil fit"* (from nothing grows nothing) and *"Nil fit ad nihilum"* (nothing leads to nothing), applying them to the "power to fall," to motion, and to heat; what is of permanent value in his paper is that he gives a reasonably correct value for the mechanical equivalent of heat. How he obtained his value, he does not tell until 1845; his computation is one still familiar, from the difference in the two specific heat capacities of perfect gases, where he assumes by implication, but correctly, that their internal energy is independent of the volume. Ludwig August Colding (1815-1888) obtained almost precisely the same value in 1843 from experiments involving friction; however, his justification for the general conservation law appears to us even more fantastic than the one given by Mayer. The latter considers electric and biological processes already in his second publication, while in his third, in 1848, he raises the question of the origin of solar heat, explains the incandescence of meteors from their loss of kinetic energy in the atmosphere, and applies the law of conservation to the theory of tides. Quite obviously, Mayer fully realized the significance of his discovery. Nevertheless, at first he remained quite unkown and received the recognition due him only much later. Men like Joule and Helmholtz cannot be blamed for not having known at first of Mayer's sparsely distributed works and therefore for not having quoted him.

Whatever we may think of Mayer's arguments, this much we

must admit: Since it is the task of physics to discover the general laws of nature, and since one of the simplest forms of a general law is to assert the conservation of some particular quantity, the search for constant quantities is not only a legitimate line of inquiry, but is exceedingly important. This approach was always present in physics. We owe to this approach the early conviction concerning the constancy of electric charge. The actual decision, whether a quantity believed to be subject to a conservation law does really possess that property can, of course, be reached only by experimentation. The energy principle is an experimental law just as much as the law of conservation of electricity. But Mayer really took the road of the experiment in determining the mechanical equivalent of heat. For other fields of physics, the principle remained for him a program, to be carried through by others.

As the second contributor we must mention James Prescott Joule (1818-1889), who early in 1843 wrote a paper on the thermic and chemical effects of the electric current (this paper was not printed until 1846). He established by measurements that the heat developed in the electric wire of a galvanic cell (which later, appropriately, was called *Joule's heat*) equals the chemical heat of reaction if the reaction takes place in an open-circuited cell, and provided, as we must add today, that the current is produced by the cell without the development of heat. Shortly after and again in 1845, Joule reports determinations of the mechanical heat equivalent, in which he converts mechanical work into heat either directly, electrically, or through the compression of gases.

However, the man whose universally educated mind enabled him to develop the energy principle with all its implications was Hermann Ludwig Ferdinand von Helmholtz (1821-1894). Like Mayer, whose works he did not know and whose results he had to obtain independently, he approached the principle starting from medical investigations. In 1845 he had corrected, in a short paper, an error of Justus von Liebig's (1803-1873), by pointing out that one could not simply equate the heat of the combustion of food stuffs in the animal body to the heat of combustion of the constituent chemical elements; at the same time, he had made a brief survey of the implications of the energy principle for the different fields of physics.

His lecture before the Physical Society of Berlin, on July 27, 1847, goes farther into the ramifications of this idea. In contrast to Mayer, Helmholtz adopted the point of view of the mechanical nature of all processes of nature, to be comprehended by the assumption of attractive and repulsive central forces, as did most of his contemporaries. In this point of view he saw a sufficient and (erroneously) necessary condition for the impossibility of the *perpetuum mobile*. But in his deductions he did not use the mechanistic hypothesis at all, but derived the various expressions for the energy directly from the impossibility of the *perpetuum mobile*—if for no other reason than that the reduction of all processes to central forces had by no means been carried through. Thus, his results did not depend on the mechanistic hypothesis and therefore were able to survive it. His original contributions included the concept of potential energy (*"Spannkraft"*—stress) for mechanics, the expressions for the energy of gravitation, for the energy of static electric and magnetic fields, and his energy considerations applied to the production of electric current in galvanic cells and thermocouples as well as to electrodynamics, including electromagnetic induction. When, today, we compute the energy of a gravitational field as the product of masses and potentials, that of an electrostatic field as the product of charges and potentials, we are employing Helmholtz's methods directly.

It would lead us too far to go into the details. The further development of the principle cannot be treated here either. The final formulation only, due to William Thomson (later Lord Kelvin of Largs, 1824-1907) may be mentioned: "We denote as energy of a material system in a certain state the contributions of all effects (measured in mechanical units of work) produced outside the system when it passes in an arbitrary manner from its state to a reference state which has been defined *ad hoc*." The words "in an arbitrary manner" contain the physical law of the conservation of energy.

Helmholtz's considerations were not at all generally accepted; the older of his contemporaries were afraid of a revival of the phantasies of Hegel's natural philosophy, against which they had had to fight for such a long time. Only the mathematician Gustav Jakob Jacobi (1804-1851), who has made his own important contributions to mechanics, saw in them the logical continuation of the ideas of those mathematicians of the eighteenth century who had built up the science of mechanics. When, however, by about 1860 the law of energy had finally received general recognition, it became very soon a cornerstone of all natural science. Now every new theory, particularly in physics, was evaluated first by examining whether it was consistent with the law of energy. About 1890 many scientists, such as the well-known physical chemist Wilhelm Ostwald (1859-1932), were so enthralled by it that they not only undertook to deduce all other natural laws from it, but they actually made it the central thesis of a new *Weltanschauung*, energetics. Such exaggerations, however, were soon brought to an end by less excitable contemporaries.

The notion of energy also penetrated into engineering. Every machine was judged according to its balance of energy, i.e., the extent to which its energy input is transformed into the desired form of energy. Nowadays the energy concept is part of the working knowledge of every educated person. Only in regard to atomic physics, about 1924, was the principle of energy seriously doubted. For a time Niels Bohr, H. A. Kramers, and J. C. Slater thought that energy was not conserved in the individual scattering process involving x-rays or γ-rays, but only as the average for many such processes. But in 1925 the famous coincidence experiments by Hans Geiger (1882-1845) and Walter Bothe established that their views were in error.

The problem of basing mechanics solely on the energy principle arose also in the epoch of energetics. We shall state the answer here, because it holds in modern relativistic mechanics even though originally it was obtained on the basis of Newton's mechanics. The law of momentum cannot be deduced from the principle of energy alone; it contains more than it. But if we add the principle of relativity—at that time of course only that of Galileo—to the law of energy, according to which there is not only one correct system of reference for the fundamental equations of mechanics but an infinite number of them, all of which move with respect to one another with constant velocity, in other words if we require that the sum of potential and kinetic energy is conserved in *each* system of reference of this kind, it necessarily follows that the total momentum of the closed system considered remains constant.[1] The connection between the two laws of conservation which is hereby revealed, is related to the inertia of energy, toward which our presentation is aimed.

But when the principle of energy was found to hold beyond mechanics, it first seemed to lose this connection entirely. It had to be accepted as being much more comprehensive than the purely mechanical law of momentum. How the law of momentum, too, gradually grew beyond the sphere of mechanics we are going to show in the following sections.

IV. The Theory of the Flow of Energy

Time changed, the knowledge of physics became more profound. No sharp dividing line, however, separates the epoch which concluded with the triumph of the principle of energy from the following period which is characterized by the displacement of the theories of action at a distance by the theories of local action, which better correspond to the principle of causality. The dates in our presentation clearly show that the transition was gradual and that the two epochs partly overlap.

---

[1] Let us consider an isolated system of any number of mass-points m_i with the velocities q_i relative to a first system of reference, the potential energy of which is a function of the relative co-ordinates of the m_i, such as Φ. From the law of energy we have:

$$\tfrac{1}{2} \sum m_i\, q_i{}^2 + \Phi = C,$$

where C is a quantity independent of time.

In a second system of reference which moves with the constant velocity $\mathbf{v}$ relative to the first system, the mass-point m_i has the velocity $q_i - \mathbf{v}$. Relative to this system the law of energy becomes:

$$\tfrac{1}{2} \sum m_i\, (\mathbf{q}_i - \mathbf{v})^2 + \Phi = C'$$

Again C' is independent of time; Φ has the same value in both cases. Subtracting the first equation from the second we therefore obtain:

$$\tfrac{1}{2}\mathbf{v}^2 \sum m_i - (\mathbf{v} \cdot \sum m_i\, \mathbf{q}_i) = C' - C.$$

According to this equation the scalar product $(\mathbf{v} \cdot \sum m_i\, \mathbf{q}_i)$ is independent of time, no matter what direction and amount $\mathbf{v}$ may have. And this is possible only if $\sum m_i\, \mathbf{q}_i$, the total momentum of all mass-points, is constant with time.

The principle of local action and that of finite velocity of propagation, even in a vacuum, which is connected with it, first triumphed in electrodynamics; we are convinced of it, since Heinrich Hertz (1855-1894) discovered the electromagnetic waves in 1888. Nowadays we are also convinced that gravitation progresses with the speed of light. This conviction, however, does not stem from a new experiment or a new observation, it is a result solely of the theory of relativity. But that belongs to a later period.

Of course, the idea of local action for all domains filled with matter was known to former physicists. The oldest theory involving local action is contained in the theory of elastically deformable bodies, including fluid dynamics. The origins of that theory date back to the life-time of Newton. Not only was the *total* potential energy of a stressed body calculated without difficulty, but the potential energy could be localized, i.e., its share could be attributed to each part of the body. It was also generally accepted that a fluid moving under pressure not only conveys energy by transport, but also conducts an additional amount of energy, which is proportional to its velocity and pressure. In 1898 this theory was completed by Gustav Mie, when he taught us how to calculate the flow of energy for any motion of elastically stressed bodies. The assumption that energy flows like a substance can be carried through quite generally. In the driving belt, which connects the motor with a machine consuming energy, the energy flows against the motion of the stretched half of the belt. In the rotating and twisted shaft, which connects the engine of the ship with the propeller, it flows parallel to the shaft axis, i.e., at right angles to the velocity of the material parts.

For electromagnetic processes Helmholtz's method at first furnished merely a formula for the total energy; as long as one believed in action at a distance without a transmitting medium, the question of localization lacked meaning. But Michael Faraday (1791-1867), in the course of his long career of scientific investigation, developed the concept of the *field* as the medium transmitting such action; the field was considered as a change in the physical state of a system which was essentially located in

the dielectric, or even in the empty space between the carriers
of electric charge and electric current and between the magnets.
With this approach, the problem of localization became significant; Maxwell's theory of electricity and magnetism, proposed
in 1862, does, in fact, contain the expressions for calculating the
energy density which is composed additively of an electric and
a magnetic term. This development is a necessary supplement
of the field concept.

J. H. Poynting (1852-1914) led the theory a step farther,
by adding to it, in 1884, the notion of a *flux* of electromagnetic
energy, long before Mie carried through this idea for the
theory of elasticity. He took this step on the basis of a mathematical conclusion from Maxwell's equations, but accomplished
much more, the creation of an entirely new physical concept.
According to him, there is a flux of electromagnetic energy
wherever an electric and a magnetic field are present at the same
time. Now it was possible to determine the route by which the
chemical energy, which in the galvanic cell is transformed into
electromagnetic energy, gets to the wire that completes the circuit, where that energy is converted into Joule's heat; likewise
we can trace the energy on its way into the electric motor which
transforms it into mechanical work. For us, this approach has
become almost a matter of course; during Poynting's time, it
was the cause of considerable conceptual difficulties and took a
long time to gain acceptance.

For a special case the concept of a spatially distributed energy
and its flow through empty space had already been developed,
and this circumstance greatly facilitated the assimilation of
Poynting's innovation. A body which radiates light or heat
loses energy; this energy will not appear as the energy of a
particular body until the radiation strikes another body. Therefore, if the sum total of all energies of the system is to remain
constant, the radiated energy must in the meantime exist as
radiation energy. And now Maxwell's theory, confirmed so
brilliantly by Hertz's experiments, reveals light and heat radiation to be electromagnetic vibrations; its formulas for the
density and for the flux of electromagnetic energy turned out
to correspond precisely to the customary ideas concerning radia-

tion. Thus, physicists of the last decade of the nineteenth century gradually learned to appreciate the new concepts also for other electromagnetic fields.

But the concept of linear momentum required a similar generalization. Clerk Maxwell (1831-1879), in his comprehensive work, *Treatise of Electricity and Magnetism*, 1873, had shown that a body which absorbs a light ray experiences a force in the direction of the ray; its magnitude per unit cross section of the ray equals the energy flux S, divided by the velocity of light c. This assertion was confirmed experimentally much later, by P. Lebedew (1901), E. F. Nichols and G. F. Hull (1903), and, with an accuracy of about two parts in a hundred, by W. Gerlach and A. Golsen (1923). But even earlier there arose the question of the validity of the law of momentum.

Now it is true that the body which emits a ray experiences the opposite force of the one which absorbs it; and, since emission and absorption take equally long times, the two changes in linear momentum eventually compensate for each other exactly. However, while the ray passes from one body to the other, the total mechanical momentum is certainly different from that measured, either before the process of emission or after absorption. If we wish to maintain the law of conservation of momentum, we cannot but ascribe to the ray an *electromagnetic momentum* and to assert the law of conservation for the sum of mechanical and electromagnetic momenta. And then one cannot but extend this new concept to all electromagnetic fields, instead of restricting it to rapidly vibrating fields like heat and light radiations. It turns out that the field must contain momentum of the magnitude of S/c^2 per unit volume, where the symbol S denotes the magnitude of electromagnetic energy flux; both of these vectors possess the same direction.

$$g = S/c^2$$

is the momentum density of the field. Science owes this fundamental step to Henri Poincaré (1854-1912); his publication is contained in the Lorentz Anniversary Volume of 1900.

According to this theory, static fields, too, may give rise to energy flux, if only electric and magnetic fields overlap. The paths of this flow, though, are always closed, the energy current leads back into itself without being converted anywhere into other forms of energy. This conclusion has occasionally been used as a counter-argument in discussions of Poynting's law. As a matter of fact, in energy considerations it is perfectly permissible to disregard this closed energy current entirely.

But according to Poincaré, in such static fields we shall also encounter linear momentum. For the field as a whole, the total momentum is always zero; but the local momenta will in general give rise to an angular momentum whose sum total is different from zero. A system consisting of electric charges and of magnets at rest represents an electromagnetic top whose angular momentum corresponds to that of a mechanical top. As long as the state of the system remains unchanged, the angular momentum of either top remains unobservable. However, any change of the electromagnetic field, affecting either the magnitude or the direction of the angular momentum, must produce a torque on the material carriers of the electric charge and on the magnets, because the change in angular momentum of the field must be compensated for by a corresponding change of the mechanical angular momentum. This conclusion, which at first may appear surprising, actually results merely in the well-known forces experienced by moving charges in a magnetic field and by moving magnets in an electric field, once the calculations are carried out. But it is clear now that the electromagnetic momentum is observable not only in heat and light radiation.[2]

Of greater importance is another conclusion from the equation $g = S/c^2$. If we displace a carrier of electric charge, then the motion of the corresponding electric field gives rise to a magnetic field, and their coexistence leads both to a current

[2] If we permit ourselves in passing to operate with a (fictitious) single magnetic pole of magnitude m and if we form a system containing in addition a single electric charge of magnitude e, then the angular momentum of the field has the direction from e toward m, if both are positive or both negative (otherwise the direction is reversed), and its magnitude is independent of the distance and equals em/c. Starting with this law, and by applying vector addition, we can get the angular momentum for a charge in the field of a magnetic dipole and also for more complicated cases.

of energy and to a momentum; if the system satisfies certain symmetry conditions, e.g., if the body is a sphere, these two vectors are parallel to the velocity of the body. Here, for the first time we encounter the *inertia* of electromagnetic energy; for this additional momentum represents an additional inertial mass. True, for a macroscopic body this additional mass is negligible for all charges that are experimentally feasible. But for the electron, considered a rigid sphere with a radius of about 10^{-13} cm, it was not difficult to find out that this additional inertial mass is of the same order of magnitude as the observed mass; in fact, it was suspected that the whole mass of the electron might be of electromagnetic origin. Many physicists tended toward this view soon after 1900. This hypothesis was examined most carefully by Max Abraham (1875-1922) in a famous investigation in 1903; the most striking result was that the electromagnetic momentum is proportional to the material velocity only for very small velocities, but otherwise increases more rapidly, in fact it increases without limit as the velocity of the electron approaches the velocity of light, c. The differentiation between two masses, both of which depend on the velocity, the *longitudinal mass* and the *transversal mass*, originated with this investigation; but it also showed that this result modifies the basic structure of mechanics only slightly. These investigations stimulated the performance of many experiments in which the deflection of fast electrons by electric and magnetic fields was measured with ever increasing accuracy. The results showed uniformly that the momentum increases more rapidly than the velocity; but even more rapidly than is predicted by Abraham's mechanics. These results led subsequently to a decision between his mechanics and relativistic mechanics.

For small velocities, both of the masses postulated by Abraham go over into the rest mass m, which is related to the electrostatic energy of the electron, E_0, by the equation

$$m = \frac{4}{3} \frac{E_0}{c^2}.$$

Theoretical investigations of the dynamics of cavity radiation inside a uniformly moving envelope are part of the same general approach. Since Planck's radiation law of 1900, the problem of cavity radiation at rest was completely settled. In 1904, F. Hasenöhrl (1874-1915) began to generalize the theory for cavities in motion, and K. v. Mosengeil and M. Planck completed the investigation with an improved theoretical approach. At rest all rays, no matter what their direction of propagation, have the same intensity, whereas in motion those are more intensive which form an acute angle to the direction of motion. As a consequence, we have a resultant momentum in the direction of motion. This momentum increases with the velocity, but more rapidly than the latter, and it would increase beyond all limits, if the velocity should approach that of light, c, but even more rapidly than in the case of Abraham's model of the electron. What is common to both cases is the relationship between the rest mass m and the rest energy E_0. We have here a special case of relativistic dynamics, but treated without explicit reference to the principle of relativity; the derivation from Maxwell's theory by itself assures consistency with that principle.

In the case of the sphere as well as in the case of cavity radiation, the total linear momentum is parallel to the velocity. In most other cases, however, the total momentum possesses a component at right angles to the velocity. Even when the motion is purely translatory, the angular momentum will change, and, to compensate for this change, the material carriers of the charge must experience a torque which will produce this compensatory change in the mechanical angular momentum. Thus it appeared reasonable that an electrically charged condenser, if suspended so that it could turn freely, would assume a particular orientation relative to the velocity of the Earth, the one in which that angular momentum vanishes. This conclusion is inescapable in Newtonian mechanics. However, in 1903 Fr. T. Noble and H. R. Trouton searched for this effect in vain, and even the much more accurate repetition of their experiment by R. Tomaschek (1925-26) showed no trace of the effect. Their result is just as convincing a proof of the principle of relativity as Michelson's interference experiment. Both of these experiments proved the necessity for a new mechanics; Michelson's experiment because it showed the contraction of moving bodies in the direction of motion, and the experiment by Trouton and Noble because it showed that an angular momentum does not necessarily lead to a rotation of the body involved.

Thus, a new epoch in physics created a new mechanics. This epoch, too, partly overlaps with the preceding one; it began, we might say, with the question as to what effect the motion of the Earth has on physical processes which take place on the Earth. Hendrik Anton Lorentz (1853-1928) had centered the general interest on this question through a famous essay in 1895. But in this case we can assign to the dividing line between epochs a precise date: It was on September 26, 1905, that Albert Einstein's investigation entitled "On the Electrodynamics of Bodies in Motion" appeared in the *Annalen der Physik*. Our presentation here need not report on the theory of relativity as a whole; we shall restrict ourselves to the question, how this theory led to the recognition that *all* forms of energy possess inertia.

And here we must first of all take exception to a prime example of national-socialist forgery of history, this time in the field of physics. Because of the work of Fritz Hasenöhrl which was mentioned above, Philipp Lenard and his cronies tried, during the period of the "Third Reich," to give credit for the law of inertia, which had received the limelight of attention because of its applications in nuclear physics, to this worthy physicist, who had long since died. But an examination of the literature shows conclusively that Hasenöhrl in 1904 applied the then current notion of the inertia of electromagnetic energy with partial success to the problem of cavity radiation. The idea of the inertia of other forms of energy occurred to him no more than to other physicists prior to Einstein.

Incidentally, we must emphasize that our division into epochs applies only to macrophysics. Simultaneously, the development of molecular physics proceeded at a different pace; initially it received more stimulus from macrophysics than it was able to return. Since Planck's law of radiation, which is based on molecular-statistical considerations, this relationship has undergone a gradual change, so that for later times we can no longer speak of two separate approaches in physics; but for our present purposes, this is rather unimportant.

V. The Inertia of Energy

The recognition of the inertia of energy as such was published by Einstein in 1905 (*Ann. d. Physik, 18*, 639), in the same year as his basic paper on the theory of relativity. Einstein derived this law relativistically. And, in fact, a rigorous derivation must start from there. But a year later Einstein gave another presentation which is merely approximate, but which possesses the great advantage of being more intuitive and of avoiding the relativistic foundation. For our purposes, it will be sufficient to trace the second argument.

Let a large cylindrical cavity which has been evacuated float in empty space; let its length be L and its mass M. Placed on its end faces there are two bodies, A and B, respectively, whose masses are sufficiently small compared to M that they can be disregarded in all sums involving M (Fig. 1). Let A transmit

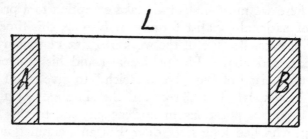

Fig. 1

to B an amount of energy ΔE in the form of Hertz vibrations or as light, and let B absorb that energy completely. The time required for emission and the equal time required for absorption shall be small compared to the time $T = L/c$, which is the time of travel through the interior of the cavity. During emission the body A receives a total impulse $G = \Delta E/c$, because of the radiation pressure, and through A, the cylinder as a whole receives the same impulse; the center of mass of the cylinder will therefore assume a velocity $q = G/M$ and, since it will retain this velocity during the time T, it will undergo a displacement

$$qT = \frac{L\Delta E}{Mc^2}$$

in the direction $B \to A$.

After the body B has stored the energy received in some arbitrary form, we displace it by means of forces which originate inside the cylinder until it touches A. If we denote the mass of B at this stage by m_1, then the center of mass of the cylinder will be displaced by an amount Lm_1/M in the direction $A \to B$. Now let B transfer the energy ΔE back to A and subsequently return B to its original position, again by means of internal forces. If the mass of B is m_2 after it has lost the energy ΔE, then the displacement of the center of mass will amount to Lm_2/M in the direction $B \to A$. In the final state the distribution of energy is the same as it was initially: But there remains a resultant displacement of the center of mass of magnitude

$$\frac{L}{M}\left(\frac{\Delta E}{c^2} + m_2 - m_1\right)$$

in the direction $B \to A$.

Shall we believe that the cylinder can shift its center of mass (and, therefore, in effect, itself) without any action from without and without any change in its interior? Such a possibility is not only inconsistent with mechanics but with our whole physical intuition, which, after all, contains a good deal of ancient valuable experience, even if that experience is often unconscious or uncomprehended. But the displacement will be zero only if the mass m_1 of the body possessing greater energy exceeds m_2, in fact if

$$m_1 - m_2 = \frac{\Delta E}{c^2}.$$

This is the amount by which the mass of a body must increase when it receives the energy ΔE, no matter in what form.

If q_1 was the velocity of B while it was moving toward A, then its momentum was

$$m_1 q_1 = \left(m_2 + \frac{\Delta E}{c^2} \right) \cdot q_1.$$

Let us divide this expression through by the volume V of the body B in order to obtain the momentum density (momentum per unit volume) and the energy density

$$\epsilon = \frac{\Delta E}{V},$$

to the extent that these quantities depend on the energy ΔE.

$$g = \frac{\epsilon}{c^2} q_1$$

is then the contribution of ΔE to the momentum density. On the other hand ϵq_1 is the flux S of the energy carried along convectively. As a result, we find the relationship

$$g = \frac{S}{c^2}$$

for the momentum density due to energy carried convectively.

Now we can modify the conceptual experiment which we have described by returning the energy ΔE to A not convectively, but for instance by means of a shaft which extends between A and B and which is rotated and twisted. We saw in Section IV that in such a shaft mechanical energy passes along the axis. Or, alternatively, we could return the energy by means of heat conduction. With every such type of energy flow there must be present an impulse in the same direction, if the center of mass of the cylinder is to return at the end to its original location. We require no lengthy calculations to show that momentum density and energy flux must always obey the same relationship indicated above.[3] Following Max Planck, who was

[3] If S is the density of the energy current in the shaft or in the heat conductor that returns the energy ΔE to A, if Q is the cross section of the carrier of this energy current and T' the time that it takes the current to return the energy ΔE, then we find

$$SQT' = \Delta E.$$

On the other hand, if G is the momentum possessed by the shaft or heat conductor

the first to point out this relationship in 1908, we consider it the most general expression for the inertia of energy. The formula

$$m_1 - m_2 = \frac{E}{c^2}$$

makes use of the concept of mass, which loses its significance when momentum and velocity are no longer parallel to each other. And this is usually not the case, as was pointed out repeatedly; the rotating shaft is merely one striking instance.

Now if for a material body there is a difference in direction between its momentum and its velocity, then a purely translatory motion will change its angular momentum according to our previous remarks. Because of the law of conservation of angular momentum, it will require an angular momentum to *prevent* angular acceleration. This is the explanation for the experiment by Trouton and Noble. The condenser is stressed elastically by the forces of its own electric field. Its mechanical momentum therefore is inclined toward its velocity. The torque which, according to Section IV, the field exerts on the condenser is just sufficient to make possible its translatory motion.

---

because of the energy current in the direction $B \rightarrow A$ and g the momentum density, then

$$G = gQL,$$

and

$$G/M = gQL/M$$

is the velocity which the center of mass of the cylinder receives because it must acquire the compensatory momentum $-G$; the direction of the velocity is from A toward B. During the time T', the center of mass will travel a distance

$$G'T'/M = GQLT'/M.$$

Now this displacement must equal the preceding displacement in the direction $B \rightarrow A$.

$$L \cdot \Delta E/Mc^2 = SQLT'/Mc^2,$$

and we conclude again that

$$g = S/c^2.$$

In this connection, one should not object that in the event of heat conduction or other irreversible processes the entropy will increase and that at least in this respect the initial condition of the system cannot be recovered. Increase in entropy by itself cannot cause a displacement of the center of mass, if for no other reason than that the direction of the displacement would remain completely undetermined.

But if an angular momentum is associated with translatory motion, is not the original law of inertia cancelled or at least its validity severely restricted? This law stated that a body *free of external forces* conserves its state of motion. Not at all! In the case of a force-free body (an isolated static system, in technical language), the momentum is always in the direction of the velocity. Only for parts of the system can the momentum deviate from that direction. The material parts of the condenser are not free of force, they are subject to the action of the field. However, the physical system which consists of the condenser plates and the field is an isolated static system. Thus we must conclude that the condenser will not begin to rotate just because it participates in the translatory motion of the Earth.

Energy possesses inertial mass. Can, then, *all* of the inertial mass of a body be ascribed to its energy content? Do we have the farther reaching relationship $m = E/c^2$? The theory of relativity has given a positive answer to this question from the beginning. That is why it was able to combine the energy density, energy flux, and momentum density into a single mathematical quantity, the energy-momentum tensor. This development is due to Hermann Minkowski (1864-1909) who, in an exceedingly beautiful mathematical representation, introduced this quantity and rewrote the two conservation laws in the form of a single brief formula. Much more clearly than in Newtonian mechanics, we recognize here the fusion of the two laws with the help of a relativity principle. Experience has subsequently confirmed the validity of this daring step in a surprising manner. The last Section (VI) will deal with these developments.

First, however, we must explain why Abraham's model of the electron as well as cavity radiation yield the different relationship $m = (4/3) (E_0/c^2)$. The reason is the same in both cases. The electromagnetic field is not capable of existing by itself alone, it requires certain supports of a different nature ("material supports"). Cavity radiation can exist only within an envelope, and the charged sphere would fly apart if it were not for certain cohesive forces. In both cases, motion will give rise to an energy current within the material supports which is directed opposite to the motion. It contributes to the total momentum a negative amount and reduces the factor 4/3 to 1. (We are disregarding here the energy inherent in the supports themselves.) For the sphere, we have to consider in addition that, in contradiction to Abraham's assumptions, a moving sphere, because of its contraction in the direction of motion, turns into a rotational ellipsoid. That is why the dependence of the momentum on the velocity obeys relativistic dynamics rather than Abraham's.

The generalized law of the inertia of energy then provides that every inertial mass is due to energy, every momentum due to energy flux. The concept of mass, formerly a basic concept of physics and a measure for the quantity of matter as such, is demoted to a secondary rôle. The law of conservation of mass is eliminated; for the energy of a body can be changed by the transfer of heat or work. What is left of that law is absorbed by the energy law. On the other hand, the energy concept is expanded tremendously. We have reason to doubt that we know all forms of energy at the present time. But quite independently of that question, we can determine the total amount of energy in a body from its mass. We thereby get rid of the arbitrariness of the zero point of energy which the former definition of energy (cf. Section III) was forced to introduce. There are not merely energy *differences*, as before; the energy possesses a physically meaningful absolute value.

One type of energy, however, the new physics must eliminate from its list, and that is kinetic energy. For the energy E of a body possessing the velocity q, relativistic dynamics furnishes the equation

$$E = \frac{E_0}{\sqrt{1 - \left(\dfrac{q}{c}\right)^2}},$$

in which E_0 is the energy in the state of rest. Each type of energy therefore increases in the same manner as a result of motion. And in fact, if we consider all of the inertia as an attribute of energy, then we cannot base a particular type of energy in turn on the inertia. That is how fundamental the changes are which the law of the inertia of energy causes in our whole picture of the physical universe.

How do these conclusions agree with the conservation of mass as established by experiment, in particular with the accurate confirmations that Landolt achieved by his investigations of chemical reactions (cf. Section II)? After all, the reagents occasionally lose considerable amounts of heat in the course of the reaction.

Let us consider, as an instance, the combination of one mol of oxygen with two mols of hydrogen to form two mols of liquid water. If we compute from the well-known heat of reaction of this chemical reaction the corresponding loss of mass, we find that it amounts to less than the 10^{-10}th part of the total mass involved. Landolt's limit of accuracy was of the order of 10^{-6}. Thus he could not possibly have ascertained the relativistic loss of mass. For all changes of phase, such as the condensation from the gaseous state to a liquid or solid, or the solidification of a liquid, the mass losses are even much smaller.

However, already in his first paper, Einstein pointed out one possibility for determining the loss of mass connected with the transfer of energy: In radioactive nuclear transformations the amounts of energy liberated are much larger relative to the masses involved than even in the most powerful chemical reactions. The same is true of artificial nuclear transformations, about which we have learned so much since Lord Rutherford's great discovery in 1919. This aspect will be the topic of our last Section.

VI. The Inertia of Energy in Nuclear Physics

The chemist Jean Charles Galissard de Marignac of Geneva (1817-1894) in 1865 wrote in a paper concerned with completed and planned determinations of atomic weights in *Liebigs Annalen* as follows:

If in these future determinations we should find to the same extent elements whose atomic weights approach integral values so remarkably close, then it appears inevitable to me that Prout's law be placed beside those of Gay-Lussac and Mariotte and that we recognize the presence of an essential cause according to which all atomic weights should exhibit simple numerical ratios, with secondary causes accounting for slight deviations from these ratios.

In all probability, Marignac merely expressed an opinion which was widespread at the time. Prout's hypothesis of the composition of all atoms from one or a few common original building stones has always been fascinating. Of course, science had to travel a long way before this opinion could assume definite shape. One of the preliminary conditions was, for instance, the discovery of isotopes by Frederic Soddy in 1910. Nowadays we know several atoms of different atomic weight at nearly each point of the periodic table; if we define the "unit of mass," by setting the atomic weight of the most frequent oxygen-isotope equal to 16.000 units, the atomic weight of each kind of atoms is really very close to an integer, the "mass number." This assertion, however, does not hold for the chemical elements composed of several isotopes. Another preliminary condition was the discovery of the neutron by J. Chadwick in 1930. Soon thereafter Jg.Tamm and Ivanienko, a little later W. Heisenberg, found that the composition of all atomic nuclei of protons and neutrons (which have nearly the same weight) is the essential cause for the integral numbers of the atomic weights, and that the energy loss accompanying the combination of these elementary particles and the loss of mass due to the inertia of energy is the secondary cause for the deviations from this law.

Two examples may show this: the atomic weights of the neutron and of the proton are 1.00895 and 1.00813 respectively; their sum is 2.01708. The deuteron, however, which consists of a neutron and a proton, has only the atomic weight of 2.01472. The difference, amounting to 0.00235 units of mass, is the mass defect of the deuteron, the result of an energy loss of 3.51×10^{-6} erg due to the fusion of a neutron and a proton. The nucleus of a lithium atom consists of 3 neutrons and 3 protons; but this atom does not have the weight 3 times $2.01708 = 6.051124$, but only 6.01692; the mass defect, therefore, is 0.03432, corresponding to a loss of energy of 5.11×10^{-5} erg when this atomic nucleus is formed from its components. The mass defect increases with the atomic number up to 0.238 for uranium. The example of lithium shows that it can be as much as half a percent of the mass; this is quite a different order of magnitude from the above defect of 10^{-10} when water is formed.

The accuracy of the law of inertia, $E = m c^2$, was proved by W. Braunbeck (*Zs. f. Physik* 107, p. 1 (1937)), by calculating the velocity of light c according to that equation for a series of nuclear reactions for which the loss of energy and the masses of the reacting atoms before and after the reaction are measured independently of each other. For instance, he finds a mass defect of 0.02462 units of mass for the transmutation of the above-mentioned isotope of lithium with the mass number 6 plus a deuteron into two atoms of helium; this mass defect corresponds to $4.087 \times 10^{-26} g$; the loss of energy is 3.534×10^{-5}. This results in the velocity of light of 2.94×10^{10} cm/sec. Forming the mean value over many different transmutations of nuclei, Braunbeck obtains the value 2.98×10^{10}, which is only 0.4 per cent below the value of 2.998×10^{10} cm/sec, measured electrically or optically.

All these tests, however, concern only the *variations* of energy and mass, not the entire mass of body. All the more important was a quite unexpected observation made in the Wilson chamber in connection with C. D. Anderson's discovery of the positron, the electron with a positive charge. In the proximity of an atomic nucleus, which serves only as a catalyst, γ-radiation can be transformed into a pair of electrons, a negative and a positive one. Not each γ-radiation can do this; its frequency ν has to be so high, its quantum of radiation $hν$ so great, that it is above 1.64×10^{-6} erg. As the rest mass of an electron—be it negative or positive—amounts to $9.1 \times 10^{-28} g$, it has a rest energy of 8.2×10^{-7} erg. This means: the γ-quantum has to be large enough to supply two electrons with their rest energy; what remains is used to give the electrons a certain velocity. The law of conservation of the electric charge is not disturbed here. The electron pair has the total charge zero.

Also, the reverse process of pair formation is possible. It is true, we have never observed in the Wilson chamber how a negative and a positive electron annihilate each other while emitting γ-radiation. But otherwise this annihilation radiation is well known experimentally; for example, Jesse DuMond measured its wave length in 1949 with a crystal spectrometer at 2.4×10^{-10} cm. According to all these observations, the law of inertia may be considered to be one of the results of physics which is best confirmed.

Thus we have followed the history of the laws of conservation of momentum and energy up to their amalgamation in the recent state of physics. Every thinking person cannot but be strongly impressed by the last consequence, which is extreme, but confirmed by experience, that at least for electrons the mass is nothing but a form of energy which can occasionally be changed into another form. Up to now our entire conception of the nature of matter depended on mass. Whatever has mass, —so we thought—, has individuality; hypothetically at least we can follow its fate throughout time. And this is certainly not true for electrons. Does it hold for other elementary particles, e.g., protons and neutrons? If not, what remains of the substantial nature of these elements of all atomic nuclei, i.e., of all matter? These are grave problems for the future of physics.

But there are more problems. Can the notions of momentum and energy be transferred into every physics of the future? The uncertainty-relation of W. Heisenberg according to which we cannot precisely determine location and momentum of a particle at the same time—a law of nature precludes this—, can, for every physicist who believes in the relation of cause and effect, only have the meaning that at least one of the two notions, location and momentum, is deficient for a description of the facts. Modern physics, however, does not yet know any substitute for them. Here we feel with particular intensity that physics is never completed, but that it approaches truth step by step, changing forever.

Max von Laue

Max Planck Institute of Physics
Göttingen, Germany

20

Herbert Dingle

SCIENTIFIC AND PHILOSOPHICAL IMPLICATIONS OF THE SPECIAL THEORY OF RELATIVITY

SCIENTIFIC AND PHILOSOPHICAL
IMPLICATIONS OF THE SPECIAL
THEORY OF RELATIVITY

E INSTEIN'S theory of relativity is unique among the
great epoch-marking ideas of the world in that it caused
a revolution by keeping to tradition; its heterodoxy lay in the
strictness of its orthodoxy. The outstanding characteristic of the
movement which in the seventeenth century inaugurated the
modern scientific age was the requirement that every conception used in the description of phenomena should be directly
referable to experience. Ideas not so referable were "hypotheses"
or "occult qualities" according to Newton, and "mere names"
according to Galileo; such ideas "put a stop to philosophy,"
and their avoidance was a prime necessity of right scientific
thinking.

It is easy to accept a general principle while violating it
in particular applications. The physicists of the nineteenth
century were not conscious of having been caught in the trap
against which Newton had warned them, when they spoke of
the length of a moving body without having convinced themselves in detail whether such a quantity could be unambiguously
determined. They had forgotten that Galileo had written: "I
will endeavour to show that all experiments that can be made
upon the Earth are insufficient means to conclude its mobility,
but are indifferently applicable to the Earth moveable or im-
moveable;" and, if this passage had been brought to their
attention, they would doubtless have replied that Galileo's outlook was too limited, without considering the possibility that
it might have been their own which was too confused. By the
beginning of the twentieth century the simple, essential principles of Galileo and Newton had become so entangled in the

network of incompatible physical theory that a genius as great
as theirs was needed to bring those principles again to light.
It is the glory of Einstein and the good fortune of the present
age that he possessed that genius.

Now that the ground has been cleared it is comparatively
easy to survey the fallen structure of post-Newtonian physics
and see wherein it was essentially faulty. It is not so easy to
build a more lasting structure; but here also Einstein has
shown the way—or at least *a* way—in which it can be begun.
The special theory of relativity reiterated the essential relativity
of uniform motion; the general theory extended that relativity
to all motion of the kind called "gravitational," and so rendered
still less valid the Aristotelian distinction between natural and
violent motions. The next extension—to motions in the electromagnetic field—though not yet so definitely established, bids
fair finally to abolish the Aristotelian distinction altogether, so
far as non-living matter is concerned, and to comprehend the
whole science of motion in one supreme generalisation. It is
indeed amazing that out of a simple recall to the Galilean
principle of relating conceptions to experience, so mighty an
issue should have come.

From another point of view it is perhaps equally surprising
that, the potentiality of that principle having been established,
it should not have been immediately applied to other physical
phenomena; for in at least one other field of study (namely,
that of temperature, or "black body," radiation) the same over-
sight has occurred. We observed motion of one body with
respect to another, and quite illegitimately we ascribed to each
an absolute motion, which we had no means of detecting.
Similarly, we observe radiation from one body to another, and
ascribe an absolute radiation to each, which we have no means
of detecting. If two bodies were relatively at rest we said their
absolute motions were equal, and so postulated two superfluous
unobservable processes which neutralised one another. Similarly,
if two bodies are at the same temperature we say that their
exchanges of absolute radiation are equal, and so postulate two
superfluous unobservable processes that neutralise one another.
The medium—an aether—which we invoke to serve as the

vehicle of these absolute radiations is the same as that which we invoked, and have now discarded, to serve as the frame of reference for the absolute motions. In order to construct laws of motion on the basis of the assumed absolute motions we found it necessary to assume two properties of bodies—inertial mass and gravitational mass—which were mysteriously equal. Similarly, in order to construct laws of radiation on the basis of the assumed absolute radiations we find it necessary to assume two properties of bodies—radiative power and absorptive power—which are mysteriously equal.

Now it seems clear that the principle which demanded a revision of classical mechanics, because of its detachment from possible experience, demands equally a revision of classical radiation theory for the same reason. Prévost's theory of exchanges is equivalent in one domain to motion with respect to the aether in the other. Moreover, the correspondence just indicated suggests that the actual technique employed in re-expressing the laws of motion might be effective also in re-expressing the laws of radiation. The parallelism is, of course, not exact; there is above all the great difference between the phenomena of motion and radiation which is usually expressed by saying that the laws of motion are reversible and those of radiation are not, so that the matter of the universe can exhibit eternal movement but not eternal radiation. But such differences are, from the technical point of view, matters of detail; they will lead us to expect equations of different form, but not needing a different mode of derivation. Again, there is no reason to suppose that the Stefan-Boltzmann law of radiation is inaccurate, as was the classical law of composition of velocities. We have found it applicable sufficiently close to the limiting temperature—the "absolute zero"—to make unlikely a modification similar to that which mechanical relativity demanded in the neighbourhood of the limiting velocity, viz., the velocity of light. We may suppose rather that the present laws of radiation correspond to the classical laws of motion with the Lorentz transformation formulae substituted for the Newtonian. Many of the phenomena observed will then be consistent with them, but they will lack the power of generalisation to cover more complex situations than those corresponding to radiation at uniform temperature, and so act as a barrier to progress without showing marked disagreement with observation in a limited field.

From the purely *scientific* point of view, therefore, it seems most desirable to explore the possibility of applying to the phenomenon of radiation the treatment which has been so successful with motion; from the general *philosophical* point of view the argument is compelling. We cannot urge the necessity of building only on experience in one part of physics and evade that necessity in another. Let us see, then, how the reform can be achieved.

The first thing to do in attempting to generalise a theory is to express that theory in the most suitable form for the purpose. An outstanding example of this is, of course, afforded by the theory of relativity itself. It is well known that, in its original form, all efforts at extending the application of the theory from uniform to accelerated motions were unsuccessful. Only when Minkowski gave it a geometrical expression was Einstein able to show how the generalisation could be made. Minkowski made no essential change in the theory: he simply expressed it in a different way. Our first task, therefore, is to see how the theory of mechanical relativity can be expressed so as to make clear the way in which its principle can be applied to the phenomenon of radiation.

To do this let us suppose we are about to start the study of motion, having no preconceptions in the matter at all. We must first devise some method of *measuring* motion; i.e., of representing each movement we observe by a number obtained by a strictly specified process. There are various processes which we could choose. We could construct some form of speedometer, or make use of the displacement of spectrum lines known as the Doppler effect, or construct a scale of movements such as that suggested by P. W. Bridgman,[1] or doubtless, if we are ingenious, invent other ways of achieving our purpose. Actually, however, physicists have chosen none of these devices, but, following Galileo, they have measured motion by the space covered by the moving

[1] P. W. Bridgman, *The Logic of Modern Physics*, 99.

body in a given time. This choice is so fundamental in physics that it is often assumed to be not a choice at all but a necessity. That is not so, however; and it is important to realise this at the outset, because when we come to compare motion with radiation we shall see that a similar choice is open there; radiation may be measured by candle-power, by the stellar magnitude scale, by a number of other observable quantities, or by the energy or entropy emitted by the radiating body in a given time. Naturally we shall choose the method indicated by the previous choice for motion.

Having decided, then, to measure motion by the space covered in a given time, we must now decide how to measure space and time. Here again considerable freedom of choice is open, but (taking space first) we select the familiar process based on the adoption of a rigid rod as a standard of length. This choice has been criticised by E. A. Milne[2] on the ground that a rigid rod is indefinable. He has usually been answered by the contention that definition is unnecessary, provided that physicists are consistent in their practice. I would agree with Milne that a definition is desirable, but I would not agree that it is impossible. The definition, which in fact is implied in modern physical theory, is that a rigid rod is a rod such that, if a source of monochromatic light and a spectroscope be placed at one end and a mirror at the other, the spectra seen by direct and reflected light always coincide. Whether the standard metre at Paris fulfills this condition we do not know, for the observation is too difficult to carry out with sufficient exactitude, but that this definition actually is implied by modern physics is clear from the following consideration. In the periodical comparisons of standards of length made at the National Physical Laboratory in England it is found that systematic changes occur. In the year 1936, for instance, the standard bar known as P.C.VI was found to be shrinking with respect to the Imperial Standard Yard at the rate of 1.92×10^{-7} cm. a year.[3]

[2] Cf. e.g. *Astrophysical Journal*, 91, 138 (1940).

[3] Report by the Board of Trade on the Comparisons of the Parliamentary Copies of the Imperial Standards with the Imperial Standard Yard, etc. (H. M. Stationery Office, 1936).

This, though certainly an actual change and not an error of observation, was regarded as practically negligible. For most purposes, of course, it is; but, taking the rate of recession of the nebulae as 528 km. a second per megaparsec (i.e., 5.4×10^{-8} cm. a year per metre), it is evident that one standard is expanding with respect to the other at nearly four times the rate of the expansion of the universe. Consequently, the universe may be expanding with respect to one and contracting with respect to the other. We are therefore not justified in saying, as Eddington does, for example,[4] that the universe is expanding with respect to "the standards of length ordinarily accepted—the metre bar, for example." The nebular spectrum shift, however, is unambiguously towards the red, and therefore the only standard with respect to which we can say definitely that the universe is expanding—or, more generally, that a Doppler red-shift indicates recession—is one whose rigidity is guaranteed by the Doppler effect itself. We do not know which, if any, of our standards that is.

Let us take it, however, that we know how to measure space: the next thing is to decide how to measure time. Broadly speaking, we can choose between two types of process. We can choose a series of recurring events—pulse beats, maxima of a variable star, passages of a particular star across the meridian, etc.,—and call the time intervals between successive events equal; or we can choose a process in which a measurable quantity changes continuously, and define equal times as those in which it changes by equal amounts. Examples of such continuous changes are afforded by a moving body (continuous change of position in space), a radio-active body (continuous change of mass), a radiating body (continuous change of energy), etc. The current practice in physics on this point is exceedingly ill-defined. Officially we choose an example of the first type; the standard in the C.G.S. system of units is the mean solar second, which is a certain fraction of the interval between successive passages of a star across the meridian, i.e., a certain fraction of the sidereal rotation period of the Earth. But it is now generally

[4] *The Expansion of the Universe*, Chapter III.

agreed that the Earth's rotation is gradually slowing down, and for this to be conceivable an unnamed ulterior standard of time measurement must be implied. Examination of the evidence for the slowing down of the Earth shows that this ulterior standard is that defined by Newton's first law of motion—equal times are those in which a moving body free from forces covers equal spaces. That law therefore ceases to be an assumption to be tested and becomes a definition of the time-scale used.

Einstein introduced a formal change in this definition: for a moving body free from forces he substituted a beam of light *in vacuo*. It is, of course, possible to maintain a time-scale defined by Newton's first law and regard the relativity postulate of the constancy and invariance of the velocity of light as an assumption vulnerable to experiment. This, however, would be a very unsatisfactory procedure, for it would mean that the whole structure of physics would rest on an assumption which it was impossible to test in actual practice. By taking the constancy of the velocity of light as a definition of the time-scale used we avoid all assumptions and introduce into physics for the first time a practicable time-scale which leads to simple expressions of natural laws. The ideal clock then becomes a beam of light travelling along a rigid space-measuring scale, and the time at any instant is the reading of the scale at the position of the wave-front.

The point of fundamental importance in this is that, having decided to represent motion as change of position in space with time, we choose to measure time in terms of space. We thus get a measure of time peculiarly fitted to express laws of *motion* (but not necessarily laws of radiation or anything else), for whatever effect motion has on space-measurement is necessarily carried over into time-measurement also. Thus, if we find that a space-measuring scale is contracted with motion, we must also find that the time-scale is contracted, for the space-scale is an essential part of our ideal clock. It is therefore because of our voluntary choice of measuring processes that we can speak of the "union" of space and time into "space-time." This has nothing to do with any philosophical notions of space and time in themselves; it is a consequence of the wisdom of making sure that, after expressing motion in terms of space and time, the measurement of time shall depend on the measurement of space. Only on this account is it possible, as Minkowski did, to represent the time-co-ordinate as a fourth space-co-ordinate and describe motion geometrically as a track in a four-dimensional continuum.

The next step is to obtain the equations of transformation connecting measurements made with one set of instruments (measuring-rod and clock) with those made with another set moving with uniform velocity with respect to the first. In each set, of course, the measuring-rod and clock are relatively stationary: i.e., the rod used for the measurement of space is stationary with respect to the similar rod which forms part of the ideal clock. It is a basic principle of the theory of relativity that no state of motion is fundamentally different from any other, so that, if we have a large number of pairs of instruments, all moving at different uniform speeds, the same laws of motion must be equally applicable to them all. Experiments such as that of Michelson and Morley indicate what the transformation laws must be in order that this shall be so: we obtain the well-known Lorentz equations, from which the measurements appropriate to any of our pairs of instruments can be calculated, when those made with a set moving with a known uniform velocity with respect to it are known. This completes the essential structure of the special theory of relativity; all that remains follows by calculation.

This description of the fundamentals of Einstein's achievement has been framed, as was indicated earlier, with the view of affording the easiest possible passage from the relativity of motion to the relativity of radiation. The procedure to be adopted is clearly first to represent radiation as a change of some measurable quantity (η, let us call it) with time; and secondly to measure time in terms of η. We may then construct an η-time which in the theory of radiation will play the rôle of space-time in the theory of motion. The whole apparatus of the tensor calculus and the geometry of the particular manifold arrived at will then be applicable to derive laws of radiation along the lines which Einstein has established for the laws of mechanical motion.

The measurable quantity which seems best fitted to serve as η is obtained as follows.[5] Suppose the radiating body under consideration has a Kelvin temperature θ. Let its radiation be received isothermally by one gram-molecule of a perfect gas at a temperature θ_0, and suppose that in consequence the pressure of the gas changes during a certain interval from p_1 to p_2. We choose for η the quantity $\beta \log_e (p_2/p_1)$, where β is a constant to be chosen to give the unit a convenient value. It is easy to see that this is closely related to the entropy received by the gas (or by the η-measuring instrument, as we will call it), for the energy received is, by the well-known formula, $-R\,\theta_0 \log_e (p_2/p_1)$ (where R is the universal gas constant) and θ_0 is the temperature. Radiation is thus measured by the η recorded by the instrument in unit time.

We must now define the time-scale, in which η will play the part played by space in the time-scale for the study of motion. Just as the ideal mechanical clock was a beam of light travelling along a space-measuring scale, so the ideal radiation clock will be a body at constant temperature radiating to an η-measuring instrument. Choose for this body one gram-molecule of a perfect gas having the same volume as the initial volume of the gas in an η-measuring instrument, but a slightly higher pressure ($p_1 + dp_1$ instead of p_1, say), and let its volume and pressure be maintained constant. We know that it will then have a slightly higher temperature ($\theta_0 + d\theta_0$) than the temperature of the η-measuring instrument and so will continuously radiate to the latter. Time is then measured by the reading of the instrument, unit time being that in which it records unit (or any other convenient) quantity of η.

These instruments—the η-measuring instrument and the radiation clock—provide measurements by which the process of radiation can be described in terms analogous to Einstein's description of the process of motion. We have now, following our pattern, to derive transformation equations for pairs of instruments in different states of uniform radiation—or, in more

[5] For a fuller treatment see *Phil. Mag.* 35, 499 (1944).

ordinary language, at different temperatures. For this purpose we have the experimental result embodied in the Stefan-Boltzmann law, namely that the gross rate of energy radiation is proportional to the fourth power of the Kelvin temperature of the body, the net rate, of course, being obtained by subtracting from this the radiation received from the surroundings. This is the "Michelson-Morley experiment of radiation," and it is easy to show that it is sufficient to solve our problem.

Let $d\eta$ represent the change of reading of the η-measuring instrument at Kelvin temperature θ_0 when a given body at constant temperature θ radiates to it for a time dt as measured by the radiation clock. We write

$$\tau \equiv \frac{d\eta}{dt} \qquad (1)$$

and clearly τ will be a measure of the temperature of the body, whose Kelvin temperature is θ, referred to an arbitrary zero of temperature represented on the Kelvin scale by θ_0. τ, of course, will measure temperature on a different scale from the ordinary ones, but that is because we do not ordinarily measure temperature in terms of a temporal process: we deliberately choose to do so here in order to be able to follow the procedure of mechanical relativity. τ is now analogous to velocity, defined as $V \equiv ds/dt$, whereas the Kelvin temperature scale is more analogous to a measure of velocity in terms of the Doppler effect, e.g., $V \equiv c\, d\lambda/\lambda$, in that time is not explicitly involved. For the measuring instruments themselves, as indicated, $\tau = 0$, for if a body at the same temperature as the instruments is presented to them, the η-measuring instrument will clearly record nothing.

Now let the same body, at Kelvin temperature θ and temperature τ on the τ-scale when measured by instruments at Kelvin temperature θ_0 and τ-scale temperature zero, be presented to instruments at Kelvin and τ-scale temperatures θ_1 and τ_1, respectively. The problem is, what will be the values of $d\eta'$, dt' and τ', corresponding to $d\eta$, dt and τ with the former instruments, when these new instruments define the arbitrary zero of temperature? (In the case of motion the corresponding problem is this: let a body moving with velocity V and travelling a distance ds in time dt, when measured by a measuring-rod and clock at rest, be examined by a measuring rod and clock moving with velocity V_1; what will be the values of ds', dt' and V' with these instruments?) The algebra is given elsewhere;[6] here we need only the result—"the thermal Lorentz equations"—namely,

$$dη' = \frac{dη - τ_1 dt}{(1 + τ_1/ζ)^{1/4}}$$
$$dt' = (1 + τ_1/ζ)^{3/4} dt$$
$$τ' = \frac{τ - τ_1}{1 + τ_1/ζ}$$
$$(2)$$

Here $ζ$ is a constant whose numerical value depends on the arbitrary choice of the increment of pressure, dp_1, in the clock (i.e., in effect on the unit of time chosen) and which corresponds to the temperature on the $τ$-scale of the Kelvin absolute zero. It is easily seen that it is a limiting temperature, having the same value for all "co-ordinate systems," and that it plays the same part in these equations as the velocity of light, c, in the Lorentz equations.

One difference is at once noticeable between these equations and the corresponding kinematical ones, namely, that these are unsymmetrical; it is not possible to interchange primed and unprimed quantities in them. That is because the limiting velocity is the same in opposite directions, but the limiting temperature is $+∞$ in one direction and $-ζ$ in the other. The difference, however, is not intrinsic in the nature of the phenomena; it is introduced by differences in the kinds of measurement chosen.

The process can be carried further. Just as the interval ds^2 in the relativity theory of motion, defined by

$$ds^2 ≡ c^2 dt^2 - dx^2 - dy^2 - dz^2$$
$$(3)$$

is invariant to a Lorentz transformation, so the "thermal interval," $dσ^4$, defined by

$$dσ^4 ≡ dt(dt + dη/ζ)^3$$
$$(4)$$

is invariant to the transformation (2). It is easily seen that whereas $dη$ corresponds to the net loss of entropy suffered by

[6] Loc. cit. in fn. 5 above.

the radiating body after the radiation by the η-measuring instrument back to the body has been taken into account, $d\sigma$ corresponds to the *gross* loss of entropy. It is the invariance of $d\sigma$ in this view of the process that corresponds to the "absoluteness" of the Kelvin temperature according to the ordinary view.

Just as equation (3) permits a geometrical interpretation of motion, so equation (4) permits a geometrical interpretation of radiation. The manifold indicated, however, ("η-time," it may be called), differs from the Euclidean—or, in its general form, Riemannian—manifold ("space-time") used in the description of motion in that it is two-dimensional instead of four-dimensional and, on the other hand, has a metric of the fourth degree instead of the second. The suggestion is inevitable that a generalisation along the lines of Einstein's general theory should be attempted. The most general laws of radiation would be expected to be given by the vanishing of a tensor derived from the metric

$$d\sigma^4 = g_{\alpha\beta\gamma\delta}dx^\alpha dx^\beta dx^\gamma dx^\delta \qquad (\alpha, \beta, \gamma, \delta = 1, 2). \qquad (5)$$

The mathematical difficulties, however, appear very formidable. "Spaces" of this character have been studied by Cartan[7] and Berwald,[8] among others, and their work seems to indicate that, even if the right tensor were identified, the mere labour of the application to a particular case would be excessive. That, however, is not of prime importance for our present purpose. It is sufficiently evident that the great clarification of the foundations of physics which Einstein achieved, and the mathematical technique which he employed, not only provide a solution of problems in the particular field of study with which he was concerned, immensely important though that was, but open the possibility of a much farther-reaching generalisation. Let us consider briefly the possible implications of this extension.

We may conveniently divide them into scientific and philosophical implications, though there is no clear dividing line between these classes. On the scientific side it is first to be noted that equations (2) and (4) are simply a re-expression, without

[7] "Les Espaces de Finsler" (*Act. Sci. et Indus.*, No. 79, 1934).
[8] *Math. Zeits*, 25, 40 (1926).

modification, of existing radiation theory. A generalisation of the metric might lead to new knowledge, but the "special" theory of thermal relativity, in its actual existing state, is precisely equivalent to what is already known and accepted; it is in its potentiality that its advantage lies. In this, as has already been pointed out, it differs from the special theory of mechanical relativity, which introduced new equations of transformation entailing consequences (e.g., the dependence of mass on velocity) not previously known.

The greater potentiality of the new expression lies first in its suggestion that phenomena in which radiation plays an essential part should be invariant to the transformation (2); i.e., that the laws of such phenomena should not depend on the temperature of the instruments used for investigating them. By an application of this requirement, for instance, it has been possible to show[9] that the electrical resistance of a pure metallic conductor should be proportional to its Kelvin temperature, a result which agrees with observation as closely as could be expected from the inexactness with which the ideal conditions are realisable in practice. Of greater interest is the application to the spectrum of black body radiation.[10] If it be accepted that radiation is associated with a continuous range of frequencies, then the law of distribution of the radiation among the frequencies, when these are reckoned on the thermal time-scale, should be invariant to the transformation (2). This condition, though necessary, is unfortunately not sufficient to determine the law, but it is possible to show that the Planck distribution law satisfies it, whereas the Rayleigh-Jeans law does not. In general, indeed, it may be said that the new expression places at the disposal of the theory of radiation the powerful apparatus of the tensor calculus, and so creates the possibility of a wide range of consequences which cannot be immediately foreseen.

As an example of the kind of simplification which the relativity expression might make possible, consider the following problem: given a sphere of known material, placed at a known initial temperature in an enclosure maintained at a constant and

[9] *Phil. Mag.*, 37, 58 (1946).
[10] *Phil. Mag.* 37, 47 (1946).

uniform lower temperature, to determine the surface temperature of the sphere at any instant during its cooling. It is difficult to imagine an intrinsically simpler radiation problem than this; yet in terms of present conceptions it cannot be solved. We need to know the laws of variation of specific heat and thermal conductivity with temperature, and we know them only approximately and semi-empirically. This would appear to be clear enough evidence that such concepts as specific heat and thermal conductivity, however necessary for engineering purposes, are unsuitable for the expression of theoretically simple laws. In the thermal relativity theory they would be expected to be as irrelevant as mass and force in mechanical relativity, and the theoretically important and tractable quantities would be the components of a tensor from which the specific heat and thermal conductivity, if needed, could be calculated.

Of more general interest is the prospect of a new system of thermodynamics. The existing science of thermodynamics, whether considered in the macroscopic or the microscopic form, is an interpretation of thermal phenomena in terms of classical Newtonian mechanics. Tolman[11] has indeed considered how the thermal quantities must be transformed when the kinematical co-ordinate system is changed; but this is more of the nature of a correction to a fundamentally Newtonian thermodynamics than the creation of a thermodynamics essentially relativistic. The problem which now suggests itself is that of amalgamating the Riemannian manifold of mechanics with the more general manifold corresponding to (5), so that both thermal and mechanical measurements can be expressed in terms of characteristics of the same "space." Such a union of the two sciences might be expected, among other things, to throw light on problems of the remote history of the physical universe.

Turning to the philosophical aspects of the theory, the first point to be noticed is the light which it throws on *the meaning of time* in physics. This has been perhaps the most widely misunderstood part of Einstein's theory. It has been supposed that the relativity theory gives us some insight into what is called the "nature" of time, and has shown that it is at bottom identi-

[11] *Relativity, Thermodynamics and Cosmology*, Sections V and IX.

cal with the nature of space, so that these two things are simply arbitrarily separated parts of an objectively existing entity called space-time. It must be confessed that Minkowski's famous remark, "From henceforth space in itself and time in itself sink to mere shadows, and only a kind of union of the two preserves an independent existence," lends itself naturally enough to this interpretation; although Einstein himself has always insisted that the theory has no metaphysical implications. The fact is that time has become associated with space in physics simply because we have chosen to measure time in terms of space measurements. The choice is voluntary, and, although this is completely revealed by Einstein's original theory when that is carefully considered, it becomes immediately obvious when we find that by measuring time in terms of other measurements, such as η, an "η-time" appears which is analogous in all essential respects to space-time. If, instead of η (or entropy), it had been found convenient to measure radiation in terms of the *energy* radiated per unit time, there would have been an "energy-time," no more and no less philosophically important than space-time or η-time. What relativity theory illuminates is not the metaphysical nature of time, but the function which time measurement can perform in physics. It appears to be a most powerful means of studying any phenomenon which can be represented as a temporal process, i.e., as the variation of some measurable quantity with time. You then choose to measure time in terms of that quantity and so create a manifold of measurements amenable to treatment by generalised geometrical methods. Such an enlargement of the scope of scientific method is altogether more significant than any of the speculations concerning the mystic nature of time which seem, unfortunately, to have been inspired by this development.

It should be pointed out, however, that the various systems of time measurement thus envisaged do not necessarily give different time *scales* in the sense of giving discordant measurements of the same duration. It is indeed a fundamental principle of relativity, considering even the relativity of motion alone, that a wide variety of such discordant scales are legitimate; although in practice one is so much more convenient than the others that it is the obvious choice to make. It happens that this same scale is the obvious one for radiation also; that is to say, the time-scale, according to which the velocity of light is constant, is also the time-scale according to which a body at constant temperature radiates uniformly. It is thus not necessary for physicists to keep a variety of clocks; for at a given temperature and in a given state of motion our ordinary familiar clocks can be used for either phenomenon. This identity of time-scales clearly suggests itself as a starting-point for constructing the relativistic thermodynamics already mentioned. The importance of adapting the system of time-measurement to the phenomenon studied lies not in the values of the clock-readings yielded but in the nature of the transformation to be used when we change the state of motion, the temperature, etc. of the instruments used; for the laws of the phenomenon in question are determined by the fact that they must be invariant under such transformations.

Another important philosophical implication of this extension of the relativity principle lies in its bearing on the question whether the physical world is fundamentally continuous or discontinuous in character. Hitherto a large and important part of physics (including universal gravitation) has been explicable only in terms of conceptions of continuity—field theory, as it is called—whereas another large and important part (atomic physics) has been explicable only in terms of conceptions of discontinuity. True, a part of the latter, which involves the discontinuity of matter only, has been amenable to treatment also in continuous terms (thus we have classical thermodynamics and statistical mechanics as alternative descriptions of the same set of phenomena), but the more fundamental part, which involves the discontinuity of energy, in which Planck's constant, h, appears, has so far resisted any interpretation which does not imply such discontinuity. Poincaré, in fact, went so far as to say that no interpretation of the spectrum of black-body radiation was possible without the basic conceptions of the quantum theory.[12]

The relativistic treatment of radiation, however, suggests that this statement might need revision. It has been stated above that

[12] *Journ. de Phys.*, January 1912.

Planck's formula satisfies the condition of invariance to the transformation (2), but is not the only formula to do so. It is, of course, a characteristic of the relativity technique that it imposes necessary, but not always sufficient, conditions on possible laws of nature; but in this case the number of mathematical alternatives is unfortunately large. It is not impossible, however, that they are reducible by macroscopic considerations alone, and, to make the most modest claim, we may say that Poincaré's dictum can no longer be accepted as final. The most general form of Planck's equation which satisfies the condition of invariance involves only one constant, B, to be determined by observation, and this is proportional to θ_0^2 (ah/kR), where θ_0 is the Kelvin temperature of the instruments used (B, though constant in any one thermal "co-ordinate system," is not invariant to change of system), a is Stefan's constant, h, Planck's constant, k, Boltzmann's constant, and R the universal gas constant. Hence we have a relation between an experimental constant, whose significance is purely macroscopic (continuous) and a combination of constants whose significance is purely microscopic (discontinuous).

The implication of this is that the alternatives of continuity and discontinuity have nothing to do with nature but are applicable to our conceptions alone; and, further, that a possibly complete parallelism might exist between the descriptions of the world in terms of the respective conceptions. Even if only one phenomenon in which hitherto the atomicity of energy has seemed inevitable should be found to be describable in terms of continuity (or even if, by an appropriate choice of β, determining the unit of η, in terms of Boltzmann's constant, k, the resulting value of ζ could be related to h, so that the atomicity of energy could be shown to depend on that of matter), the present complete antagonism of microscopic and macroscopic physics would have been broken down, and the view now so widely held, that the microscopic scheme of things, with its attendant conceptions of probability, uncertainty and the like, is the essential framework of nature itself, would no longer be tenable. Such a scheme, though legitimate as a means of expression of natural laws, would be seen as an alternative to a possibly equally comprehensive expression in purely macroscopic terms. Its elements would be no longer inherent in the physical world, but characteristics of a possible way of describing the physical world. Admittedly this is not yet established; but its likelihood must be taken into account by the scientific philosopher.

From our present point of view, however, the main purport of this article is to indicate what a profound and far-reaching achievement Einstein accomplished when he first recalled to physicists the forgotten principles of their own philosophy and next introduced to them the technique by which those principles could be applied to derive the ultimate laws of nature. In a survey of the phenomena with which the physicist is concerned, two stand out above all others as universally and eternally significant—motion and radiation. Unless we are altogether deceived, two pieces of matter placed anywhere at all in an otherwise empty universe will necessarily influence one another in two ways, and, so far as we know, in two ways only: they will affect one another's motion, and they will affect one another's temperature. The genius of Einstein explicitly derived the law of operation of the first phenomenon; it now appears that at the same time it implicitly derived the law of operation of the second.

HERBERT DINGLE

UNIVERSITY OF LONDON
LONDON, ENGLAND

Kurt Gödel

A REMARK ABOUT THE RELATIONSHIP BETWEEN RELATIVITY THEORY AND IDEALISTIC PHILOSOPHY

A REMARK ABOUT THE RELATIONSHIP
BETWEEN RELATIVITY THEORY
AND IDEALISTIC PHILOSOPHY

ONE of the most interesting aspects of relativity theory for the philosophical-minded consists in the fact that it gave new and surprising insights into the nature of time, of that mysterious and seemingly self-contradictory[1] being which, on the other hand, seems to form the basis of the world's and our own existence. The very starting point of special relativity theory consists in the discovery of a new and very astonishing property of time, namely the relativity of simultaneity, which to a large extent implies[2] that of succession. The assertion that the events A and B are simultaneous (and, for a large class of pairs of events, also the assertion that A happened before B) loses its objective meaning, in so far as another observer, with the same claim to correctness, can assert that A and B are not simultaneous (or that B happened before A).

Following up the consequences of this strange state of affairs one is led to conclusions about the nature of time which are very far reaching indeed. In short, it seems that one obtains an unequivocal proof for the view of those philosophers who, like Parmenides, Kant, and the modern idealists, deny the objectivity of change and consider change as an illusion or an appearance due to our special mode of perception.[3] The argu-

---

[1] Cf., e.g., J.M.E. McTaggart, "The Unreality of Time." *Mind*, 17, 1908.

[2] At least if it is required that any two point events are either simultaneous or one succeeds the other, i.e., that temporal succession defines a complete linear ordering of all point events. There exists an absolute partial ordering.

[3] Kant (in the *Critique of Pure Reason*, 2. ed., 1787, p. 54) expresses this view in the following words: "those affections which we represent to ourselves as changes, in beings with other forms of cognition, would give rise to a perception in which the idea of time, and therefore also of change, would not occur

ment runs as follows: Change becomes possible only through the lapse of time. The existence of an objective lapse of time,[4] however, means (or, at least, is equivalent to the fact) that reality consists of an infinity of layers of "now" which come into existence successively. But, if simultaneity is something relative in the sense just explained, reality cannot be split up into such layers in an objectively determined way. Each observer has his own set of "nows," and none of these various systems of layers can claim the prerogative of representing the objective lapse of time.[5]

This inference has been pointed out by some, although by surprisingly few, philosophical writers, but it has not remained

---

at all." This formulation agrees so well with the situation subsisting in relativity theory, that one is almost tempted to add: such as, e.g., a perception of the inclination relative to each other of the world lines of matter in Minkowski space.

[4] One may take the standpoint that the idea of an objective lapse of time (whose essence is that only the present really exists) is meaningless. But this is no way out of the dilemma; for by this very opinion one would take the idealistic viewpoint as to the idea of change, exactly as those philosophers who consider it as self-contradictory. For in both views one denies that an objective lapse of time is a possible state of affairs, *a fortiori* that it exists in reality, and it makes very little difference in this context, whether our idea of it is regarded as meaningless or as self-contradictory. Of course for those who take either one of these two viewpoints the argument from relativity theory given below is unnecessary, but even for them it should be of interest that perhaps there exists a second proof for the unreality of change based on entirely different grounds, especially in view of the fact that the assertion to be proved runs so completely counter to common sense. A particularly clear discussion of the subject independent of relativity theory is to be found in: Paul Mongré, *Das Chaos in kosmischer Auslese*, 1898.

[5] It may be objected that this argument only shows that the lapse of time is something relative, which does not exclude that it is something objective; whereas idealists maintain that it is something merely imagined. A relative lapse of time, however, if any meaning at all can be given to this phrase, would certainly be something entirely different from the lapse of time in the ordinary sense, which means a change in the existing. The concept of existence, however, cannot be relativized without destroying its meaning completely. It may furthermore be objected that the argument under consideration only shows that time lapses in different ways for different observers, whereas the lapse of time itself may nevertheless be an intrinsic (absolute) property of time or of reality. A lapse of time, however, which is not a lapse in some definite way seems to me as absurd as a coloured object which has no definite colours. But even if such a thing were conceivable, it would again be something totally different from the intuitive idea of the lapse of time, to which the idealistic assertion refers.

unchallenged. And actually to the argument in the form just presented it can be objected that the complete equivalence of all observers moving with different (but uniform) velocities, which is the essential point in it, subsists only in the abstract space-time scheme of special relativity theory and in certain empty worlds of general relativity theory. The existence of matter, however, as well as the particular kind of curvature of space-time produced by it, largely destroy the equivalence of different observers[6] and distinguish some of them conspicuously from the rest, namely those which follow in their notion the mean motion of matter.[7] Now in all cosmological solutions of the gravitational equations (i.e., in all possible universes) known at present the local times of all *these* observers fit together into one world time, so that apparently it becomes possible to consider this time as the "true" one, which lapses objectively, whereas the discrepancies of the measuring results of other observers from this time may be conceived as due to the influence which a motion relative to the mean state of motion of matter has on the measuring processes and physical processes in general.

From this state of affairs, in view of the fact that some of the known cosmological solutions seem to represent our world correctly, James Jeans has concluded[8] that there is no reason to abandon the intuitive idea of an absolute time lapsing objectively. I do not think that the situation justifies this conclu-

[6] Of course, according to relativity theory all observers are equivalent in so far as the laws of motion and interaction for matter and field are the same for all of them. But this does not exclude that the structure of the world (i.e., the actual arrangement of matter, motion, and field) may offer quite different aspects to different observers, and that it may offer a more "natural" aspect to some of them and a distorted one to others. The observer, incidentally, plays no essential rôle in these considerations. The main point, of course, is that the world itself has certain distinguished directions, which directly define certain distinguished local times.

[7] The value of the mean motion of matter may depend essentially on the size of the regions over which the mean is taken. What may be called the "true mean motion" is obtained by taking regions so large, that a further increase in their size does not any longer change essentially the value obtained. In our world this is the case for regions including many galactic systems. Of course a true mean motion in this sense need not necessarily exist.

[8] Cf. *Man and the Universe*, Sir Halley Stewart Lecture (1935), 22-23.

sion and am basing my opinion chiefly[9] on the following facts and considerations:

There exist cosmological solutions of another kind[10] than those known at present, to which the aforementioned procedure of defining an absolute time is not applicable, because the local times of the special observers used above cannot be fitted together into one world time. Nor can any other procedure which would accomplish this purpose exist for them; i.e., these worlds possess such properties of symmetry, that for each possible concept of simultaneity and succession there exist others which cannot be distinguished from it by any intrinsic properties, but only by reference to individual objects, such as, e.g., a particular galactic system.

Consequently, the inference drawn above as to the non-objectivity of change doubtless applies at least in these worlds. Moreover it turns out that temporal conditions in these universes (at least those referred to in the end of footnote 10) show other surprising features, strengthening further the idealistic viewpoint. Namely, by making a round trip on a rocket ship in a sufficiently wide curve, it is possible in these worlds to travel into any region of the past, present, and future, and back again, exactly as it is possible in other worlds to travel to distant parts of space.

This state of affairs seems to imply an absurdity. For it enables one e.g., to travel into the near past of those places where

[9] Another circumstance invalidating Jeans' argument is that the procedure described above gives only an approximate definition of an absolute time. No doubt it is possible to refine the procedure so as to obtain a precise definition, but perhaps only by introducing more or less arbitrary elements (such as, e.g., the size of the regions or the weight function to be used in the computation of the mean motion of matter). It is doubtful whether there exists a precise definition which has so great merits, that there would be sufficient reason to consider exactly the time thus obtained as the true one.

[10] The most conspicuous physical property distinguishing these solutions from those known at present is that the compass of inertia in them everywhere rotates relative to matter, which in our world would mean that it rotates relative to the totality of galactic systems. These worlds, therefore, can fittingly be called "rotating universes." In the subsequent considerations I have in mind a particular kind of rotating universes which have the additional properties of being static and spatially homogeneous, and a cosmological constant < 0. For the mathematical representation of these solutions, cf. my paper forthcoming in *Rev. Mod. Phys.*

he has himself lived. There he would find a person who would be himself at some earlier period of his life. Now he could do something to this person which, by his memory, he knows has not happened to him. This and similar contradictions, however, in order to prove the impossibility of the worlds under consideration, presuppose the actual feasibility of the journey into one's own past. But the velocities which would be necessary in order to complete the voyage in a reasonable length of time[11] are far beyond everything that can be expected ever to become a practical possibility. Therefore it cannot be excluded *a priori*, on the ground of the argument given, that the space-time structure of the real world is of the type described.

As to the conclusions which could be drawn from the state of affairs explained for the question being considered in this paper, the decisive point is this: that for *every* possible definition of a world time one could travel into regions of the universe which are passed according to that definition.[12] This again shows that to assume an objective lapse of time would lose every justification in these worlds. For, in whatever way one may assume time to be lapsing, there will always exist possible observers to whose experienced lapse of time no objective lapse corresponds (in particular also possible observers whose whole existence objectively would be simultaneous). But, if the experience of the lapse of time can exist without an objective lapse of time, no reason can be given why an objective lapse of time should be assumed at all.

It might, however, be asked: Of what use is it if such conditions prevail in certain *possible* worlds? Does that mean anything for the question interesting us whether in *our* world there

---

[11] Basing the calculation on a mean density of matter equal to that observed in our world, and assuming one were able to transform matter completely into energy the weight of the "fuel" of the rocket ship, in order to complete the voyage in t years (as measured by the traveller), would have to be of the order of magnitude of $\dfrac{10^{22}}{t^2}$ times the weight of the ship (if stopping, too, is effected by recoil). This estimate applies to $t \ll 10''$. Irrespective of the value of t, the velocity of the ship must be at least $1/\sqrt{2}$ of the velocity of light.

[12] For this purpose incomparably smaller velocities would be sufficient. Under the assumptions made in footnote 11 the weight of the fuel would have to be at most of the same order of magnitude as the weight of the ship.

exists an objective lapse of time? I think it does. For, (1) Our world, it is true, can hardly be represented by the particular kind of rotating solutions referred to above (because these solutions are static and, therefore, yield no red-shift for distant objects); there exist however also *expanding* rotating solutions. In such universes an absolute time also might fail to exist,[13] and it is not impossible that our world is a universe of this kind. (2) The mere compatibility with the laws of nature[14] of worlds in which there is no distinguished absolute time, and, therefore, no objective lapse of time can exist, throws some light on the meaning of time also in those worlds in which an absolute time *can* be defined. For, if someone asserts that this absolute time is lapsing, he accepts as a consequence that, whether or not an objective lapse of time exists (i.e., whether or not a time in the ordinary sense of the word exists), depends on the particular way in which matter and its motion are arranged in the world. This is not a straightforward contradiction; nevertheless, a philosophical view leading to such consequences can hardly be considered as satisfactory.

KURT GÖDEL

INSTITUTE FOR ADVANCED STUDY
PRINCETON, NEW JERSEY

[13] At least if it required that successive experiences of one observer should never be simultaneous in the absolute time, or (which is equivalent) that the absolute time should agree in direction with the times of all possible observers. Without this requirement an absolute time always exists in an expanding (and homogeneous) world. Whenever I speak of an "absolute" time, this of course is to be understood with the restriction explained in footnote 9, which also applies to other possible definitions of an absolute time.

[14] The solution considered above only proves the compatibility with the general form of the field equations in which the value of the cosmological constant is left open; this value, however, which at present is not known with certainty, evidently forms part of the laws of nature. But other rotating solutions might make the result independent of the value of the cosmological constant (or rather of its vanishing or non-vanishing and of its sign, since its numerical value is of no consequence for this problem). At any rate these questions would first have to be answered in an unfavourable sense, before one could think of drawing a conclusion like that of Jeans mentioned above. *Note added Sept. 2, 1949:* I have found in the meantime that for *every* value of the cosmological constant there do exist solutions, in which there is no world-time satisfying the requirement of footnote 13. K.G.

22

Gaston Bachelard

THE PHILOSOPHIC DIALECTIC OF THE CONCEPTS OF RELATIVITY

THE PHILOSOPHIC DIALECTIC OF THE CONCEPTS OF RELATIVITY*

I

PHILOSOPHERS have removed the great cosmic drama of Copernican thought from the dominion of reality to the dominion of metaphor. Kant described his Critical philosophy as a Copernican revolution in metaphysics. Following the Kantian thesis, the two fundamental philosophies, rationalism and empiricism, changed places, and the world revolved about the mind. As a result of this radical modification, the knowing mind and the known world acquired the appearance of being relative to each other. But this kind of relativity remained merely symbolic. Nothing had changed in the detail or the principles of coherence of knowledge. Empiricism and rationalism remained face-to-face and incapable of achieving either true philosophical co-operation or mutual enrichment.

The philosophic virtues of the Einsteinian revolution could be quite differently effective, as compared to the philosophic metaphors of the Copernican revolution, if only the philosopher were willing to seek all the instruction contained in relativity science. A systematic revolution of basic concepts begins with Einsteinian science. In the very detail of its concepts a relativism of the rational and the empirical is established. Science then undergoes what Nietzsche called "an upheaval of concepts," as if the earth, the universe, things, possessed a different structure from the fact that their explanation rests upon new foundations. All rational organization is "shaken" when the fundamental concepts undergo dialectical transformation.

Moreover, this dialectic is not argued by an automatic logic, as is the dialectic of the philosopher too often. In relativity,

* Translated from the French manuscript by Forrest W. Williams.

the terms of the dialectic are rendered solid and cohesive to the point of presenting a philosophical synthesis of mathematical rationalism and "technological" empiricism. This, at least, is what we would like to show in the present article. First, we will present our view in respect to the "shaking" of some isolated concepts; then, we shall endeavor to show the value of the philosophical synthesis which is suggested by Einsteinian science.

II

As we know, as has been repeated a thousand times, relativity was born of an epistemological shock; it was born of the "failure" of the Michelson experiment. That experiment should contradict theoretical prediction is in itself not a singular occurrence. But it is necessary to realize how and why a negative result was, this time, the occasion for an immense positive construction. Those who live in the realm of scientific thinking doubtless do not need these remarks. They are nonetheless polemically indispensable for assessing the philosophical utility of relativity.

For this notion of the negative quality of experiment must not be allowed to subsist. In a well-performed experiment, everything is positive. And Albert Einstein understood this fact when he pondered over the Michelson experiment. This pseudo-negative experiment did not open upon the mystery of things, the unfathomable mystery of things. Its "failure" was not even a proof of the ineptitude of rationalism. The Michelson experiment proceeded from an *intelligent* question, a question which had to be asked. Contemporary science would be hanging "in mid-air," if the Michelson experiment had not been conceived, then actualized, then meticulously actualized in the full consciousness of the sensibility of the technique; then varied, then repeated on the floors of valleys and the peaks of mountains, and always verified. What capacity for self-doubt, for meticulous and profound doubt, for *intelligent* doubt, was contained in this will to test and measure again and again! Are we sure that Michelson died with the conviction that the experiment had been well performed, perfectly performed, with the conviction that the *negative* bases of the experiment had been reached? Thus, instead of an universal doubt, an intuitive doubt, a Cartesian doubt, technological science yields a precise doubt, a discursive doubt, an implemented doubt. It was as a consequence of this explicit doubt that the mechanistic dogmatism was shattered by relativity. To paraphrase Kant, we might say that the Michelson experiment roused classical mechanics from its dogmatic slumber.

For the negative aspect of the Michelson experiment did not deter Einstein. For him, the experimental failure of a technique thus scientifically pursued suggested the need for new theoretical information. It became indispensable to hope for a minute "Copernican revolution" in which all philosophy of reality and of reason must begin a new dialectic. In order that this dialectic may possess its full instructive value for the philosopher, it is necessary to beware of sweeping philosophical designations. It is not highly instructive to say, with Meyerson, that Einstein is a *realist*. Without a doubt, Einstein submits to experience, submits to "reality." But must we not inquire: to what experience, to what reality? That of the infinitesimal decimal upon which the Michelson experiment turned, or that solid reality of the whole number, of solid, ordinary, common, gross verification? It would seem that the philosopher who acknowledges the lessons of relativity must at the very least, envisage a *new reality*. And this *new reality* enjoins him to *consider* reality *differently*.

Where, then, must the philosophy of science find its initial convictions? Must it give precedence to the lessons to be found in the beginning of experience, or in the end of experience? By building upon the first structures or upon the final structures? We shall see that the latter is correct, that it is *l'esprit de finesse* which reveals the foundations of *l'esprit géometrique*.

III

Which, then, are the concepts that are "shaken"? Which concepts undergo at the rational level, in the superb light of rational philosophy, a Nietzschean transmutation of rational values?

They are the concepts of:

> absolute space,
> absolute time,
> absolute velocity.

Is so little required to "shake" the universe of spatiality? Can a single experiment of the twentieth century annihilate—a Sartrian would say "*néantiser*"—two or three centuries of rational thought? Yes, a single decimal sufficed, as our poet Henri de Regnier would say, to "make all nature sing."

Upon what, in fact, did the notion of absolute space rest? Did it rest upon an absolute reality or upon an absolute intuition of the Kantian variety? Is it not philosophically strange that absoluteness could be attributed as well to a *reality* as to an *a priori intuition*? This double success of a raw realism and an over-simple intuitionism seems spurious. This twofold success makes a double failure. Therefore, it is necessary to investigate this double possibility of philosophical interpretation from the standpoint of the precision of modern scientific experiment. Uncriticized experience is no longer admissible. The *double philosophy* of the experience of space—realistic philosophy and Kantian philosophy—must be replaced by a *dialectical philosophy* of space, by a philosophy which is at once experimental and rational. In short, the philosophy of ultra-refined experience and the philosophy of physical theory are firmly *coupled* in relativity. The new philosophy of science will prove to be a critical philosophy more subtle and more synthetic than was Kantian philosophy in respect to Newtonian science. Relativistic criticism does not limit itself to a revoluton of means of explanation. It is more profoundly revolutionary. It is more *génial*.

Thus, we come face-to-face with the fundamental assertion of Einstein: the *position* of an absolute space as the affirmation of a kind of materialization of immobility and as the residence of an unconditioned subject in the center of all the conditioned relations, is a *position* without proof. Therefore, one must— Copernican revolution at the level of an unique concept— formulate the essential relativity of the intuition of localization and the experience of localization, which simultaneously destroys two absolutes: first, the intuition of an observer has no absolute character; and secondly, the extension of an objective world has no absolute character. The essentially discursive method of reference will, therefore, always have to be explicitly considered in relation to the real phenomena studied in the extremity of scientific precision. Extreme experimental dexterity will underlie any knowledge of space. The Michelson experiment, at first sight so particular in character, will form the basis of the most far-reaching generalization.

It is, moreover, quite striking that the Michelson laboratory was, properly speaking, *cosmic*. There, the most artificial physics imaginable was referred to the space of the world. The decimal which they wished to reveal by means of the interferometer, the decimal which is of the order of three-fourths of the wavelength of a vibration of light, was related to the orbital speed of the earth, a speed of the order of eighteen miles per second. The precision of such a question posed by this technique in respect to the space of the world, this attempt to experience the immobility of space in its cosmic significance, ought to set the metaphysicians thinking who study the place of man in the world; if only these metaphysicians would give their attention to the lengthy discursive processes which lead science to build new intuitions.

IV

The new intuitions of time likewise demand lengthy preparation. They must struggle against the blinding clarity of common intuitions, and against the equally over-hasty formulation of Kantian criticism.

Here, the concept which experiences the "Nietzschean upheaval" is that of *simultaneity*. In regard to this concept, so evident, so familiar, the Einsteinian claim is pregnant. This claim collides with common sense; it is contrary to common experience; it puts in question again the very basis of classical mechanics. It demands therefore, a decisive intellectual mutation which must reverberate among the most fundamental philosophical values. More precisely, if the notion of simultaneity, which was not *criticized* by Kant, must receive a *neo-critical* examination, empiricism and rationalism must, at the same time, be *rectified* and related to each other in a new way.

To formulate a doubt concerning the notion of simultaneity is, in our opinion, to transcend the hyperbolic doubt of Cartesian philosophy. A doubt attaching to so simple, so positive, so direct a notion no longer bears the marks of a formal doubt, an universal doubt. As long as one remains within the horizons of Cartesian doubt, one is in the contingency of doubt. The Einsteinian revolution demands a necessary doubt regarding a notion which has always passed for fundamental. Concomitantly, the putting in doubt of a rational and realistic notion cannot remain provisional. Such a doubt will always carry with it a decisive pedagogical effect. It will remain an imprescriptible cultural fact. Whoever, for the rest of time, would teach relativity would have to put in doubt the absolute character of the notion of simultaneity. This necessity constitutes, in some sense, an *electro-shock* for rationalistic philosophies and hardened realistic philosophies.

Granting a renunciation of the right to posit an absolute space, what is the Einsteinian claim in regard to the simultaneity of events which occur at two different points in space? Einstein demands that one define a *positive* experiment, a *precise* experiment expressible in well-defined scientific terms. There is no longer any question of retreating into the intuition of internal sensibility, whether this intuition be Kantian or Bergsonian, formalistic or realistic. One must be able to describe and institute objective experiments which enable one to *verify* this simultaneity. Immediately, a metaphysical nuance appears which the philosopher too often neglects. Here we have a *verified* reality in place of a *given* reality. Hereafter, if an idealist must make an initial declaration, he will be forced to do so from a point one step closer to a rationalism which is linked with reality. He cannot be satisfied with repeating after Schopenhauer: "The world is my representation;" he must say, if he is to assume the full extent of scientific thought: "The world is my verification."

More precisely, the objective world is the aggregate of facts verified by modern science, the world rendered by the conceptions verified by the science of our time. Further, *experimental verification* implies the *coherence* of the experimental method. Since a science is founded upon the Michelson experiment, this Michelson experiment must be comprehended in the very definition of simultaneity. To be sure, we are concerned with the Michelson experiment as it is, not as it was for a long time thought to be. The Michelson experiment, as it is, then, must assign reality at the outset to the convention of signaling.

Without a doubt, any number of conventions of signalling could have been adopted. One could create a meta-acoustics based upon a simultaneity verified by the transmission of sounds. But physics would gain nothing from such specialization. Hereafter, physics is cosmic. The most rapid and reliable signals which are both human and universal are light signals. The Michelson experiment discloses a privileged character which accrues to these signals. They require no support; they are not conditioned by a medium, by a transmitting ether. They are independent of the *relative* movements of the observers who utilize them. They are truly the most "reasonable" (*"rationalisables"*) of all signals. Thus, one would define the simultaneity of two events which occur in two different places in terms of an exchange of light signals and of the result, henceforth regarded as positive, of the Michelson experiment which justifies the following postulate: the velocity of light is the same in all directions irrespective of the observers who measure it, regardless of the relative motion of these observers.

This *operational* definition of simultaneity dissolves the notion of *absolute* time. Since simultaneity is linked to physical experiments which occur in space, the temporal contexture (*contexture*) is one with spatial contexture. Since there is no absolute space, there is no absolute time. And it is due to the solidarity of space-experiments and simultaneity-experiments that a reconstitution of space and time must accompany any thorough examination of space and time. Therefore, from the standpoint of philosophy, it is evident that scientific thought requires a rebuilding of the notions of space and time in terms of their solidarity. As a consequence of this necessity to provide a new basis for space and time, relativity will emerge philosophically as a *rationalism of second order* (*rationalisme de deuxième position*), as an enlightened rationalism which necessitates a new departure.

But before building, one must destroy. One must convince oneself that any analysis which from the outset separates spatial characters and temporal characters is a crude analysis. Doubtless, such an analysis is valid for common knowledge, and no less valid for an enormous quantity of scientific thought. But for its denunciation one need only note that it masks certain well-defined problems. Looking to the new synthetic notion of space-time, henceforth indispensable for a grasp of electromagnetic phenomena, one can perceive the philosophical weakness of any attempt at vulgarization. It is not a matter of basing a synthesis upon an analysis. One must conceive the *a priori synthesis* which underlies the notion of space-time. All the tales of passing trains which signal an observer standing in a station, of aviators who smoke cigars in lengthened or contracted periods of time—to what purpose are they?—or, more precisely, for whom are they designed? Surely not for those who have not understood the *mathematical organization* of relativity. And those who have understood the *mathematical organization* of relativity require no *examples*. They install themselves in the clear and certain *algebraism* of the doctrine. It is on the basis of the synthesis of algebraism and scientific experiment that one may correctly designate the rationalistic revival implied in the doctrines of Einstein. Let us demonstrate this neo-Kantian aspect. It did not escape Léon Brunschvicg, who wrote: "The advancement on Kant (effected by these new doctrines) consisted in transporting the *a priori* synthesis from the region of intuition to the region of intellect, and this is decisive for the passage to physics."

And, in fact, any Kantian philosophy holds that space is not a concept drawn from experience of the external world, since the intuition of space is a *sine qua non* condition of experience of the external world. A similarly inverted formulation is enunciated in respect to time, which is given as the *a priori* form of internal sensibility. The *sine qua non* is the pivot of the Copernican revolution of intuitions of space and time.

And, in the same manner, in the same philosophical fashion, if one would determine the epistemological function of the space-time notion in relativistic science, one must say that the *space-time algebraic complex* is a *sine qua non* condition of the general validity of our knowledge of electromagnetism. Knowledge of electromagnetic phenomena during the nineteenth century was co-ordinated by the laws of Maxwell. Reflection upon these laws led to the conviction that they must remain *invariant* for any change of reference system. This invariance defined the transformation [formulas] of Lorentz. It established a Lorentz group which possesses the same philosophical significance for relativity geometry which the group of displacements and similitudes possesses for Euclidean geometry. Thus, it is the Lorentz transformation which underlies the notion of space-time, and the Lorentz group which forbids the separation of spatial co-ordinates and temporal co-ordinates. The notion of space-time takes shape in a perspective of *necessity*. To see in it a mere linguistic structure, a mere condensation of means of expression, would be to underestimate its philosophical significance. It is a conception, a necessary conception. If the rôle of the philosopher is, as we believe, to think thought, then he must think space-time in the totality of its functions, in its algebraic nature, and in its informing value for scientific phenomena.

If one adds now, that due to the operational definition of simultaneity the velocity of light enters into geometrical-mechanical references, and if one recalls that light is an electro-magnetic phenomenon, one reaches the conclusion that the notion of space-time is hereafter a basic notion for an ultra-precise understanding of phenomena.

Thus, the concept of space-time, as suggested by Lorentz, as achieved by Einstein, appears as an *a priori* form, functionally *a priori*, permitting the comprehension of precise electromagnetic phenomena. It is of little importance, philosophically, that this form occurs tardily in the history of science. It is installed as functionally *primary* by the *enlightened rationalism* which constitutes one of the most clear-cut aspects of the theory of relativity. Once having aligned oneself with this enlightened rationalism, one sees that there is a *naïve rationalism* in the same sense that there is a *naïve realism*. And if one would reap all the philosophical benefits of scientific culture, one must realize psychologically the soundness of the *new foundations;* one must abandon the old points of departure, and *begin again.* At the close of the eighteenth century, in his history of astronomy, Bailly maintained that calculated astronomy procured a *peace of mind* in contrast to any theory of imaginative astronomy. Newtonian thinkers, he said, "chose to adopt the notion of attraction to fasten their imagination, to rest their thoughts."

The function of Einsteinian rationalism is likewise salutary The algebraic notion of space-time rids us of vulgarizing images. It frees us from a falsely profound reverie upon space and time. In particular, it precludes the irrationalism associated with an unfathomable duration. The mind *rests* in the truth of its constructions.

Once the *algebraic* nature of the Einsteinian formulation is realized, one is prepared for a philosophic inversion of the abstract and concrete characters of scientific culture; or, to speak more precisely, one accedes to the *abstract-concrete* character of scientific thought. One may well say that the concept of *space-time* is more concrete, despite its intellectual character, than the two separate notions of space and time, since it consolidates two perspectives of experience. Naturally, the notion of space-time will, whenever necessary, be divided and analyzed so as to reinstate those separate functions of time and space, in view of the *simplifications* which are useful in classical mechanics. But relativity will be on guard against all *simplifications.* It *rests* upon the summit of its synthesis. From this vantage point, it judges confidently all analytical perspectives.

How shall philosophers be led to this summit? But philosophers no longer care, it seems, for synthetic thoughts. They do not wish to found knowledge upon its highest achievement. They claim to cut Gordian knots at a time when science is striving to *knit together* the most unforeseen relations, at a time when physico-mathematical science resolutely declares itself abstract-concrete.

Rather than to return ceaselessly to the base of common knowledge, as if what suffices for life could suffice for knowledge, we have the means, by pursuing Einsteinian science, to develop a terminal rationalism, a differentiating rationalism, a dialectical rationalism. This differentiaton, this dialectic appears in knowledge at a second stage of approximation. In short, there occurs an inversion in [the order of] epistemological importance. The first approximation is only the opening move. Common knowledge regards it as basic, though it is only provisional. The structure of scientific understanding emerges only from refinement, through an analysis as thorough as possible of every functionality.

One may, in application, limit these functionalities, cognizant that a potentiality remains unrealized, that a sensibility is smothered. One would recognize that in quantum mechanics in numerous cases there occurs *degeneration* ("*dégénérescence*"), that is to say, extinction of a structural possibility. But the new theories yield the whole hierarchy of rationalistic and empiricist values. Classical science and common knowledge have their [respective] places in the system of epistemological values. The dialectic of relativistic mechanics and classical mechanics is an enveloping dialectic. It seems that relativity risked everythng which lent certainty to the classical conception of reality, but, having risked all, lost nothing. It has retained all that was scientifically known during the last century. A shift of the finer structures reveals the ancient bonds. Thus, relativity permits a retrospective re-enactment of the entire history of mechanistic rationalism.

V

This possibility of recurring to simplified philosophies will be better understood if we can now show the notably firm nature of the coupling of rationalism and realism effected by relativity. To this end, it will suffice to consider the algebraic form, *space-time*, in its ordering functions in mechanics and electromagnetism.

Space-time is not merely a simple epistemological necessity evoked by reflection upon the conditions of invariance stipulated by the Maxwell equations. This initial synthesis propagates its ordering power. The notion of space-time conditions quadrivectors which accentuate the synthetic character of the relativistic [mode of] organization.

For example, by extending the classical conception of mechanical impulsion, which is a vector of three-dimensional space, relativity attains the conception of the impulsion of the universe as a quadrivector of four-dimensional space. This impulsion has the three components of classical momentum as its spatial component, and energy divided by the velocity of light as its temporal component. But the quadrivector of the impulsion does not consist of a simple juxtaposition of the momentum- and energy-aspects. So powerful a conceptual fusion is achieved that the principle of the conservation of momentum and the principle of the conservation of energy are summated. In an isolated material system, the geometric sum of the quadrivectors of the impulsion remains constant when applied to different bodies in the system. Recalling that Descartes formulated his mechanics in terms of the notion of momentum whereas Leibniz advanced the notion of mechanical energy, one would perceive, from the summit of this synthesis, the historical recurrence as a profound synthesis of Descartes and Leibniz achieved by Einstein.

This same inspiration led to Einstein's discovery of the algebraic homogeneity of energy and mass. This discovery of mathematical, *rationalistic* origin had considerable *realistic* import. The mass-energy amalgam, first established for kinetic energy, clearly extends to all forms of energy. Doutbless the philosopher who thinks in words, who believes that scientific concepts have an absolute root in common notions, is shocked by the phrase *"inertia of energy."* And yet it is this concept of the inertia of energy which marks Einsteinian science as a new science, as a conceptually synthetic science.

In effect, the realistic aspect of this mass-energy amalgam consists in none other than the union of the so different classical principles of the conservation of mass and the conservation of energy. Considered in their historical evolution, the concepts of mass and energy appear bereft of an *absolute*. Now it is necessary to establish between them a profound *relation*, an ontological relation.

In other words, in order to realize this relativization of so realistic a principle as that of the conservation of mass, one must accept once more the Copernican revolution of relativity, one must install mathematics at the *center* of experience, one must take mathematics as the inspiration of scientific experiment. For, after all, experiments as precise as those of chemistry cast no doubt upon the principle of Lavoisier. Chemistry was, in this respect, the recital of an immense success. Chemistry codified the *absolute* character of a materialism of balances. *Scientific* realism was, on this point, on a par in conviction with *naïve realism*. Let us firmly underscore that efficacious thought proceeds in the direction of rationalism → realism. Primacy belongs, not to the principle of conservation (in realistic fashion), but to a principle of invariance (in rationalistic fashion). It is the conditions of invariance in the mathematical expression of the laws which permit a definition of the meaning and validity of the true *principles of conversation*. Insofar as it was thought possible to characterize the philosophy of relativity by the too-simple label of "realism" from the sole fact that relativity substantiates principles of conservation, this epistemological evolution must be the more definitively formulated. For our part, we are of the opinion that the manner of conserving is more important than what is conserved. To conserve mass and energy in a single formula is not really to ground one's faith in the reality conserved but, rather, to become conscious of the rationalistic power of the invariance of the laws.

Doubtless, experiment in its most refined, meticulous forms sanctioned the ingenious views of Albert Einstein; consequently, [the concept of the] inertia of energy possesses hereafter an undeniably realistic character. But these very *conceptions* were *original* and *inspired;* they were not psychologically *natural* and they led to scientific experiments which were quasi-*supernatural*. For example, the entirety of nuclear physics falls within the jurisdiction of the principle of *inertia of energy*. And the power of nuclear physics has been sufficiently emphasized, perhaps to the neglect of its ultra-phenomenal character. The scientist has already smashed more uranium nuclei in the space of five years than Nature in a millennium. The laboratory technician has succeeded in *implementing* by means of the atomic pile the Einsteinian principle of inertia of energy. The reality which slumbered in his materials was *provoked* by mathematically-founded experiments. Seen from the nuclear level, one might well say that matter evokes a neo-materialism in which substance and energy are interchangeable entities. Reality is no longer nature pure and simple. It must be wrought to become the object of scientific experiment. Thus, the philosophy of contemporary science as it issued from the revolutions of the beginning of the century appears as a dialectic of enlightened rationalism and elaborated realism. In order to lose none of the philosophical implications of science the two concepts of invariance and conservation must be synthesized in an *abstract-concrete* philosophy by introducing an additional unifying trait in the form of an *invariance-conservation*. Here is a philosophical *doublet* which would be mutilated by an unilateral philosophical interpretation, whether rationalistic or realistic. Science requires hereafter a bi-certitude. It must satisfy the requirements of mathematical coherence and minute experimental verification.

VI

We have followed rapidly a development of relativistic thought to a synthetic center of the science of mechanics. The synthesis on the side of electromagnetism was not less important. The components of the two tri-dimensional vectors by which classical physics defined separately the electric field and the magnetic field are recognized by relativity as the components of a single tensor. This fact endows the Maxwell-Lorentz equations with an extreme generality which goes hand in hand with an extreme algebraic condensation.

It is not the least paradoxical character of general relativity to find in the development of its doctrine this dialectic of rational condensation and extension of empirical significations. When enlightened rationalism takes hold of reality by such condensed symbols, one experiences, there too, a great peace of mind. Tensor calculus, Paul Langevin liked to say, knows relativity better than the relativist himself. Tensor calculus becomes, in some manner, charged for us with subaltern thought; it is our guarantee of forgetting nothing; it arranges for particular analyses. These symbols are in no way mystical. They are translucent to the mathematician and they render the physicist perspicacious. The unifying formulas of general relativity are philosophical syntheses which reunite rationalism and realism.

VII

If we were to consider dialectically the *principle of equivalence* of inert mass and heavy mass, the principle which founded general relativity, we would be led to the same philosophical conclusions.

In effect, to reunite *inert mass* and *heavy mass* in a single concept amounts to amalgamating inertia, a quality inhering in a given body, and weight, a quality whose seat is, in some manner, external to the body in question. Thus, we have a prime example of the correlation of a force and a structure of space-time. This correlation inscribed in the Einsteinian principle of equivalence is greatly extended in the development of the doctrine.

Here, again, the philosopher may find instruction; for the principle of equivalence constitutes a denial of the [supposed] logical priority habitually assigned to force over against its manifestations. In fact, force is contemporaneous with phenomena. There is no circuit of being which assigns being to matter, then to its forces, then to the deformations of matter. As Eddington said, "Matter is not a cause, it is an index."[1] All exists together as the structure of space-time.

Relativity, therefore, seems to us to modify philosophically the principles of *"causalism"* in quite as thoroughgoing fashion as those of *realism*. *Abstract-concrete* philosophy will have to be formulated in terms of a new trait of metaphysical union and will have to think of scientific phenomena as *cause-functions*. There occurs an endosmosis of mathematical consequences and physical causes.

[1] A. S. Eddington, *Space, Time and Gravitation* (Cambridge, 1921), 191.

Thus, relativity ceaselessly calls scientific thought to a philosophical activity which is both *central* and *dialectic*. The traditional problem of the dualism of mind and body is posed in a precise central locus, with the benefit of an extreme sensibility. Here the most rigorous mathematician and the most meticulous physicist agree. They understand each other. They instruct each other. Thought would become empty, experience would become obscure, if one were not to accept, in the regions in which relativity functions, the synthesis of enlightened rationalism and elaborated realism.

GASTON BACHELARD

THE SORBONNE
PARIS, FRANCE

23

Aloys Wenzl

EINSTEIN'S THEORY OF RELATIVITY, VIEWED FROM THE STANDPOINT OF CRITICAL REALISM, AND ITS SIGNIFICANCE FOR PHILOSOPHY

EINSTEIN'S THEORY OF RELATIVITY, VIEWED FROM THE STANDPOINT OF CRITICAL REALISM, AND ITS SIGNIFICANCE FOR PHILOSOPHY*

THE battle in epistemology is, in the final analysis, conditioned by the various degrees of confidence in our capacity to know. It could be said that the issue is that of finding the right Aristotelian mean between the extremes of naïveté and scepticism. Naïve realism as well as so-called subjective idealism drop out from the beginning if what we are concerned with is real and significant knowledge; for if science and philosophy are to be pursued seriously, they certainly cannot be satisfied with an uncritical acceptance of our impressions of the outside world as faithful reproductions of the same, nor carry doubt so far that our determinations are seen as nothing more than our ideas, our perceptions as nothing more than our imaginings. This would also lead to a splitting of theory and practice. The (only) applicable epistemological points of view, therefore, are the critical idealism of Kant, positivism, and critical realism. Kant emphasizes that he can and wants to make assertions only concerning appearances, although he acknowledges a reality independent of consciousness as the cause of those appearances. Positivism in its various forms wants to limit itself to mastering of experience under the viewpoint of usefulness, simplicity, and uniformity; it merely wishes to bring the facts of experience into an ordered system. Critical realism is concerned with combining criticism and the positive knowledge of reality. It appears inconsistent [to the critical realist] to destroy the bridge between appearance and reality, and unsatisfactory to the human striving for knowledge to be satisfied with merely useful or

* Translated from the German manuscript by Paul Arthur Schilpp.

even with the most useful ordering of the variety of experiences; this would not be knowledge and [certainly] no justification of the motive of all scientific endeavor to arrive at the most responsible world-picture. In Germany we do not understand under critical realism quite the same thing as what is thus named in America; but we do assert our faith in the programmatic theses, formulated by the *Critical Realism* of 1920, that, although the things-in-themselves do not enter our consciousness, appearances are by no means merely subjective, but that there is such a thing as objective truth and that logic is valid. In Germany critical realism is connected with the names of Eduard von Hartmann, Hermann Lotze, Hans Driesch, Oswald Külpe, Erich Becher, Bernhard Bavink, *et al.*: to the perceptual appearances, relations, and qualities correspond the relations and qualities of objective reality; neither the sense-qualities of color, of sound, etc., nor the spatial and temporal distances are objective or absolute, but they do correspond to qualities and relations which are independent of consciousness; out of the agreement between deduced suppositions and their conclusions with experience, moreover, we may conclude concerning the truth content of the proffered hypotheses.

It is thus that critical realism becomes the basis for an inductive metaphysics, i.e., it is possible to posit, even if only hypothetically, a unitary picture of the world which does most justice to experience and is scientifically [respectable] responsible. A theory is, therefore, neither a [mere] ideational work of art nor a mere convention, but a pointer with external and inner probability on the basis of validation and consistency; and its scientific character remains preserved even in its hypothetical nature by virtue of the fact that the presuppositions of the accepted assumptions are stated. It is only on such a point of view that from the standpoint of critical realism, a theory actually contributes to what we call knowledge. What, now, are the philosophically most important results of Einstein's theory of relativity. We consider them to be the following:

1. The equal validity of all straight-line equally moving systems not only as regards the laws of mechanics, but also as concerns those of electro-magnetism, of optics, and

the constancy of the *velocity of light,* the two axioms, that is to say, from which the relativizing of spatial and temporal measurements follow and which demand the co-ordination into a four-dimensional continuum.

2. The equivalence of mass and energy, which is expressed in the already classical equation $E = mc^2$ and which connects the concepts of *mass and energy,* which had played the rôle of substance in classical physics and in natural philosophy.

3. The formation (curvature) of the space-time continuum by mass and energy in such fashion that the *metric* becomes the expression for the reality of what appears to us as material-energic. True, this conception of matter and its fields as a realization of the metrical characteristics of the space-time continuum has thus far been carried through in Einstein's general theory of relativity only for the field of gravitation; but one is confident that the charges and the electromagnetic fields will also be capable of being interpreted metrically.

4. The *cosmological* development: the world is a spatially limited, finite non-Euclidean continuum, its radius increases and the universe expands.

5. The *cosmogonic* development: our universe originated in an "explosion" or "expansion" of a "cylindrical world" or else by means of the increasing formation of material particles (P. Jordan).

The philosophical problematics includes, therefore:

1. The problem of space-time, especially as concerns the reality of time and of motion—the problem which already had its inception with the opposition between the philosophy of the Eleatics and that of Heraclitus.

2. The problem of substance and of the original stuff, which began with the antique problem of the ether—viz., of the still indeterminate *apeiron* of Anaximander—continues in Aristotle's and scholasticism's concept of the *materia prima,* and which was contained also in the modern problem of the physical ether. Since Democritus the doctrine of continuity, which dominates these theories, has been

opposed by a theory of discontinuity; the opposition and the question of a [possible] synthesis of continuity and discontinuity reaches right down to the present and constitutes the basic problem as regards the union of the theory of relativity and quantum theory.

3. The Pythagorean-Platonic Ideal: Reality is the realization of mathematical ideas, "God is always doing mathematics."

4. The cosmological-cosmogonic theories, which reached their first height in Kant's "theory of the heavens," but which has by no means proved itself unobjectionable.

5. There must be added the problem of determinism, related on the one hand to the problem of time, and, on the other hand, to the opposition between the theory of relativity and quantum theory; an old philosophical problem also, which was central [in importance] from Augustine to Spinoza, for Leibniz and Kant, as well as for Schopenhauer and Fechner.

We now shall take a stand on these problems from the point of view of critical realism.

1. The Constancy of the Velocity of Light

Philosophically the most exciting assertion and therefore the one which has aroused most philosophic opposition is the second axiom of the special theory of relativity, viz., the constancy of the velocity of light, from which follows the relativity of spatial and temporal measurements. One could say, that the observers of various moving systems are like Leibniz's monads and that Leibniz's idea of a pre-established harmony finds an analogy in the theory of relativity: Just as the world is mirrored differently in each monad and yet the sights of all monads are related to each other and translatable into each other, so also does the "absolute" four-dimensional world-continuum appear in different values of spatial and temporal measurements to every observer imprisoned [as he is] in his own system, yet all sights are transformable into each other. But if, on the one hand, Hans Driesch calls Leibniz's system of the pre-established harmony bizarre, many critics of the theory of relativity have even declared its principle to be a logical contradiction:[1] if light spreads out—independently of the motion of its source —equally in all directions, if it is a reality—whether wave or corpuscle is at this point of no concern—which moves, then it can not proceed with objectively equal velocity with reference to an observer A, on the one hand, and with reference to an independently moving observer B. As a way out [of this difficulty] the explanation is offered that the axiom of the constancy of the velocity of light in all qualified co-ordinate systems is simply an arbitrary determination, which we posit. In this case it remains ununderstandable, however, that this arbitrary determination validated itself in experience and that it makes possible the astounding consistency of the mathematical forms of the theory of relativity. Objective matters of fact seem, therefore, to provide the foundation for this [arbitrary] determination, after all.

A second possibility of interpretation offers itself in the following. Spatial and temporal qualities are objectively not at all divisible, in fact, spatiality and temporality are nothing objective at all; motion is merely appearance which arises by splitting the world-continuum into space and time; it is merely our consciousness which goes along with the world-line of our body; and the objectively real is precisely the four-dimensional continuum. In this way we get to Minkowski's world, a world of absolute existence, the Eleatic world. From the standpoint of the physicist this is a thoroughly consistent solution. But the physicist will [doubtless] understand the objection, raised by philosophy, that time is by no means merely a physical matter. Time is, as Kant put it, the form not merely of our outer but

---

[1] So, among others, O. Kraus, who writes: "The proposition that velocity of light is identical in all 'Galilean' systems, uninfluenced by the motion of the source of light, does not offend habits of thought but *a priori* self-evident judgments; the relativizing of simultaneity is very much like the explanation of the principle of contradiction as a habit of thought." And P. F. Linke writes: "A proposition is absurd not only if it contradicts formal logic, but also when it asserts a proposition which contradicts the essence of the object to which it refers. That is to say, a proposition is just as absurd if its assertion does not lie within the meaning of such a propositional object, which latter can itself be given at any time in immediate confrontation, as if it were in a formal sense illogical." *Annalen der Philosophie*, Vol. II, No. 3, 1921.

also of our inner sense. Could everything which we call development [evolution] be really an untemporal order? Should our experiences of successiveness and of memory be mere illusion, our whole existence, with all its bodily conditioned and bodily expressed strivings and actions be, so to speak, already pre-existent and also still post-existent—in so far as one could speak in such an absolutely existing world of pre and post at all; should we, in the final analysis be trans-temporal beings? And with this does not the question of *freedom* receive an answer from physics alone and a negative answer at that, without regard for those experiences which have always spoken for freedom of the will, such as responsibility, shame, and regret, and without regard for the freedom which is today particularly emphasized by the philosophy of existentialism, that freedom in which every later act is, after all, dependent upon former decisions? One understands in any case that the relativizing of time, of simultaneity, of temporal dilatation, in brief, the subjectivizing of temporality as such is felt as a much greater demand than the relativizing of spatial magnitudes, as, e.g., by means of the Lorentz-contraction. And what matters is not the measurement of time, but the saving of temporality as a principle of our world as such. However, is it possible to maintain temporality in its specific quality—even in the theory of relativity time is by no means entirely homogeneous with the spatial co-ordinates, but is multiplied by the imaginary unity, and a space-like and a time-like area are differentiated—and nevertheless avoid the contradiction that a physical reality, which moves, can not move with objectively identical velocity with reference to different observers? This can, indeed, be done, but one must draw the conclusion that [in that case] light may neither be treated nor be viewed as a material body, nor as a wave which moves on in a three-dimensional space.

Already in the special theory of relativity we meet, for the first time, the inadequacy of the two sides of that "double nature," whether of the corpuscle or of the wave in any perceptual sense. Obviously we dare not regard light either as moving particles nor as real waves of a system-bound medium. On the other hand, there is no reason why light should not be regarded as a signal which actually behaves towards all systems disinterestedly and impartially, which is neither imprisoned in nor bound to a material system, but is supersystemic [or: above all systems]. Only in that case we may not regard it [i.e., light] as something already material, but must consider it as something still "immaterial," "pre-material," "potential." But what does this mean? For the concept of the potential is by no means at home merely in ancient ontology, but also in physics; considerable clarification might therefore be expected from a uniting of the often underestimated ingenuity to be found in the thought-structures erected by Aristotle and scholasticism as if out of thin air, with the concept of potentiality which is already familiar in physics from the doctrines of force and energy, and which has entered, in even an expanded degree, into modern physics. What then does it mean [to say] that light is still "above the systems"?

Let us think of two systems moving towards each other, in which A and B, on the one hand, and A' and B', on the other, stand to each other in a relatively identical relation of order, in the same relation, in the same "distance" from and for each other; and let us imagine that, at the very moment when A and A' coincide (with each other), there proceeds a signal, a disturbance, from A, resp. from A', then one can certainly see no reason why B should not be reached in the identical temporal duration as B'. "Light" is the signal of the change in existential relations, no longer and not yet materialized and therefore not yet system-bound, but rather, as the dissolution of a former material order, the mere announcement and communication of a new possibility. It is an as yet potential situation,[2] which does not refer to a *single* system, but which restores the disturbed order precisely because of its reference to all. If one wishes to retain the old concept of the ether, one simply dare not regard the ether itself again as a material reality which itself constructs or distinguishes or belongs to *one* system, but inversely, only as a field of possibility to which all systems be-

[2] The introduction of a concept of potentiality, in the sense of a real possibility, of a multi-potential being, is met with in modern biology in the notion of a germinal substance, and in psychology in that of the unconscious.

long even as do planes to space; the mathematical models, which already exist, would merely have to be interpreted in this sense. If we attribute a sphere of existence to every system, we would have to say, in traditional fashion, that their [resp.] "ethers" penetrate each other reciprocally without disturbance; which would simply mean that they are no longer to be treated materially. It would be closer to our way of thinking today to take the systems together in an over-all concept of a "space-like" area, which would require four dimensions and to permit the signal, the pre-proclamation for possible corpusculations, to move ahead in this ["space-like" area]. What moves ahead is, therefore, a potential; that is to say, in every system the changed existential situation can "announce itself" successively according to the distance relation between the origin of the disturbance and the recipient. The "geometrical location" of the appearance of a disturbance and dissolution, the possibility of the occurrence of new localized elements, photons, transmits itself uniformly in reference to all systems, and only by this process is the foundation created for the spatial and temporal measurements of the individual systems. If we are still to use a neutral designation, we would have to say that potential energy propagates itself in order to actualize itself again when it hits a "wall." Only this sounds unaccustomed; until now physics has been using the concept of potential energy in the first place for the working capacity which inheres in a body or field, but which is still restrained, not yet released; here, however, we have to form the concept of an expanding potential energy, of an expanding capacity for individuation as photons, of a disinterestedly, impartially, and super-systemically expanding possibility in such way that every system can have a basis for its measurements in its inter-systematic relations of spatial and temporal distance. If, therefore, one speaks of the undulatory and corpuscular nature of light, the contradiction, which has created so many difficulties, is solved [by pointing out] that the continuous wave-nature corresponds to energy in its potential state, to the expansion of a super-systemic field of possibilities, whereas the particle nature is to be associated with the actualization in a system. By doing this temporality is in principle preserved, without having had to demand an absolute *measurement* of time, which could have been claimed by one system. Perhaps the gap between the double nature of light and matter could also be bridged by this same procedure.

2. The Problem of Substance

For classical physics mass with its attributes of inertia and gravity was *the* substance, which remains preserved through all changes. Electromagnetism added charges and the attribute of polarity, and with that the problem of the reducibility of mechanics to electromagnetism emerged. But energy also claimed the character of substance and it seemed to play the unity-producing rôle. True, even though the equivalence-statements are valid for the comparison of mechanical and electromagnetic energy, the question is still open whether it is possible thereby to arrive at a real monism; for the conversion of Joule into *mkg* does not prove that the two forms of energy are in essence the same, just as one can not say of an electron that it *is* mass merely because one can say of it that it *has* mass. Also connected with this is the question, whether it is more suitable to retain for the absolute system of measurement the three old magnitudes of "mass, length, and time," or to introduce a fourth magnitude for the "charge." In microphysics one believed to have at last found the very original building-stones. And now the theory of relativity brought to synthetic view, by way of the famous equation $E = mc^2$, viz., mass represents localized energy, it is an agglomeration, a centre, a concentration of energy, an energy-knot, and inversely an area of space filled with energy has inertia and gravity. Both, of course—mass and energy—proved themselves as dependent upon the state of motion of the observer. The general theory of relativity made possible the compression of the conservation principles of energy and impulse; and the sum of the energy of matter and of the gravitational field proved to be invariant. In the general theory of relativity the "world-plane" with its invariants is itself the ultimate reality, the "substance." The laws of the conservation of energy and impulse follow from the equations for the field of gravitation and for the physical fields. That is to say, valid for every system is [the proposition] that in a restricted spatial area the balance between the total energy present in it and the addition or subtraction of energy by way of the surface of the area must remain preserved. But what precisely is energy? Physics defines it [viz., energy] as working capacity, that is to say as something potential; moreover, it is not merely the potential energy but the kinetic energy also which is, strictly speaking, potential: it *can* actualize itself. It is a special instance, a sub-concept of what Aristotle called *energeia*. Force, itself again a potential concept, enters constitutively into the field of energy; and mass into the kinetic energy; mass too is a potential concept, it implies space-control-potency and the tendency to lay claim to space; the mass-bodies and mass-particles are themselves bearers of the energy-content $E = mc^2$. Substance, therefore, whether mass or energy, is from the beginning a capacity to make itself effective according to mathematical order; spatially-temporally, therefore, material reality appears to us where and only where potentiality actualizes itself and where, by so doing, it becomes comprehensible for us.

3. THE METRIC OF THE WORLD-CONTINUUM

To the question, what both: matter and energy, are, the general theory of relativity gives us the [following] answer: they are that which creates the metric. The metric of the space-time-continuum is the expression of the intensity of the stresses of their essence, which is unknown to us, of their "inner," to use the expression employed by Hermann Weyl and Richard Woltereck. The measurement-worthiness, the metric, the space-curvature, space-determination, space-signing, or however we care to put it, is the expression of the potency of this "inner." The Riemann continuum really refers to the fields, the masses are really asymptotic-symmetrical positions; Hermann Weyl speaks of "channels" along the world-line; the energetic events, the actualizations of the potency represent singularities.

The most noteworthy fact, object of marvelling which can not be great enough, is this: that it is possible to comprehend and represent the physical magnitudes (mass, impulse, force, energy) as producers of geometrical characteristics as they occur in the theory of planes, and to be able to treat the field-forces also [in terms of] differential geometry. For this is by no means self-evident nor simply the invention of a great mathematico-artistic ingenuity; yet *in this possibility lies the decisive objective epistemological value of the general theory of relativity.* The name [of this theory] already shows that it arose out of the (now called "special") theory of relativity by looking for and finding an invariant form of natural laws not merely for Galilean systems of inertia but for any [number and types of] accelerated systems. That was still a matter of mathematics, a mathematical problem. The enlightening main thought, by which this general theory of relativity became the theory of gravitation was the equivalence of inert and heavy mass and, along with that, of accelerated systems and gravitational fields. The classical example for this, which has become famous, is the thought experiment of the indistinguishable nature of a free fall in an elevator which is at rest in a gravitational field, and a body at rest in an elevator which is accelerated upwards in gravitation-empty space. It is also possible, therefore, to regard the co-efficients of the line-elements in an accelerated system without gravitational field as the co-efficients in a gravitational field at rest. In proceeding this way, however, it must not be overlooked that it is true that every accelerated system can be thought of as substituted by one at rest in a gravitational field with appropriate distribution of masses, but that it is not possible to substitute an accelerated system for every gravitational field. In spite of this, with the g_{ik} and with the differential-geometrical tensors, vectors, and scalars, which can be formed out of the g_{ik}, one possesses the tool with which the gravitational fields can be treated as metrical fields. And this means that matter and energy impress a geometrical structure upon the world, fields of force are producers of metric and inversely the metric expresses itself dynamically.

What has occurred is a return to Descartes on a higher plane of mathematical and philosophical development: in Descartes extension was the attribute of matter. Leibniz raised the objection to this that extension is no real attribute at all, that it is force which is real (in one of his discussions with Descartes he actually found the law of the conservation of "living force"). Now the characteristics of space—although not those of extension but of metrical structure—viz., its characteristics of curvature, have become *the* attribute of matter after all; which latter [namely, matter] actually creates the physically real space by means of those characteristics. Geometry itself has become real. Instead of saying, matter produces a field of force under whose influence the motions result, one can now say, reality means the formation of the world-continuum, the creation of a metric field, in which the movements follow on the principles of variation. What we call material and physical is an "inner," which expresses itself mathematically and which, therefore, is capable of being mathematically expressed. Material reality is actualized mathematics. True, in the general theory of relativity this is valid only for the gravitational fields; the metrical representation of electromagnetic fields is still an unsolved problem.

4. THE PROBLEM OF COSMOLOGY AND COSMOGONY

If we turn our attention to the external world as a whole, the first question which arises is whether space, filled with matter and energy, is finite or infinite. For the naïve unprejudiced person it is difficult to assume infinity, but he is more or less forced to it by the idea of an unbounded Euclidean space; and it is, moreover, the commitment to the principle of sufficient reason which thus forces him. Why should the space filled with material and energic reality come to an end at some boundary and beyond that be nothing but infinite unfilled space? This thought, of course, is by no means logically conclusive; in fact, it would lie close to our ideational requirement to think of an asymptotic fulfillment which approximates to the limiting value of zero. However, from the standpoint of natural science the objection raised against this [view] is that it is pure speculation, and, from that of philosophy, that empty space is here spoken of as if such were a reality. However, through the development of the general theory of relativity the question has taken on a completely new look: The universe is finite, but not a universe which is subsumed in Euclidean space, lives in such space or is embedded in it; but the universe is finite just as a non-Euclidean space of finite radius is finite (just as the surface of a three-dimensional "ball" in a four-dimensional continuum). This closed non-Euclidean space is not something which exists prior to or alongside of material reality, but is produced by it and at the same time together with it; the question concerning "something beyond" makes no sense, since one dare not make the mistake, almost always made by the mathematical layman, to think of a non-Euclidean continuum in a Euclidean one of equally as many dimensions. By the way, mathematicians and philosophers often talk past each other at this point; the former insists that through the physical theory of the closed space it is now decided that "space" is not Euclidean; and the latter declare that, on the basis of our powers of perception, it is impossible that "space" could be anything but Euclidean. Actually the matter stands as follows: Even though the physically filled space with its relationships corresponds to a closed non-Euclidean system of relations, it nevertheless remains true that the Euclidean space plays not merely a mathematical but also a psychologically excellent rôle, insofar as Euclidean geometry is in fact the only one which corresponds to our powers of perception. Inversely: Although I must proceed from this form of perception in all empirical investigations, it nevertheless remains true that the cohesion of all observations may demand a system of relations which is not Euclidean. The closedness and finitude of the universe relates, therefore, to matter-filled space as a whole and declares that a body or a ray, which moves in one direction without deviating towards any of the three perceptual dimensions, nevertheless returns upon itself, just as the idea of red, moving towards orange and yellow, returns upon itself. It is true that, if we want a perceptual model for this imperceivable fact, we shall have to have recourse to an analogy: Just as we must imagine the band of colors in the last named example, we would have to imagine the progression of the ray or of the moving body in a continuum of four dimensions. The fourth dimension would be that one in which the body on a sphere returns to its point of departure; since, however, our power of imagination does not suffice for four dimensions, we must suppress one dimension and imagine, for example, the progression of a beam of light on a plane, one of the dimensions of which is the not perceivable, not appearing "fourth dimension." To the mathematician all of this is so familiar that it becomes actually difficult for him to note and recognize the epistemological difficulty.

But, back to the issue: Physical space is a non-Euclidean continuum of finite radius. Matter and space are indissoluble from each other. Matter manifests itself as actualization of a many-dimensioned continuum which appears to us in space and time. And now came the next step. The radius itself grows, the universe expands.

And with that a double problem is raised. Temporality enters again into the physical consideration and the cosmological problem becomes at the same time a cosmogonic one. What is the situation at the beginning?

The idea which has dominated all cosmogony-schemes of a physico-astronomic kind until now has been essentially the Kant-Laplace theory: The becoming of our world of experience arose out of a chaotic primeval fog. Against the carrying through of this idea there arose, however, quite aside from all references to a teleological element in the world order, physical objections also, which C. F. von Weizsäcker has recently attempted to remove by [means of] supplementary hypotheses. Within the framework of the theory of relativity itself Einstein's cylindrical world could be regarded as an ideal state of equilibrium, from which the expansion took place. What, however, was the cause of this, and how would this cylindrical world have come to be? Most recently P. Jordan attempted a radical solution, which unites microphysical and macrophysical problems, the becoming of the material world from a minimum number of particles, say two neutrons, which move away [from each other] and in so doing make "space" for the appearance of new particles.

Jordan rejects the question concerning any "before" as meaningless; for time arises precisely as does space with matter.

What, however, can not be rejected is the question concerning the "before" in the causal sense: What causes the first particles to form themselves? No man can disregard the *"ex nihilo fit nihil."* Even for religious faith the world is a creation out of nothing only insofar as matter itself had a beginning; but not insofar as its appearance came out of nothing; rather in the sense of the story of creation it is the will and idea of God— to whom himself is ascribed timeless eternity—which constitute the ground for the genesis of space, time, and matter. Consequently one would still have to imagine pre-posited a potential state without any materialization of corpuscles before the cosmogony of Jordan; a potential state whose transition to the empirical form of being introduced at the same time a temporal becoming. Once again, therefore, potentiality would precede actuality. But, in the final analysis, this means: Every physical cosmogony comes necessarily to the boundary of transcendence and must end with an unsolved problem. And every attempt at a solution [of this problem] on the part of philosophy will only be able to be a speculation. If the philosopher risks such [a speculation]—and he may do this, if only to assert that it is only a speculation, an idea, which he creates for himself—he will have to organize it into a transcendent *Weltanschauung*, which would have to be called "Real-Idealism" (*Real-Idealismus*).

In any case we desire to express the basic thought of such an interpretation: What appears to us as external reality is the putting itself forward of a will; matter is the expression of a mathematically expressible form of its inner essence. Its will finds its expression in the actualization of mathematical structures. Were we to resolve the differential equations, which constitute the basic laws of the universe, and give to arbitrary functions and constants, which occur in the resolution, a definite value, we should have created the world, which appears in a way which is binding for all beings. In an epistemological sense such a world structure would be realism, because it recognizes a reality independent of consciousness. Metaphysically speaking it would be idealism, because the essence of what appears would be the "will to appear," and because the mathematical structures, in which it appears, or which are at least ideationally implied, are the expression of a non-material "inner" (understanding this word approximately in the sense of Hermann Weyl and Richard Woltereck). But, as already stated, this reaches way beyond experience and is merely interpretation.

5. BOUNDARY PROBLEMS OF THE THEORY OF RELATIVITY

However imposing and impressive the intellectual work of art of the general theory of relativity, nonetheless great is the suspense with which both theoretical physics and the philosophy of nature await the solution of the riddles which are propounded by it. These are:

1. The description of the electromagnetic fields in analogy to the fields of gravitation by means of metric characteristics of the space-time world. This demands a mathematically-formal differentiation of the metric of the general theory of relativity, a refinement of its geometry, and a refinement of the existential concepts of such nature that the polarity of the charges and their relation to the mass is included, i.e., that the dualism of mechanics and electromagnetism is resolved by placing both on a common foundation.

2. A synthesis of the continuum and discontinuity views and, with that, of the two lines of development of modern physics: the theory of relativity and the quantum theory, macrophysics and microphysics, in the sense of the old philosophical problematic: the doctrine of original substance and of the hypothesis of original building-blocks. All of these problems of a refined structure of the theory of relativity on the one hand, and of a synthesis on the other, are obviously very closely connected with each other.

Philosophy will enter this problematic mainly from the standpoint of the problem of determinism. The general theory of relativity rates as an avowedly deterministic doctrine. Quantum mechanics has led to the indeterminacy relation of Heisenberg, which at least leaves open the possibility of some play for freedom in the area of elementary events, or, more carefully, let's say a threshold of indeterminacy. This possibility will at least have to be taken into consideration. For the attempt to save determinism at all events by interpreting the indeter-

minateness of the two complementary factors as mere inde-
termin*able*ness (because of the impossibility of knowing exactly
the respective present, and because of the disturbing interference in the case of an experiment), this attempt only pushes
the problem back [a step] and does not explain that the product
of the imprecisions of impulse and location, or of energy and
time, is precisely equivalent to such an important universal constant, and that the final equations, at which we arrive, are equations of probability; that possibility and probability, therefore,
are not anything secondary, but something primary. But, entirely aside from this, philosophy cannot make its attitude to
the problem of determinism become dependent merely upon the
formation of physical theories. We already have weighty reasons to assume that life-events are taking place not *merely*
according to mathematically formulable laws, such as Hamil-
ton's principles, for example; and that [life] does precisely
not run its course according to laws of probability; that, shall we
say, the arbitrary functions which enter into the solution of
differential equations leave great latitude for meaningful and
complete (*ganzheitliche*) events. Perhaps the formative forces
of life make use of a wide range of indetermination in the
microphysical realm. However, even independently of these
theories we need to cling to what is given us in life's experience "existentially," to use the word which is so common today.
And here it must be stated that we cannot get by [without
recognizing] the experience of a double freedom: If there is
not to loom up an unbridgeable gulf between theory and practice, and if we are not to discount our confidence in our immediate and most important experience as just nothing, then we
must acknowledge that as original phenomenon we are confronted by:

1. The experience of arbitrary decisions, which, although
they may not at all be of any particular consequence, are not
unequivocally determined by the situation; the hypothesis that
we are deceived by unconscious motives must not be generalized
to such an extent that nothing but illusions remain; otherwise
one would unnecessarily have to invent nothing but hypothetical causes.

2. Above all, however, the experience of moral responsibility; without the acknowledgment of moral freedom the concepts of guilt and expiation become just as empty fictions as the emotions of indignations, of shame and of remorse. From the "inner point of view," to use a word of Planck's we are free. The "external point of view," the view which considers every event as unequivocally causally determined, is not applicable there. We make the [causal] presupposition in order to carry on science and to make predictions; but we may, of course, reach limits; and the presupposition is [only] an hypothesis, whereas the consciousness of freedom is obvious in experience. If, however, existence at the human level demands freedom, or at least possibly demands it, does not then an aspect of freedom enter into all strata of existence, even into those of the vital and material? Any reality which would be nothing but driven, pushed, pulled, and kicked would be a purely passive being, and such a world would be a world of marionettes which is [merely] being played. Determinateness does not in any case belong as ideational necessity to the concept of being. To the contrary, real active being includes within itself a degree of determination of the indeterminate.

However, we neither shall nor can unroll here the question of the pro and con, but only raise it conditionally: If an aspect of freedom runs through reality at all levels of its being, is it, and how is it, compatible with the theory of relativity, what does it mean in its framework and what does the theory of relativity mean within the framework of such a view of being? Well then, the world continuum of the theory of relativity is simply the framework of possibility and of probability within which the actual happening takes place. Just as macrophysics grows out of the microphysical possibilities and actualizations, just as the macrophysical laws grow out of the microphysical laws of probability for a large number of particles and their fields, just so is the metric of the world continuum so to speak the epitome, the integral of all fields of probability. Or if, instead of proceeding from the discrete particles and moving on to the continuum as totality, we, inversely, proceed from the continuum as totality: Just as the fields of probability are not mere mathematical-ideal structures, but rather the lead fields of a super-individual potentiality for the occurrence of actual elements, just so is the metric not merely a mathematical-ideal structure, but the world continuum is the all comprehensive field into which all microfields are bedded. The indeterminateness of the elementary events would, therefore, mean a refined structure of the world-plane just as [is the case with] a vitally or psychically conditioned event; but it would have as little meaning for the macro-structure as the falling of a bit of dust for the path of the earth. Indeterminism in microphysical events would therefore be just as compatible with the theory of relativity as are the autonomy of life and the psychic conditioning of the behavior of living things.

How, then, is it with the double nature of light and matter? Already when discussing the constancy of the velocity of light in the special theory of relativity we hit upon the necessity of depriving the expanding radiation of the characteristics both of particles as well as of those of a system-bound wave. We said: an immaterial signal expands in the entire space-like area (really on the boundary of the temporal); the geometrical location for the possibility of the occurrence of photons expands itself super-systemically and thereby creates the foundation for the systematic space- and time-measurements. In this process the contradiction disappears that a physical reality could not propagate itself objectively equally rapidly with reference to systems and observers moving at different rates of speed. Therewith the other contradiction disappears also which seemed to exist between the undulatory and the corpuscular nature in microphysics. As one and the same reality the same something can indeed not at one and the same time be corpuscle, viz., be localized, and be wave, viz., be not localized. But nothing stands in the way of referring the localization only to the actual occurrence in energy and in situations of energic character, or of referring the nature of waves only to the progress of possibilities and of geometrical locations to the occurrence of corpuscles. As a matter of fact—and this is particularly important from the positivistic standpoint—we must clearly recognize that what we at any particular time observe experimentally are always particles and that what makes us conclude that there are waves, [namely] the interferences, refers only to expansion. We reach, therefore, so to speak, the following proportion: Wave nature is to the nature of particles what super-individual potentiality is to individual actuality. For, for the so-called waves of matter—because of their excess over the speed of light—immateriality, i.e., pure potentiality, is valid from the very beginning.

SUMMARY

SIGNIFICANCE FOR OUR PICTURE OF THE WORLD

In a prize essay of 1923 on "The Relation of Einstein's Theory of Relativity to Contemporary Philosophy" (which was composed in response to a prize offered by the *Annalen der Philosophie*, and to which the prize was awarded by a committee of judges consisting of Max von Laue, Ernst von Aster, and Moritz Schlick, and which was also favorably adjudged by Albert Einstein) the author had already pointed out the compatibility of the theory of relativity with critical realism and had contended for its significance for our scientific worldpicture. Favoring the objective epistemological worth of the theory of relativity in the sense of critical realism is, on the one hand, the possibility of its consistent execution, which is by no means self-evident, and, on the other hand, its validation within experience. Today I would summarize this significance in the following manner:

1. The order of things and events which appears to us as space, and that which appears to us as time with regard to the external world, are, of course, not interchangeable, but neither are they separated by a sharp boundary. There is, therefore, a space-like and a time-like "sphere." A "distance" in the sense of merely being apart from each other may, according to differing conditions, appear as a more spatial or as a more temporal [kind of a] distance.[3] This is connected with the fact

---

[3] The order becomes unequivocally temporal only if a cause and effect relation is involved. Without such [a relation] it makes no sense to speak of any objective simultaneity or after-each-other; for finite system-bound beings could not establish such; and for an infinite being, capable of surveying everything, there could be no temporality at all.

that reality, which is the foundation of all appearances, is obviously a many-dimensional arrangement of order, which demands more dimensions than are at the disposal of our perceptual capacity. And this in turn is connected with the fact that before that which becomes real there lies a greater richness of possibilities. What appears to us as matter in an unformed Euclidean space and in an homogeneous time is something which creates a four-dimensional Riemannian continuum which, for a "graphic" description of its intensity, would require a ten-dimensional Euclidean space.[4] If we were to conceive of the four-dimensional continuum as a whole (under neglect of two dimensions) as a plane in a three-dimensional (actually: five-dimensional) space, and do this with regard to the expansion of the universe as a plane whose cross-sections have an increasing radius, then a thus described world would have at its disposal a fifth dimension for a stratum of possibilities.[5]

2. The invariants occur in the four-dimensional synopsis. This does not mean the elimination of time as such, but points to the fact that spatial and temporal extensions and distances, which are bound to each other, belong to real being and happening. The fact should be pondered that even in microphysics, in Planck's equation $E \cdot \tau = h$ and in Heisenberg's uncertainty-relation we are confronted by this solidarity of spatial and temporal extensions.

3. The reality of the external world is not so material as was held by materialism, which got its bearings from the ideas of classical physics of impenetrable, fixed, extended and well-defined bodies. What is it possible to say concerning it today at all? Nothing, except that it is a [type of] reality which effectively confronts us and which is so well mathematically describable that it can be regarded as the realization of mathematical structures and forms, as something which realizes mathematically expressible relations of order (space-time struc-

---

[4] It is possible to say that a Riemannian space of four dimensions lies in a Euclidean space of ten dimensions. In this case tensors can be interpreted geometrically by extensions which bring about a deformation of space. (Cf. Herbert Lang, *Zur Tensor-Geometrie in der Relativitätstheorie:* Dissertation, 1919).

[5] Compare the author's *Wissenschaft und Weltanschauung* (Leipzig, 1st ed., 1935, p. 280; 2nd ed., 1949), 308f.

tures). Being effectual for each other and towards us, being the expression and the expressibleness of the orderly relations in mathematically couchable forms: these are today the attributes of "material reality." Is this peculiar? Mathematical expressibility, we already said, is marvellous. But what lies at the base of material appearance is a being-related-to and a becoming-effectual: this simply lies in the concept of being. For being means nothing else than "being for itself" or "being for someone," expressing itself with regard to other being, making an appearance and becoming effective.

If we raise the question at all concerning the essence, concerning the "inner nature" of matter, concerning the bearer of the orderly relations, we must recognize the fact that we shall either have to waive any claim to any answer—which would still be no reason for saying that the question has become meaningless; for questions are meaningless only if they already contain within themselves a contradiction or a lack of relation between subject and predicate[6]—or else we shall have to weigh the possibility of placing the "inner nature," the "essence" of the being of matter in analogy with the only being with which we cannot connect any meaning at all, namely with the becoming effective, which is grounded upon a "will." This appears to be pure speculation. In fact, however, not one of the however greatly differing *Weltanschauungen* has been able to get around the necessity—nor will any such ever be able to get around it—of taking into account a volitional element which expresses itself in actuality. The religious *Weltanschauungen* speak of the will of the creator; the pantheists have a dim notion of the will of the soul of nature; Schopenhauer made the will itself the principle of the world; Nietzsche misinterpreted it as the mere will to power, and by doing so made it empty of meaning; in Eduard von Hartmann it received its content from an unconscious; in Bergson it appeared in the form of an *élan vital*; but in a dynamic conception of nature

---

[6] Questions today are all too readily cut off by the dictum that they are meaningless. The question is meaningless as to whether a primary number is red, or which integral co-efficients must have an equation of the n'th degree, amongst whose roots the circular number and the basis of natural logarithms occurs. But a question is not meaningless because it is empirically unanswerable.

also is the idea of the will—not, of course, in an anthropo-
morphizing sense—basic. Whether we regard matter as the
appearance of a divine or of a natural will, of a meaningful or
of a blind will or as the expression of an inner dynamic—and
we offer no opinion on the subject—, the content of this "will"
is, in any case, of such a nature that it seems at one and the
same time to arise out of a both irrational and rational principle. In the realization of the principles of mathematical
order there expresses itself the content of a will which we
would have to call Logos; in the distribution [on the other
hand there seems to be] a contingency, chance, arbitrariness:
for the empirical world does not appear to be what one would
call a harmonious whole. Here we confront a bifurcation of
the roads which try to interpret the world meaningfully: Is
there a divided principle at the foundation of the world? Or
is the arbitrary element, the aspect of chance included in the
self-willedness of finite beings who nevertheless are under
meaningful direction?

The theory of relativity has simultaneously made us freer
and richer by showing in the realm of physics, not merely by
way of abstract advice but in concrete performance, that our
intellectual capacity of knowledge reaches farther than our
sensory capacity of perception. It is the same step in the realm
of ideas as that in geometry from Euclidean to non-Euclidean
geometry. Our perceptual capacity is limited to three dimensions of a homogeneous continuum of the curvature zero. Our
thought-capacity reaches farther. We do not feel ourselves imprisoned in the world of appearances and of the workaday
world. But neither do we need to resign ourselves so much, as
did Kant, who could say nothing aside from his forms of perception and the forms of thought. We do not assert that with
the theory of relativity we have reached reality as such; concerning its inner essence we shall never be able to speak otherwise than by analogy and suppositions. But we have obviously
come closer to objective reality than by way of our perceptual
capacity. Philosophically this means at the same time that we
have moved farther away from materialism even through the
development of physics. For we now assert of matter only that

it is something which is expressed and can be expressed differential-geometrically, by means of differential equations for a many-dimensioned continuum. Our cautiousness must go so far that we are willing to leave undecided whether there is such a thing as a continuous existence of world-bodies and particles, or whether only discrete actual events take place in the interplay of energy, so that only super-individual potential being can still be thought of as continuous. In the continuous world of potentiality, within the "frame" of being, temporality has become a mere dimension which enters into the world continuum just as do the dimensions of space. Only in actual individuation does a real temporalisation and localisation occur again.

Alongside of the tasks of theoretical physics named above there will be the task of creating a clear system of concepts in a new physical ontology, concepts which are demanded by the evolution of physics and which can now only be intimated.

ALOYS WENZL

PHILOSOPHISCHE FAKULTÄT
UNIVERSITÄT MÜNCHEN
GERMANY

24
Andrew Paul Ushenko

EINSTEIN'S INFLUENCE ON CONTEMPORARY PHILOSOPHY

EINSTEIN'S INFLUENCE ON CONTEMPORARY PHILOSOPHY

1. A GENERAL SURVEY

EINSTEIN'S influence on philosophy has taken many forms. This means that no complete account can be expected within the space of the present essay. At the same time, the writer, if he is not to appear arbitrary, must explain his choice of contents. Such influence as is mainly negative in character or effect will be disregarded. Accordingly, the story of the setback, after a period of unprecedented success, of Bergson's philosophy of absolute time—unquestionably under the impact of relativity—is not to be told here. Again, there will be no adequate discussion of Einstein's influence on thinkers who would not go beyond the boundaries of tradition in philosophy. Many able men have tried to assimilate the new physics within the context of a congenial type of classical philosophy without realizing the necessity of reciprocal adjustments: their efforts have not led to a new metaphysics. For example, physicists, as a rule, have interpreted relativity within the frame of some classical version of idealism. Eddington advocates some sort of Kantian apriorism; Jeans goes for neo-Platonism enriched with a mathematician God; Weyl concocts a mixture of ideas derived from Leibniz and Husserl; Dingle is a phenomenalist; and Einstein himself occupies an intermediate position between Cassirer's neo-Kantianism and Mach's positivism. Interesting as such attempts to interpret relativity in terms of traditional philosophy may be in some instances, I shall disregard them all in favor of philosophers who were inspired by Einstein in starting an entirely new departure of metaphysics, including both epistemology and ontology. Philosophers to be examined have managed to render the traditional issue between idealism and materialism obsolete by showing that the distinction between "mental" and "physical" is epistemological and not ontological. Preoccupation with the novel departure in philosophy, in the spectacular form of its presentation by Whitehead and Russell, enables me to interpret the title of this paper in the following narrow but literal sense. I shall be dealing with Einstein's conceptions in philosophy which are characteristic of contemporary mentality, as contrasted with tradition. Accordingly, my chief concern is to connect certain tenets of relativity physics with the philosophical principle which, either in the negative form of exposing "the fallacy of bifurcation," or, in a positive formulation, as "neutral monism," has been embedded in a metaphysics of events to be opposed to the traditional metaphysics of material or mental things. Concentration upon the philosophies of events has a further advantage of forming a link between the Einstein volume and its predecessors in *The Library of Living Philosophers*. Thus I have an opportunity of straightening the matter whenever misunderstanding of the relation between Einstein and the philosophies of Whitehead and Russell has led some contributors to the third and fifth volumes of the *Library* towards unfair criticism; and correction of misinterpretation is particularly important in the case of Whitehead who was unable to write a reply to his critics. This accounts for the critical discussion, in the second and third sections (of this paper), of articles by F. C. S. Northrop, and E. Nagel. The outcome of the examination of the above philosophers is the conclusion, in fulfilment of the intention to trace a connection between this and the third and fifth volumes, that Whitehead and Russell present a "united front" with regard to the concept of nature, and that they differ from Einstein in ways which are more subtle, and at the same time less profound, than their explicit pronouncements may lead one to expect. (*The Library of Living Philosophers* will be referred to by initials, as "LLP.")

On certain points Einstein's influence on Whitehead and Russell may have been indirect. For example, Russell tells me in a letter of December 12, 1946, that it was Whitehead who led him, around 1914, "to abandon Newtonian absolute time and space and also particles of matter, substituting systems of events." Russell's conviction that the philosophy of events "fitted in well with Einstein," as he puts it, "confirmed me [i.e., Russell] in the views I got from Whitehead, but Einstein was not their source for me, and I think not for Whitehead." If Russell is right concerning Whitehead, the latter may have developed his philosophy of nature under Einstein's indirect but formative influence, for example, through contact with T. P. Nunn or S. Alexander. However this may be, there are other important points, such as the principle that contemporary events are physically independent of one another, where the influence could have hardly been anything but direct.

Reduction of the scope of discussion to a concern with two philosophers, together with some doubt about the measure of Einstein's positive influence, makes us wonder why the number of metaphysicians who have studied relativity physics to their profit is unquestionably smaller than it should be. I believe the explanation is that metaphysicians generally do not consider themselves sufficiently competent to deal with technical physics, while feeling that popular expositions are unreliable. And, if the explanation is satisfactory, the only remedy short of turning metaphysicians into professional physicists, the only way which would enable philosophers to assimilate the ideas of relativity, is to raise the level of popular presentation. Although abundance of allegories and metaphors, in such popularisers as Eddington and Jeans, is stimulating to imagination, it leaves a philosopher at a loss in his effort to understand the logic of modern physics. Even Einstein himself, as explained in the second section, has misled philosophers on the crucial point of the relativity of simultaneity, although the book in which he gives the misleading illustration[1] can be recommended as a model of popular account. These remarks give additional support to a rejection of an alternative explanation, according to which metaphysicians are not interested in contemporary

[1] *Relativity: the Special and General Theory.* (Henry Holt & Co., 1921.)

physics simply because physics and metaphysics have nothing in common.

I am not raising here the issue of the possibility or meaning of metaphysical statements. I fully agree with Einstein when he tells us that the fear of metaphysics is a "malady of contemporary empiricistic philosophizing"[2] and I expect that the days of anti-metaphysicians are numbered. I am concerned with the current opinion, shared by men who show a respect for metaphysics, that physics is neutral with regard to philosophy. To illustrate the opinion in question let me quote from an able physicist-philosopher. In his presidential address, prepared for the Pacific Division of the American Philosophical Association, V. F. Lenzen says: "It is a thesis of the present discussion that it is desirable, and indeed possible, to expound the concepts of science in a manner that is neutral with respect to theory of knowledge."[3]

Neutrality, of course, may mean several things. And I should agree with Lenzen, if he merely meant to point out that science does not logically entail, in the sense of formal logic, any particular type of theory of knowledge or ontology, say realism, to the exclusion of other types. Accordingly, I grant that there is no contradiction in a belief which combines science with any self-consistent metaphysics whatsoever. The point is, however, that entailment is not the only kind of conformity or requiredness. Science may require a particular metaphysics because of a peculiar relation of fitness or harmony between the two. This is to call the reader's attention to the kind of exclusive relevance which the scientist himself recognizes at least in practice. In plotting the graph of a completed continuous process, of which only a finite number of disconnected observations is available, the scientist joins the points that represent the data of observation by a "smooth" curve which he chooses, on the grounds of simplicity, to the exclusion of any of the infinite number of odd or "irrelevant" curves, although the latter are logically equally consistent with the same data. Simplicity is not

[2] *LLP*, v. 5, 289.
[3] *The Philosophical Review* (July, 1945), 341.

required by formal logic; whether a requirement of aesthetics or economy, the principle of simplicity stands for an extra-scientific consideration. And the fact that science must rely on such extra-scientific considerations proves that science is biased in favor of, and not neutral, with regard to, the latter. If I am asked to mention some particular metaphysics which clearly does not fit in with the theory of relativity, I should name solipsism. This I am prepared to do in spite of H. Dingle's disapproval in a review of my *Philosophy of Relativity*.[4] For an essential part of the meaning of the term "relative property," as is brought forth by such pronouncements as "The shape A is a square in relation to a particular observer $O1$ but is elongated in relation to another observer $O2$, provided these observers are in relative motion," implies the existence of at least two observers. A solipsist, even with a split personality, could not actually move in relation to his alter ego. This, as well as other considerations, may or may not mean that relativity and solipsism are logically incompatible; but, at any rate, they enable me to hold, contrary to Dingle, that solipsism does not fit in with, or is not naturally conformable to, relativity or, for that matter, any physics. As Russell has pointed out, "relativity physics, like all physics, assumes the realistic hypothesis, that there are occurrences which different people can observe."[5] In order to avoid the ambiguity of the noun "physics" we must not overlook, in this connection, the physicist's intention to describe the nature of the external world, i.e., of facts which are there independently of his own existence. Subsequently to divorce the description from the original intention, to argue that there is nothing to describe but a private field of dreams, or to contend that the description describes nothing at all and should be treated as an instrument for successful prediction of private observations, is a travesty of truth or language. And if positive grounds enable us to eliminate solipsism, and thereby show that relativity is not neutral in regard of metaphysics, we may also expect evidence for the existence of a particular type of phi-

---

[4] *Philosophy* (1937).
[5] *The Analysis of Matter* (Harcourt, Brace & Co., 1927), 48.

losophy which is, as it were, sponsored by Einstein's physics. The philosophies of events are, as I shall attempt to demonstrate, in such a privileged position.

2. The Relativity of Simultaneity: Einstein's Illustration of the Train

In order to decide whether world-elements are things or events a philosopher must understand the bearing of the relativity of simultaneity on his problem. For in one way, which a relativist can disregard because the size of physical bodies is negligible in comparison with the astronomical scale of phenomena that he is dealing with, the bearing would seem to be noteworthy. A material thing of classical physics occupies a definite volume of space—to be recognized by all observers regardless of their state of motion—which it carries with it, from moment to moment throughout the period of its existence, and thereby provides an absolute differentiation between space, the invariant volume of the body, and time, the succession of moments. And since, theoretically, we can imagine a body of an immense size, this conception of a material thing naturally fits in with the idea of absolute simultaneity which allows for an instantaneous volume of space—the same for all observers—regardless how large the latter is required to be. On the other hand, if simultaneity of spatially separated parts of a body is relative, and observers in relative motion must associate with the body different physical configurations, the conception of a definite material thing is no longer theoretically clear. If this is understood, the paramount question in the philosopher's mind is: how compelling is the evidence for the relativity of simultaneity, and, in particular, to what extent do observable data enter into the situation? Einstein's example of the train, illustrated by Fig. 1, has the merit of providing evi-

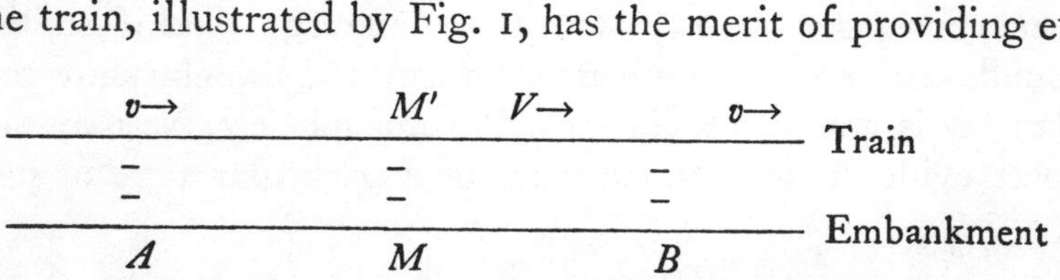

FIG. 1

dence which is, in principle, observable. A passenger seated at *M'* in a train observes two events *A* and *B*, two strokes of lightning, in close succession, while a man on the embankment at *M* observes the same events simultaneously. But such conflicting observations, assuming that they would be obtained in the case of an extremely long train moving at a superlative speed, form evidence for the relativity of simultaneity only within the context of certain plausible assumptions. Some of these assumptions Einstein has stated explicitly and clearly, but his exposition is confusing, if not confused, on the following two crucial points.

First, observation of simultaneity of spatially separated events does not imply the identification between seen simultaneity and physical simultaneity, except in the case where the observer happens to be situated midway between the physical sources of the simultaneously seen events. Accordingly, the relativist would agree with the astronomer who tells us that the explosion of a distant star happened long before the nearby flash of lightning even though both are recorded at the present moment. Second, in order to infer physical simultaneity from seen simultaneity, the observer's state of motion must be discounted as immaterial. This is to say that, in agreement with physical experiment, observers in relative motion, for example, the man on the embankment and the passenger in the train, establish the same constant velocity *c* with which light travels *in vacuo*. With these two points in mind, let us turn to Einstein's own presentation of the matter.

We suppose a very long train travelling along the rails with the constant velocity *v* and in the direction indicated in Fig. 1. People travelling in this train will with advantage use the train as a rigid reference-body (co-ordinate system); they regard all events in reference to the train. Also the definition of simultaneity can be given relative to the train in exactly the same way as with respect to the embankment. . . . When we say that the lightning strokes *A* and *B* are simultaneous with respect to the embankment, we mean: the rays of light emitted at the places *A* and *B*, where the lightning occurs, meet each other at the midpoint *M* of the length *A*—*B*, of the embankment. But the events *A* and *B* also correspond to positions *A* and *B* on the train. Let *M'* be the mid-point of the distance A—B on the travelling train. Just when the flashes (as judged from the embankment) of lightning occur, this point M' naturally coincides with the point M, but it moves towards the right in the diagram with the velocity v of the train. If an observer sitting in the position M' in the train did not possess this velocity, then he would remain permanently at M, and the light rays emitted by the flashes of lightning A and B would reach him simultaneously, i.e., they would meet just where he is situated. *Now in reality* (considered with reference to the railway embankment) he is hastening towards the beam of light coming from B, whilst he is riding ahead of the beam of light coming from A. Hence the observer will see the beam of light emitted from B earlier than he will see that emitted from A. Observers who take the railway train as their reference-body *must* therefore come to the conclusion that the lightning from B took place earlier than the lightning from A. We thus arrive at the important result: Events which are simultaneous with reference to the embankment are not simultaneous with respect to the train, and vice versa.[6]

I have italicized in this passage three words which are particularly misleading. The words "in reality" suggest that the real reason why the passenger must see two flashes in succession is his rushing towards one and away from the other, and that therefore the relative speed of the two beams of light depends on his state of motion and is not the same. The explanatory clause in brackets, inserted immediately after the words "in reality," does not help much because it can be misinterpreted in the sense that the embankment is a privileged frame of reference and that only description with respect to the embankments represents the real situation. And this misinterpretation is likely to be strengthened by Einstein's subsequent explanation which appears to require correction for the motion of the train in order to account for the disagreement between the passenger and the observer on the embankment. In other words, the explanation is given in terms which would be entirely acceptable to a classical physicist and therefore fail to make clear the new position. Under these circumstances, the italicized "must" leads to an additional misunderstanding: the reader may think that correction for the motion of the train is re-

---

[6] Einstein, *Relativity: the Special and General Theory*, 30ff.

jected because seen succession is identifiable with physical succession.

A physicist, who knows better, because of his familiarity with technical expositions, is apt to minimize the danger of misinterpretation. I can assure him that the danger is quite real. For a number of men, prominent in philosophy, have been actually misled by Einstein, exactly along the above mentioned lines, and thereby arrived at the conclusion that philosophy had better disregard the alleged relativity of simultaneity. Consider, for example, A. O. Lovejoy's article "The Dialectical Argument against Absolute Simultaneity."[7] Commenting on Einstein's example of the train, Lovejoy, first, points out that the relativity of simultaneity can follow only if the passenger, unlike the man on the embankment, "has not remained permanent at M," and then contends, in disregard of the principle that the train and the embankment are on a par as alternative frames of reference, that the fact that the passenger continues to be seated midway between two points, which Lovejoy calls A' and B', where the lightning strokes A and B hit the train, is immaterial to the argument because "it is not necessary to suppose that the observer on the train is unaware that he is moving relatively to the embankment in the direction A—B."[8] Thus, according to Lovejoy, the passenger can always correct the results of his observation for the motion of the train and establish that in reality the lightning bolts struck at the same time. However, Lovejoy believes that even if the passenger were unaware of his motion he could establish simultaneity, because

if it is still maintained that each observer can have empirical information only about events on his own system, what follows is that the signals will arrive simultaneously both at M and M' . . . since, upon the principles of relativity physics and the apparent evidence of Michelson-Morley experiment, the velocity of light is constant over equal distances on any given system irrespective of its relative motion.[9]

Let me admit that at this point Lovejoy's premises are correct,

[7] *The Journal of Philosophy* (1930), 650.
[8] *Ibid.*, 650.
[9] *Ibid.*, 650.

so that momentarily the fault is with his own reasoning for which we cannot blame Einstein. Lovejoy's error is that momentarily he overlooks (a) that the succession of flashes is assumed to be observed at M' (an assumption which he recognizes elsewhere through the requirement that observable succession must be corrected for the motion of the train), and (b) that, on the premises of the theory of relativity, observed succession of flashes at the mid-point M' can only mean that, in relation to the train, the lightning strokes A and B are *not* physically simultaneous. Lovejoy may have sensed that something is wrong with his remark because he hastens to add:

But in this case [i.e., on the premises of relativity physics] the two observers would not in fact be judging about the same pair of events; the one would be judging about events occurring at A and B, the other about events occurring at A' and B'. Hence, if their conclusions did disagree in the case supposed (though they would not), the fact would have no significance, since the two observers would be talking about different things.[10]

The additional point does not help Lovejoy, because A' occurs in the immediate neighborhood of, and therefore is virtually identical with, A, and the same is true about B' and B. And perhaps he is not easy about this point either because he relinquishes the momentary advantage of proceeding from correct premises and reverts to the original misunderstanding by concluding that Einstein himself assumes "that the observer on the train as well as the one on the embankment is judging about events occurring at A and B, i.e., at points on the embankment." The quoted conclusion is intended to reinstate what Lovejoy takes Einstein's example to imply, the privileged position of the embankment as a frame of reference.[11]

[10] *Ibid.*, 650.
[11] Lovejoy is by no means alone in his misunderstanding. F. S. C. Northrop and DeWitt H. Parker, to mention two men of reputation among philosophers, have also been misled by Einstein. In his *Science and First Principles* (The Macmillan Co., N.Y., 1932, 73), Northrop gives a lucid and correct account of the example of the train, but concludes with the following statement: "Obviously, then, if the light rays arrive simultaneously for the man on the ground, they will not

A slight modification of Einstein's example would remove the cause of misunderstanding by philosophers. For instance, two trains on parallel tracks might serve better the purpose of illustrating the parity of alternative reference systems because of a common experience, in looking out of the window of a train at another, of the inability to tell which of the trains is actually moving. Accordingly, let two passengers, P in the train T and P' in the train T', take each his own train as the frame of reference. We may imagine that a lightning stroke $L1$ hit both trains and left a burned spot A on T and A' on T', while another lightning stroke $L2$, at the opposite end of the trains, left its mark B on T and B' on T'. We further assume P to be seated midway between the marks A and B, and P' between the marks A' and B'. Under these circumstances, and because the beams of light from both $L1$ and $L2$ move with the same critical velocity in both trains, the fact that one of the passengers observes the flash coming from the engine before the flash from the rear, while the other passenger observes both flashes at the same time, can be explained only by the proposition that $L1$ and $L2$ are in succession in relation to one train, but simultaneous in relation to the other.

3. Whitehead's Conception of Simultaneity

In a penetrating essay on "The Philosophy of Whitehead," John Dewey observes that experience of causal compulsion— "the direct evidence as to the connectedness of one's immediate present occasion of experience with one's immediately past occasions"[12]—serves as the pattern of connectedness in

---

do so for the man of the train, since the latter is moving towards the ray coming from the front of the train and away from the one coming from the rear." If this statement were the explanation of the difference in observation, correction for the motion of the train would establish, in contradiction to Northrop's preceding account, the non-relative physical simultaneity of the lightning strokes. Parker, likewise, gives an excellent exposition of Einstein's illustration only to wind it up with the unaccountable contention that Einstein is not concerned with physical simultaneity but with the time when light messages reach the observers concerned: "And relativity theory gives an absolutely correct picture *with regard to the messages. . . .*" *Experience and Substance*, (The University of Michigan Press, 1941, 168).

[12] *LLP*, v. 3, 647.

nature in the metaphysics of events and thereby supports Whitehead's opposition to the traditional separation between mind and matter. On a further page of the same essay Dewey adds:

> The new philosophical departure [i.e., Whitehead's rejection of the bifurcation between mind and matter] initiated by deep reflection upon the general significance of the new physics in its contrast with Newtonian cosmology was . . . carried through by taking human experience to be a specialization of the traits of nature thus disclosed.[13]

Dewey's remarks leave no doubt as to where to look to among the doctrines of the new physics in order to establish the crucial point of Einstein's influence upon the metaphysics of events. This crucial point is the conception of the causal structure of physical space-time, the principle, that is, that because of the finite but unsurpassable velocity of light, the occurence of any event is the apex of a double light-cone which leaves the events along the alternative cross-sections of simultaneity, i.e., within the regions of space-time in-between the two cones, causally disconnected and therefore physically independent of one another. This principle, except for the identification of the critical velocity with the velocity of light *in vacuo*, Whitehead accepts *in toto* as a basis of metaphysics. "Contemporary events happen in causal independence of each other," writes Whitehead, and a footnote adds: "This principle lies on the surface of the fundamental Einsteinian formula for the physical continuum."[14]

In order to understand the importance which the principle of physical independence of contemporaries has for Whitehead, let us consider the principle in the context of the metaphysics of events, and, in particular, of Whitehead's theory of perception. As is well known, his ultimate elementary events are organized acts, or, rather, agent-acts combined, of perception—I shall call them *percipients*—where perception ranges, with respect to complexity of organization, from human experience down to blind electronic response, or sensitiveness, to the surrounding physical field. Because percipients are events im-

[13] *Ibid.*, 656.
[14] *Process and Reality* (Cambridge University Press, 1929), 84.

mutably fixed each at a definite region of space-time, mutual perception is their only way of transaction. And since perception of another event requires propagation of causal influence from the latter to the percipient, experience of causal compulsion—in Whitehead's terminology perception in the "mode of causal efficacy"—is the major ontological pattern of correlation. Conformably to this pattern, and in agreement with the conception of the causal structure of space-time, Whitehead accounts for creativity, which is his ultimate and most universal feature of process, in terms of the unique and original perception of the world which each percipient brings forth with its occurrence. This is to say that the actual world of each percipient is different from the actual world of any of its contemporaries: in each case the actual world can be represented by the unique light-cone of the past with the corresponding percipient at the apex. In this connection Whitehead explicitly refers to the theory of relativity:

> Curiously enough, even at this early stage of metaphysical discussion, the influence of the 'relativity theory' of modern physics is important. According to the classical 'uniquely serial' view of time, two contemporary actual entities define the same actual world. According to the modern view no two actual entities define the same actual world. Actual entities are called 'contemporary' when neither belongs to the 'given' actual world defined by the other.[15]

Recognition that contemporary percipients are physically independent of one another, in conjunction with the principle of "one world," or what Whitehead calls "the solidarity of one common world," lead to a complication in the theory of perception. Important as the mode of causal efficacy is, this mode is insufficient because it leaves out contemporaries, contrary to the requirement of solidarity, completely disconnected. Hence Whitehead supplements his basic perception of causal compulsion by a second mode of perception, which he calls the "mode of presentational immediacy," which is designed to provide non-causal correlation among contemporaries. In the mode of presentational immediacy a percipient is directly cognizant of the *extension* of the contemporary external world but not of the nature or character of events that happen jointly to fill up

Ibid., 90f.

this extension. This is to say that the percipient has no access to such colors, shapes, or other perceptual and physical manifestations that actually belong to the external world at the moment of perception but only to the regions of the surrounding medium where the inaccessible properties reside, in Whitehead's words, only to the "presented locus" of contemporary events. Of course, under normal conditions of the so-called veridical perception and at close range, perceived qualities are likely to be similar, or at any rate relevant, to actual manifestations; and under no circumstances is there perception of pure and bare extension. But error, not with regard to the presented locus but to perceptual presentations within the locus, is always possible, because manifestations which illustrate to a percipient his contemporary external world are in fact derived, through the mode of causal efficacy, from the past (and therefore represent the world as it was and not as it is) to be unconsciously "projected" upon the extended surroundings of the present. An important difference in the function of the two modes of perception is this: in the causal mode the world reaches the percipient where and when the latter happens to be, i.e., at the latter's spatio-temporal standpoint, whereas in the non-causal mode the percipient manages to reach, beyond the volume of its own body and by means of a felt geometrical prolongation of bodily strains, for places where contemporaries abide.[16] We may express this difference, in terms of the well

---

[16] An obvious objection against the theory of two perceptual modes, that we find no evidence for the existence of distinct kinds of perception, is met by Whitehead when he points out that *ordinary human perception* is the outcome of a pre-conscious interplay between the two modes; he calls this interplay "symbolic reference." However, Whitehead has also mentioned unusual instances when each mode operates singly. For examples of experience in the mode of causal efficacy alone see *Process and Reality*, 247f. The mode of presentational immediacy can be illustrated with the aid of the difference between our perception of a chair and as we turn around, of the mirror-image of the chair. The mirror-image *presents a region behind the mirror*, but the chair-like shape and color, which are projected upon that region, are derived from the actual chair in front of the mirror and give no idea as to the actual contents of the space thus illustrated. Another example is an astronomer's perception of the explosion of a star at a distant region in the sky: the astronomer knows that the star actually exploded long ago and therefore only an image of the past event illustrates the contemporary distant region.

known issue between direct and representative realism, by saying that the regions of a contemporary world can be presented *directly*, but the nature of events there (directly given there in the aspect of extension) is represented, and sometimes misrepresented, by characteristics that are causally derived from their antecedents. Whitehead himself sums up the matter as follows:

> Thus the presented locus must be a locus with a systematic geometrical relation to the body. According to all the evidence, it is completely independent of the contemporary actualities which in fact make up the nexus of actualities in the locus. For example, we see a picture on the wall with direct vision. But if we turn our back to the wall, and gaze into a good mirror, we see the same sight as an image behind the mirror. Thus, given the proper physiological state of the body, *the locus presented in sense-perception is independent of the details of the actual happenings which it includes.* This is not to say, that sense-perception is irrelevant to the real world. It demonstrates to us the real extensive continuum in terms of which these contemporary happenings have their own experience qualified. Its additional information in terms of the qualitative sensa has relevance in proportion to the relevance of the immediate bodily state to the immediate happenings throughout the locus. Both are derived from a past which is practically common to them all. Thus there is always some relevance; *the correct interpretation of this relevance is the art of utilizing the perceptive mode of presentational immediacy as a means for understanding the world as a medium.*[17]

I have italicized some of Whitehead's statements in order to forestall F. C. S. Northrop's contention, to be examined presently, that Whitehead and Einstein have essentially different conceptions of simultaneity because the former fails to differentiate between perceptual or phenomenal events, on the one hand, and physical events on the other. I think that the required differentiation follows from the statement that the presented locus is independent of the actual happenings which it includes, since the presented locus appears in the guise of immediately sensed events, whereas actual happenings are physical events. Furthermore, Whitehead explicitly recognizes that, in order to establish which physical events reside within the pre-

[17] *Loc. cit.*, 178.

sented locus, we must resort to interpretation, or correlation, of the data in the mode of presentational immediacy.

An examination of Northrop's contention is in order not only because in the context of his interesting article on "Whitehead's Philosophy of Science" the misinterpretation enjoys an appearance of plausibility, but also because Northrop may have succeeded in misleading Einstein. In an attempt to explain to Einstein Whitehead's position Northrop made the following statement:[18]

When Whitehead affirms an intuitively given meaning of simultaneity of spatially separated events he means immediately sensed phenomenological events, not postulated public physically defined events. . . . We certainly do see a flash in the distant visual space of the sky now, while [and subsequently?] we hear an explosion beside us. His reason for maintaining that this is the only kind of simultaneity which is given arises from his desire, in order to meet epistemological philosophical difficulties, to have only one continuum of intuitively given events, and to avoid the bifurcation between these phenomenal events and the postulated physically defined public events.

Northrop tells us that Einstein's comment on Whitehead's theory thus presented was: "on that theory there would be no meaning to two observers speaking about the same event." This comment is a *reductio ad absurdum* not of Whitehead's view but of Northrop's account of the latter.

I do not deny that Whitehead passed some adverse criticism upon Einstein's definition of simultaneity, and if E. McGilvary is right (*LLP*, v. 3, 215ff.), the criticism is questionable. But if Whitehead misunderstood Einstein, this merely shows that the philosopher assumed the existence of disagreement where there was none. In order not to exaggerate their difference, let me point out, first, that in all his publications which are subsequent to *The Principles of Natural Knowledge,* and therefore may be taken as a more considerate treatment of the matter, Whitehead has omitted his original criticism of Einstein's definition, and, second, that the point of the original criticism is not that Einstein's procedure—whereby simultaneity of spatially separated events can be ascertained by the use of light signals—is inadequate, but that, whatever the procedure, the meaning of simultaneity is the same regardless of whether simultaneous events are far apart or in immediate proximity. Apparently Northrop has missed Whitehead's point, the differentiation between the *meaning* of simultaneity and the *procedure* whereby simultaneity can be established, because he argues, as if Whitehead should reject the scientist's ways of knowing simultaneity, that simultaneity of spatially separated events is scientifically "known by postulated theory, which is confirmed indirectly through its deductive consequences and not by immediate apprehension."[19]

In support of his interpretation Northrop quotes Whitehead's statement that "Nature is nothing else than the deliverance of sense-awareness." But Whitehead's statement, an expression of his opposition to the "fallacy of bifurcation," must not be taken to mean that immediate sense-awareness discloses *everything* there is in nature. Whitehead does not even claim that perception accounts for every item of human knowledge. His position is simply that there are no *kinds* of things in nature except the kinds which, in principle, can be known directly through perception. This position leaves ample room for knowledge by inference, and application of Whitehead's own "method of extensive abstraction" provides many illustrations of such knowledge.[20] Hence there is no reason whatsoever to expect that Whitehead is unable, on the basis of his allowance for inference, to deal with the following situations:

Consider two immediately sensed explosions: one in West Haven and the other in East Haven, which are so loud that they can be heard at every point between the two places. . . . We all know it to be a

[19] *LLP*, v. 3, 194.
[20] For example, Whitehead uses the method of extensive abstraction in order to account for such scientific objects as atoms or electrons. On p. 158 of *The Concept of Nature* he describes an electron as "a systematic correlation of the characters" of events, and contrasts a scientific object, such as an electron, with both observable physical objects, such as chairs, and sense-objects, such as colors or noises. Thus Northrop is completely mistaken when he asserts that, to Whitehead, "both atoms and sense data are immediately sensed adjectives of immediately sensed events, and that an electron is 'a sensed adjective qualifying all the event particles' in a 'historical route,' i.e., a Minkowskean world-line" (*LLP*, v. 3, 190).

phenomenological fact, and hence one which Whitehead cannot escape, that if a person midway between these two explosions immediately senses them as simultaneous, then all other observers who are nearer the one explosion than the other will not. This example shows both, that we do have an immediately sensed simultaneity for spatially separated events for the individual sense awareness of the individual observer, and that this intuitively given simultaneity does not provide [rather need not provide if the observer is not midway between the two explosions or if some such interference as the wind causes the speed of sound coming from one explosion to be greater than the speed from the other] a publicly valid simultaneity the same for all observers at rest relative to each other on the same frame of reference—in this instance on the earth's surface.[21]

It is amazing that Northrop can imagine that his example should embarrass Whitehead, or that an epistemology which would be embarrassed by such examples is worth refutation. Actually Whitehead requires no more than the possibility of knowing simultaneity of spatially separated events through the deliverance of sense-awareness, for example, in the case of the observer midway between the two explosions. Whitehead recognizes the existence of a public temporal relation between two events, the same for all observers using the same frame of reference, to be established by correction for differences in distance, and the like. Thus, on p. 53 of *The Principles of Natural Knowledge*, he says: "The same definition of simultaneity holds throughout the whole space of a consentient set in the Newtonian group."[22] And, in accordance with his theory

---

[21] *LLP*, v. 3, 200.

[22] The phrase "consentient set" designates a frame of reference of the special theory of relativity. And while, as the context of the phrase shows, "the same definition of simultaneity" is to be distinguished from Einstein's procedure of establishing public simultaneity within a particular frame of reference (because actually light signals do not travel *in vacuo* and therefore represent only an approximation to the constant velocity c, however close this approximation may be), Whitehead's recognition of the existence of alternative consentient sets, even when observers in relative motion pass by each other at virtually the same place and therefore momentarily have the same field of vision, proves that he does not identify public simultaneity with sensed simultaneity of spatially separated events. The distinction between a consentient set and the associated perceptual space reappears, with a greater measure of elaboration, in *Process and Reality* in the form of the differentiation between a "locus in unison of becoming" (with the

of perception, he would say, concerning Northrop's example, that there is no public physical sound at the sources of the explosions by the time a distant observer hears the noise. The inevitable conclusion is that there is no essential disagreement between Whitehead and Einstein of the special theory of relativity, at any rate not on the distinction between seen and physical simultaneity.

The truth is that Einstein's influence on Whitehead is, if anything, excessive. For the principle of independence of contemporaries is strictly valid only if events are understood in Einstein's sense of world-points. According to Whitehead, on the other hand, an event or a percipient is not without extension but a quantum of duration, a protensive entity. And when the duration of an event, as exemplified by the specious present in human experience, takes an appreciable fraction of a second,

---

given percipient) and the associated "presented locus." The additional elaboration brings Whitehead even closer to Einstein: "Thus the *loci* of 'unison of becoming' are only determinable in terms of actual happenings of the world." (*Process and Reality*, 180.)

There is, of course, much difference between the physical theories of Whitehead and Einstein, but I am not concerned with this aspect of the matter. And, in so far as a physical theory is conditioned by a philosophy of nature, I think Whitehead exaggerates his departure from Einstein, when he opposes his conception of "contingent" physical laws superimposed upon the uniform structure of space-time to the conception of the general theory of relativity, according to which spatio-temporal curvature expresses the presence of matter. As Whitehead himself has pointed out in the "Preface" to *The Principle of Relativity*, his requirement of uniformity would be satisfied by an elliptic or hyperbolic as well as by a flat space-time. Furthermore, Whitehead's prolongation of the presented *locus* beyond the set of strains of the percipient's body cannot be expected to disclose the exact structure of space-time on an astronomical scale; and on the scale of terrestrial transaction the validity of Euclidean geometry can be ascertained within the errors of observation. On the other hand, the general theory of relativity is concerned with astronomical distances, and proceeds upon the premise of a large scale uniformity of space-time: the relativist either assumes a uniform and static distribution of the nebulae or, if he argues for an expanding universe, systematic motions in the matter accountable for the cosmic curvature. The idea of the expanding universe practically obliterates the philosophical difference (under consideration) between Whitehead and Einstein, for, to quote from H. P. Robertson's article "The Expanding Universe," (*Science in Progress*, 2nd Series, 166), this idea leads to "a more or less unique stratification of space-time into space and time (which in a sense reintroduces a universal time), in which the geometry of space is one of the congruence geometries."

two such contemporary events can be physically interconnected, provided they are not too far from each other. Consider, for example, two men at the opposite ends of an open field. If both must strain their eyes in order to watch each other, the facial expression of strain can be perceived by each, because of the negligible amount of time required to carry a light-message from one of them to the other, before his percipient act is over. And, although Whitehead allows for a kind of "passage" from earlier to later phases within the duration of a single percept, he would not let us say that the beam of light that leaves one observer at an early phase of his percept reaches only a later phase within the percept of the other man. For this manner of speaking implies a division into earlier and later phases that occupy earlier and later intervals of physical time, a breakdown of the temporal quantum. "This genetic passage from phase to phase is not in physical time."[23] Hence contemporary percipients, on Whitehead's premise of protensive events, need not be physically independent of one another.

4. Things and Correlations of Events

Since Einstein, and still more since Heisenberg and Schrödinger, the physical world is no longer regarded as consisting of persistent pieces of matter moving in a three-dimensional space, but as a four-dimensional manifold of events in space-time. The old view resulted from an attempt to make the common-sense concept of "things" available for science; the new view means that "things" are no longer part of the fundamental apparatus of physics. . . . The essential business of physics is the discovery of "causal laws," by which I mean any principles which, if true, enable us to infer something about a certain region of space-time from something about some other region or regions.[24]

Thus, succinctly, Russell has stated the basis of the philosophies of events. On this basis his road to "neutral monism," the contention that the distinction between mind and matter is functional or epistemological but not an ontological disparity, is clear. If there is no need for material things, the ground is removed from under their alleged mental counterparts, per-

[23] *Process and Reality*, 401.
[24] *LLP*, v. 5, 701.

cipient things. And if causal laws do not unexpectedly break down when a physical stimulus causes the occurrence of a percept, we must not expect the percept to be fundamentally, or ontologically, different from a physical effect which the same stimulus would have caused at the same spot if the percipient had not been present there.

The theory that perceiving depends upon a chain of physical causation is apt to be supplemented by a belief that to every state of the brain a certain state of the mind 'corresponds,' and vice versa, so that, given either the state of the brain or the state of the mind, the other could be inferred by a person who sufficiently understood the correspondence. If it is held that there is no causal interaction between mind and brain, this is merely a new form of the pre-established harmony. But if causation is regarded—as it usually is by empiricists—as nothing but invariable sequence or concomitance, then the supposed correspondence of brain and mind involves causal interaction.[25]

As this passage shows, Russell's causal theory of perception leads to neutral monism because the alternatives, the doctrine of pre-established harmony and the notion of double effect (i.e., the notion that the same physical cause which is regularly followed by a definite physical effect is occasionally followed by an additional mental effect), are "fantastic." Although the question whether Einstein accepts the causal theory of perception, and, if he does, how far he would go with Russell towards neutral monism is very interesting, I do not have sufficient evidence for an answer. In fact, and this is the question I am concerned with, I am not sure whether Einstein would accept without qualification the basis of the philosophies of events as stated by Russell in the beginning of this section. Unquestionably there is much agreement between them:

In the pre-relativity physics space and time were separate entities. . . . It was not observed that the true element of the space-time specification was the event specified by the four numbers x_1, x_2, x_3, t. . . . Upon giving up the hypothesis of the absolute character of time, particularly that of simultaneity, the four-dimensionality of the time-space concept was immediately recognized. It is neither the point in space, nor the

[25] B. Russell, *Physics and Experience* (Henry Sidgwick Lecture, Cambridge University Press, 1945), 6.

instant in time, at which something happens that has physical reality, but only the event itself. There is no absolute (independent of the space of reference) relation in space, and no absolute relation in time between two events, but there is an absolute (independent of the space of reference) relation in space and time. . . . The circumstance that there is no objective rational division of the four-dimensional continuum into a three-dimensional space and a one-dimensional time continuum indicates that the laws of nature will assume a form which is logically most satisfactory when expressed as laws in the four-dimensional space-time continuum.[26]

Nevertheless, when it comes to dispensing with material things in favor of events, Einstein demurs. And, of course, there is no single decisive reason why we should not use both the concept of event and the concept of thing in an account of the physical world. But taken in conjunction such reasons as I have mentioned in the beginning of the preceding section are impressive. The main consideration, however, is that we can dispense with the concept "thing" because in relativity physics events are sufficient. This is to say that, although the language of things cannot do away with the events that happen to a thing, the language of events enables us to translate a statement about a thing into an equivalent statement about a sequence, or string, of events. In particular, a material particle becomes, in the language of relativity, a series of world-points along a definite world-line. "It is hardly correct to say that a particle *moves* in a geodesic; it is more correct to say that a particle *is* a geodesic (though not all geodesics are particles)."[27] In the face of this consideration Einstein's reluctance to eliminate the concept of material things requires explanation. As far as I can see, he has two reasons, the operational basis of physics and the technical meaning of the term "event," each of which I shall proceed to examine separately at some length.

Physics, including relativity, involves the use of instruments, such as clocks and practically rigid measuring rods, which must be identifiable at different dates and through displacement.

[26] A. Einstein, *The Meaning of Relativity* (Princeton University Press, 1945), 30f.

[27] B. Russell, *The Analysis of Matter* (Harcourt, Brace, & Co., 1927), 313.

And, as Einstein has pointed out, "we are still far from possessing such certain knowledge of theoretical principles as to be able to give exact theoretical construction of solid bodies and clocks."[28] Einstein's remark may mean that translation of statements about things into statements about more ultimate elements, such as events, although desirable, is premature at the present stage of science. If this were all he meant, there would be no essential disagreement between him and Russell. In this case both might agree to draw a line of demarcation between the theory of relativity, with events as basic elements, and the metatheory of physics (through the medium of which relativity is to be presented), with provisional employment of the concept, "thing." But Einstein's recent criticism of Russell shows that his present position is much more uncompromising: "Over against that [i.e., against Russell's view] I see no 'metaphysical' danger in taking the thing (the object in the sense of physics) as an independent concept into the system together with the proper spatio-temporal structure."[29] These words may show no more than disagreement with Russell's latest attempt to dispense with substances (including particular events) altogether by reducing things into bundles of qualities. But Einstein's reason for disagreement suggests opposition to reduction of any kind. His reason, as the following quotation shows, is that Russell is unable to account for the distinction between two bundles of qualities which are exactly alike except by including the differentiating spatial relations among sense data: "Now the fact that two things are said to be one and the same thing, if they coincide in all qualities, forces one to consider the geometrical relations between things as belonging to their qualities. (Otherwise one is forced to look upon the Eiffel Tower in Paris and that in New York as 'the same thing'.)"[30] Einstein's implicit criticism, I take it, is twofold: (1) A thing cannot be constructed out of, or reduced to, a set of sensory qualities, and (2) Geometrical, and presumably spatio-temporal, entities are not sense data. And this leads us to an

[28] A. Einstein, *Sidelights of Relativity* (Methuen and Co., 1922), 36.
[29] A. Einstein in *LLP*, v. 5, 291.
[30] A. Einstein in *LLP*, v. 5, 290.

examination of events in the technical sense of spatio-temporal elements or world-points.

Events in the sense of world-points are without extension. And, unless these extensionless elements of space-time can be constructed out of, or logically derived from, ordinary and extended happenings or events, there would be no advantage in sacrificing things for the sake of the latter. Of course, Russell explicitly recognizes the distinction between a world-point and an ordinary event: "The points of space-time have, of course, no duration as well as no spatial extension."[31] But a question is raised on which Einstein and Russell are apart: Is there a way to abstract, or logically derive, world-points from events that are given in sense experience? The fact that both world-points and ordinary events are identifiable by specifying a position and a date prompts us to answer "Yes." Einstein, however, says "No." For world-points are theoretical concepts, and Einstein rejects the "idea that the fundamental concepts and postulates of physics were not in the logical sense free inventions of the human mind but could be deduced from experience by 'abstraction'—that is by logical means."[32] This is not to say that Einstein denies that world-points, or any other scientific concepts, serve to correlate events of observation or sense experience; but his idea of correlation or what he calls "representation," is not correlation in Russell's sense of logical construction. As far as "representation" in terms of world-points is concerned, it consists of *assignment* of distinct world-points to distinct observations. The assignment is controlled by the condition of numerical agreement between the spatio-temporal relations among the assigned world-points, on the one hand, and the relationships, established by clock readings and displacements of measuring rods, that bind the represented phenomena, on the other. According to Einstein, "representation" of data by means of world-points is an obvious extension from three to four dimensions of the usual correlation between Euclidean geometry and actual, or possible, configurations exhibit-

[31] B. Russell, *The Analysis of Matter*, 57.
[32] A. Einstein, *The World as I See It* (Covici & Friede, N.Y., 1934), 35.

ed by solid bodies on the earth in relation to one another: "Solid bodies are related, with respect to their possible dispositions, as are bodies in Euclidean geometry of three dimensions. Then the propositions of Euclid contain affirmations as to the relations of practically-rigid bodies."[33] Hence the difference between Einstein and the philosophers of events concerning the part played by ordinary events in the constitution of nature depends on the opposition of the procedure of "representation" to that of logical construction. The question is: Which of the two conceptions of correlation is more adequate?

I believe Einstein is wrong when he asserts that such scientific concepts as points, or world-points, cannot be "deduced from experience by 'abstraction'—that is to say by logical means." The method of extensive abstraction (in the development and use of which Russell has followed Whitehead) can do just that. For example, in Chapter 28 of *The Analysis of Matter,* Russell applies the method of extensive abstraction in a successful construction of a world-point out of sets of overlapping ordinary events. Such constructions are supposed to be given exclusively on the basis of observable data, such as the sequence of overlapping notes struck one after another on the keyboard of the piano, and by means of formal logic and mathematics alone, i.e., with the aid of such terms as "the logical sum of classes," "infinite number," and the like. Furthermore, these constructions satisfy the following two conditions: (1) The constructed elements must be related to one another in agreement with the theorems of the corresponding geometry; and (2) The statement that "A region of space-time can be exhaustively analyzed into sets of points," and other statements of the same kind, must have a definite empirical meaning in terms of the constructed elements. Accordingly, construction of points, or world-points, by means of the method of extensive abstraction is a question of semantics or meaning; there is no intention to provide instruction for the purpose of locating, or exhibiting, a particular point, or world-point, in the actual set-up of practice and experiment. Hence, granted that the method is technically correct,

---

[*] A. Einstein, in *Sidelights of Relativity,* 32.

ANDREW PAUL USHENKO

the observation that the procedure of a practicing physicist is something entirely different is no objection against the method as such.[34] Yet some critics have made this observation as if it were an objection. For example, E. Nagel writes as follows:

[34] As far as I know no one has attempted to show that the method of extensive abstraction involves some logical or technical error. The usual criticism is that a geometrical "element," constructed by means of the method, is not observable because it contains an infinite number of regions. This criticism is invalid. For the infinite number (of regions) is allowed not because it is observable but because it is a legitimate concept of formal mathematics. Accordingly, the method does not require an actual exhibition of *all* regions that constitute a point; the requirement is that *any* constituent region should be, in principle, observable. In fact a weaker condition is sufficient in order to provide the construction of a point with an empirical basis. This is to say that identification of a particular region or member of a co-punctual group, i.e., within a group that forms a point by definition, is not required. All that we really need is an illustration of the *kind* of thing that the definition is about. For example, Whitehead gives the following illustration of an abstractive set. "Such a set . . . has the properties of the Chinese toy which is a nest of boxes, one within the other, with the difference that the toy has a smallest box, while the abstractive class has neither a smallest event nor does it converge to a limiting event which is not a member of the set" (*The Concept of Nature*, 79f.). The difference between the illustration and the abstractive set cannot, and need not, be illustrated because of being fully accounted for in terms of pure logic and mathematics. These considerations, I think, take care of E. Nagel's objection which runs as follows: "Assuming that events have been isolated, co-punctual groups of events must next be found. However, since a co-punctual group may have an indefinite number of event-numbers, the assertion that a given group is co-punctual will in general be a *hypothesis*. The situation does not become easier when the physicist next tries to identify those co-punctual groups which are points: the assertion that a class of events is a point will be a conjecture for which only the most incomplete sort of evidence can be available." (*LLP*, v. 5, 344.) Nagel overlooks the fact that if a co-punctual group could be perceptually given *in toto*, recognition, or identification of a point would follow by definition. On the other hand, the fact that a total co-punctual group cannot be perceptually given is immaterial in a concern with meaning, i.e., in so far as the proposed definition of a point is meaningful. I believe now that my own objection against Whitehead's definition of a point, the observation that we cannot exhibit even a part of the required abstractive set, because this presupposes an antecedent acquaintance with points and other exact geometrical figures such as sets of concentric circles (cf. *Power and Events*, Princeton University Press, 1926, 251f.), is a mistake, or, at any rate, needs qualification. For even if precision of enclosure cannot be exemplified except through some such configuration as a set of concentric circles, the definition to be understood and empirically justified, may need illustration but does not require exemplification. In other words, Whitehead's definition is a conceptual or logical construction. Furthermore, if we insist upon dealing with events of any odd shape, we can follow Russell's alternative definition without giving up the use of the method of extensive abstraction altogether.

Russell's definition exhibits no concern whatever for the way in which physicists *actually use* expressions like "point." In the first place, it is certainly not evident that physicists do in fact apply the term to structures of events. On the contrary, there is some evidence to show that they employ it in a somewhat different fashion, using it in connection with bodies identifiable in gross experience and whose magnitudes vary from case to case according to the needs of specific problems. To be sure, the application of the term is frequently sloppy and vague, and its rules cannot in general be made precise. But the vagueness and sloppiness are facts which a philosophy of science must face squarely, and they cannot be circumvented by an ingenious but essentially irrelevant proposal as to how the term *might* be used.[35]

How widely Nagel's shot misses the target becomes evident when we ascertain that Russell's philosophy of science faces squarely the facts with which Nagel is concerned. Thus, we read:

Sometimes it would seem as if the whole earth counted as a point: certainly one physical laboratory does so in the practice of writers on relativity. . . . The fact that such a view is appropriate in discussions of relativity makes it unnecessary to be precise as to what is meant by saying that two events occupy the same point, or that two world-lines intersect.[36]

But Nagel's admission that "the application of the term is frequently sloppy and vague" does not mean that there is no need for a precise meaning of the term "point." And Nagel overlooks the theoretical need for a precise meaning when the physicist is concerned with the correlation of statements which belong to different branches of physics. To illustrate: It is no longer unnecessary to be precise when a relativist contends that his own statement that "Two world-lines intersect at a world-point" and the quantum principle that "A simultaneous specification of a world-point of a particle and of its momentum and energy is impossible" are not entirely disconnected propositions.[37] The relativist may then consider that in his own practice

---

[35] E. Nagel in *LLP*, v. 5, 344f.

[36] B. Russell, *The Analysis of Matter*, 57.

[37] I cannot resist the temptation, which this illustration offers to a philosopher, of a footnote query to the professional physicist: Is the quantum principle, quoted in the illustration, in conflict with the equation of the general theory of relativity, according to which the "curvature" tensor is *equated* to the "matter" tensor?

he is dealing with an approximation, corresponding to the nature of the particular problem, to the precise meaning which is empirically justified by the method of extensive abstraction. In fact, Nagel's characterization of the practice as "sloppy and vague" would be meaningless, if he were altogether unaware of successive approximations to precision. And if the application of the term "point" were arbitrary and uncontrolled by any consideration of the precise meaning, even to the extent to which the measure of precision in the act of application may turn out to depend upon the specific nature of the problem, the successful outcome in practice, as far as correlation and prediction of observations is concerned, would be an utter mystery. Einstein himself is ready to accept the success with which scientific terms are applied to experience as a mystery that "we shall never understand."[38] But to a philosopher an epitemological mystery spells failure in analysis. Thus, whereas Einstein, on p. 23 of *The World as I See It,* says, concerning the relation between theoretical principles and phenomena: "This is what Leibniz describes so happily as a 'pre-established harmony,' " to Russell the notion of a pre-established harmony appears "fantastic."[39] And, in the case of the relation between the theoretical term "point" and observable phenomena, the philosopher has actually dispelled the mystery with the aid of the method of extensive abstraction.

The issue between Einstein and the philosophy of events has not been settled yet, however. For we must not overlook the fact that world-points are elements within the continuum of space-time; and if the latter is a conceptual scheme or order that cannot be derived from the world of experience, and therefore, in Einstein's own words, "in guiding us in the creation of such an order of sense experiences, success in the result is alone the determining factor,"[40] abstraction of an isolated world-point from a set of ordinary events is of no consequence. This consideration raises the problem of the ontological status of space-time.

[38] "Physics and Reality," *Franklin Institute Journal* (1936), 351.
[39] B. Russell, *Physics and Experience,* 6.
[40] "Physics and Reality" 351.

5. THE PROBLEM OF SPACE-TIME

"Space-time, as it appears in mathematical physics, is obviously an artifact, i.e., a structure in which materials found in the world are compounded in such a manner as to be convenient for the mathematician."[41] On the face of it Russell's statement leads beyond Einstein's semi-Kantian conceptualism toward positivism or conventionalism. For, in order to appreciate Einstein's comparatively conservative stand, we must not be misled by such phrases as "the purely fictitious character of the fundamentals of scientific theory,"[42] which serve to emphasize the part played by the scientist's creative intelligence in the advance of knowledge, but take them in conjunction with Einstein's explanation that the scientist's "liberty of choice . . . is not in any way similar to the liberty of a writer of fiction . . . , but to that of a man engaged in solving a well designed word puzzle . . . ; there is only one word which really solves the puzzle in all its forms."[43] The concept of space-time affords an excellent illustration of Einstein's epistemological position. The scientist's freedom of choice is fully exercised in the construction of a curved four-dimensional continuum, since no experience could dictate to him the idea. Yet his invention also happens to be an intuition or discovery of an objective physical reality. For spatio-temporal invariance provides the word that solves the puzzle of alternative differentiation between space and time within frames of reference which are set in relative motion. The illustration brings out invariance as the ultimate criterion of physical reality. In accordance with this criterion variable or alternative perspectives of differentiated space and time are relegated to the status of shadowy being: hence Einstein's endorsement of Minkowski's dictum that "henceforth space in itself and time in itself dissolve into shadows and only a kind of union of the two retains an individuality." Of course, to such an empiricist as Russell this sort of about face, which starts with building physics on the evidence of observations within the terrestrial frame of differentiated space and time

[41] B. Russell, *The Analysis of Matter*, 376.
[42] A. Einstein, in *The World as I See It*, 34.
[43] "Physics and Reality," 353.

only to end with casting metaphysical doubts upon the reality of the latter, is unacceptable. And to counteract the physicist's influence Russell has pointed out that space-time, as it appears in mathematical physics, is an artifact. But Russell's observation does not mean that he rejects the existence of space-time altogether. On the contrary, his statement suggests a differentiation between the artificial mathematical, and possibly metrical, structure of space-time in relativity physics, on the one hand, and space-time as the physical medium in which ordinary events are embedded and without which there could be no continuous, and therefore unobservable, causal chains from external sources to actual percepts, on the other. As a medium of events and percepts space-time is no less real than these events and percepts themselves, although their modes of reality may be different. In its capacity of a medium space-time provides distinct happenings in the world with distinct, and mutually external, regions; and this fact of externality, which is represented in experience by the opposition between the "now" or "here" and whatever takes place "elsewhere," is, however unique its mode of being may be, more than a mental act of correlating observations. This conception of space-time Russell makes explicit, and accepts as his own, in another statement: "I think it may also be assumed that one event may extend over a finite extent of space-time, but on this point the theory is silent, so far as I know."[44] As these words show, the identification of space-time with a medium of extended events appears to Russell so natural that he is prepared to take it as part of the theory of relativity although he leaves the question open. Actually, of course, there is no such question: if it is permissible to identify the theory of relativity with Einstein's position, and if my account of Einstein is substantially correct, the theory is not silent but rejects Russell's assumption. The real question is: What can be said for and against the conception of space-time as a medium?

A relativist may object to Russell's differentiation between the ontological basis of a space-time medium and the mathematical superstructure, an artifact, as follows. Either the hypothetical medium of events has a definite intrinsic structure or

---

[44] B. Russell, *The Analysis of Matter*, 57.

not. On Russell's realist premises, the second alternative, of an indeterminate space-time, would seem to be excluded. But if space-time has structure, then mathematical, and metrical, specifications in relativity physics, unless they are no more than a fairy tale, must have a certain measure of conformity to that structure. And therefore, to the extent to which there is conformity, space-time of mathematical physics is not an artifact. The argument is telling and leaves only two ways of escape.

There is Einstein's way which is closed to Russell, because of the rejection of the medium of extended events as an independent physical reality, independent, that is, of the scientist's mathematical construction. Einstein can make allowance for the conventional, or fictitious, features of mathematical space-time without raising the question of conformity to a would-be ontological counterpart. However, he has to pay a high price for his advantage. There remains the mystery—which Einstein himself is forced to recognize as such—of successful prediction. And, except for this mystery, the imposition of the conceptual order of space-time upon facts can only mean that, if physical occurrences were left to themselves, free from theoretical intervention by the scientist, they would be mutually disconnected.[45]

The second alternative, which might be acceptable to Russell, if it were not for his prejudice against the idea of potentiality, takes the medium of events, in opposition to the determinate or specific structure of mathematical space-time, to be plastic or determinable rather than fixed and fully specified. This alternative denies that the medium of space-time is a ready made, antecedently established actuality of which mathematical space-time is a conceptual copy or replica. The contention is that the

[45] Let me enlarge, in this connection, upon an earlier remark about Einstein's epistemology. If we differentiate between *a priori* meaning and truth, we may say that Einstein, following Kant, accepts the *a priori* meaning of scientific concepts and theories whereas, in agreement with the positivists, he contends that truth in science is established *a posteriori* by the success of prediction. Thus Einstein is not a positivist: the latter questions the very meaning of an empirical statement that, admittedly, cannot be derived from experience by abstraction, induction, or some other logical means. Furthermore, it would seem that Einstein relies, in addition to the pragmatic criterion of successful prediction, on the *a priori* intuition that the acceptable theory is the closest available approximation to the limit of an absolute truth.

medium exists in a state of disposition, or potentiality, to be variously specified in conception or description; and mathematical space-time of relativity is one such specification. This contention enables us to treat the peculiarities of mathematical specification, to the extent to which they go beyond the specifiable, as a matter of convention and, at the same time, to recognize a measure of conformity between theory and physical reality, in case the disposition to be theoretically specified has not been positively distorted by the subsequent theory. On the other hand, lack of specificity or actuality does not prevent the medium of events from connecting them with one another independently of, and antecedently to, the supervening correlation, by means of a mathematical construct, in the mind of a mathematician. Let me illustrate the point, first, with a three-dimensional analogue to a situation in space-time. Suppose a cone to be at rest in the frame of reference containing two observers. One of them perceives the cone from aside, in the shape of a triangle; the other from below, in the shape of a circle. The total, three-dimensional shape of the cone is not represented by either of the two actual percepts. Moreover, the total shape cannot be actual, or subject to perception, because any actual percept would exclude, or be incompatible with, the shape of a circle or a triangle. We seem to have no other choice but to admit that the cone, as contrasted with its alternative actual aspects such as a circle or a triangle, exists in the state of disposition or potentiality. This is to say that the cone is the disposition, or power, to show an actual aspect of a triangle within one perspective and some alternative aspect, for example, a circle, within another. The alternative aspects exclude each other as actual observations—no observer can have two of them at the same time—but as observable, i.e., in the capacity to appear in different perspectives, they are connected and co-exist. Of course, we also have the mathematical formula for the cone to correlate its various perspectival aspects in our minds. But the formula cannot literally *do* anything to either the cone itself or to its aspects, and the point of mental correlation is conformity to antecedent correlation in fact, even though the latter means no more than disposition or power to be actualized in alternative aspects.

We now turn to the analogue in space-time. Alternative frames of reference, moving in relation to one another, provide alternative actual aspects upon the same region of space-time. These alternative aspects are co-exclusive, because each represents a different way of separating space from time. Again there are mathematical formulas, the transformation equations of relativity, that enable us to correlate the diverse systems of space and time. But again we may assume the ontological counterpart of the mathematical correlation to be antecedent to the latter. The question is: What are the minimum requirements which the ontological counterpart must satisfy? One thing is clear. Whatever else the disposition to yield a variety of systems of space and time may be, it is, at least, just this, a disposition or power. And there is another consideration. To be susceptible to alternative separations between space and time the disposition in question must provide neutral, or impartial, grounds for all of them—as the term medium appropriately connotes—and that can only mean that the medium of potentiality exists as a fusion of space with time. The logic that leads to the invariant space-time as a medium for a variable differentiation between space and time, let us note, does not depend, except for the conception of alternative systems of space and time, on the theory of relativity. At any rate the logic does not commit us to the mathematical peculiarity of space-time in physics. Accordingly, we are in a position to accept what I take to be Russell's distinction between the ontological basis and the conventional superstructure, the artifact, of space-time.

The contention that space-time is a field of potentiality or power may be altogether unacceptable to Russell.[46] Nor is the

---

[46] Yet one line of his argument leads Russell to what he calls "ideal" elements of reality that would not seem to be essentially different from elements of potentiality. I have in mind his theory of unobserved aspects within a causal chain that terminates in a percept of a material thing. To describe an unobserved aspect Russell uses the term "ideal" with the proviso, which is directed against phenomenalism, that "the only thing rejected is the view that 'ideal' elements are unreal." (The Analysis of Matter, 215) The employment of the term "ideal" to connote reality would be awkward if Russell were not concerned with the kind of reality that, like potentiality or power, is to be contrasted with actual observation. On the other hand, in his later book, An Inquiry into Meaning and Truth, Russell has proposed a theory of particulars which would do away with any substantial medium, whether actual or potential.

present contention derived from Whitehead. Whitehead characterizes the "extensive continuum" of physical space-time as
"the most general scheme of real potentiality."[47] Yet this characterization does not enable me to claim agreement with Whitehead because he does not make his meaning, even within the
context of further elaboration, sufficiently clear. For, according to Whitehead, clarity requires that "every entity should
be a specific instance of one category of existence";[48] but he
fails to classify either the extensive continuum or potentiality
under any of his eight categories of existence. The extensive
continuum, Whitehead's own term, "scheme," and E. McGilvary's interpretation[49] notwithstanding, cannot be meant to be
an eternal object, a Platonic form, since, as Whitehead has
pointed out,[50] eternal objects are no more than pure or general
potentialities whereas space-time is said to be "the first determination of order—that is, of real potentiality—arising out of
the general character of the world." If we try the remaining
categories of existence one by one, we may conclude that only
the category "proposition," in Whitehead's peculiar sense of
"matter of fact in potential determination," appears to be ad-
justable to fit in with his description of the extensive continuum.
And if the conclusion is correct, Whitehead's extensive continuum is an aspect—to be derived by abstraction either conceptually or through perception of the "presented locus"—of
actuality. An aspect of actuality is, of course, something different from a medium of potentiality. On the other hand, his re-
fusal to follow Einstein beyond the special theory of relativity
indicates that Whitehead would be in favor of our distinction
between space-time and the mathematical specification of the
latter.

The proposed distinction enables us to justify directly, on the
grounds of observability, the conception of the medium of
events, and, indirectly, the mathematical space-time of relativity. We recognize that space-time as a whole, mathematical or

---

[47] A. N. Whitehead, *Process and Reality*, 93.
[48] *Ibid.*, 27.
[49] *LLP*, v. 3, 239.
[50] *Ibid.*, 90f.

otherwise, is beyond experience. And we know that the "curved" continuum of general relativity cannot be perceived even in parts. I may also admit that the percipient's field of experience coincides with a particular frame of reference in which space and time are set apart. Yet a glimpse into the world of dynamics, a four-dimensional fragment, is not irregular or uncommon in perception. For even within a frame of separation between space and time their union is in a measure restored in a percept of some dynamic shape the presentation of which cannot be given by an arrested figure, like a snapshot, because it requires the completion of a process or movement. The shape of a waving flag, for example, is perceivable, but only through the period of an enduring experience. And similarly with the shape of a dance. Occasionally we may even perceive the four-dimensional intersection of two distinct frames of reference, when we happen to participate in both. Whitehead gives an illustration of this possibility:

> When the bulk of the events perceived are cogredient in a duration other than that of the percipient event, the percipience may include a double consciousness of cogredience, namely the consciousness of the whole within which the observer in the train is 'here,' and the consciousness of the whole within which the trees and bridges and telegraph posts are definitely 'there.'[51]

Such fragments of four-dimensional experience, let me repeat, form direct evidence in favor of a determinable or specifiable medium of space-time. But whereas we can correlate two things, both of which lack specificity, we may wonder whether sound logic would ever establish a correlation between the indefinite and fragmentary dynamic manifestations, on the one hand, and the precise specification of space-time, on the other. Under the circumstances, neither Einstein's procedure of "representation" nor Whitehead's method of extensive abstraction appear to be serviceable. The question is whether there exists a different method of correlation.

The required principle of correlation is to bridge the gap between factual indeterminacy and theoretical precision. Hence

[51] A. N. Whitehead, *The Concept of Nature*, 111.

we can expect a form of idealization; only not the usual practice of idealization which has been discredited by entanglement in arbitrariness, dogmatism, and wishful thinking. With the need for drastic restriction in mind, let us try the following tentative statement of the principle of legitimate idealization. A theoretical conception is empirically justified if, and only if, determinable experience, a sense datum or percept, is not sufficiently specific or explicit to enable the observer positively to establish its failure as an exemplification. To illustrate the function of the principle let us consider Euclid's conception of an extensionless point. In answer to Whitehead's criticism of the conception, to the effect that there is nothing in nature that would not show under close inspection some amount of extension, we can point out that perception is part of nature and that a percept of a dot may not be determinate enough to be positively distinguishable from what would be an extensionless point. If we look from some distance at a corner of this page, we are unable to discern within the visual datum a length or width or depth: the corner of the page, as we see it, does not positively fail to exemplify Euclid's ideal. Or, to take another illustration, observe a road-map in relation to the percept of the countryside. As we drive along the highway, we understand the map to be an idealization because we do not find representation of minor curves on the road or other perceptible detail. But we accept the idealization as legitimate because we know that under different perceptual conditions, for example, while looking down from an airplane, the percept of the road would no longer be sufficiently definite and detailed to be contrasted with the outline on the map. Similarly, with the mathematical conception of space-time. If no other method except "representation" or "extensive abstraction" were available, such peculiarities of the mathematical conception as "curvature" would be entirely artificial; the principle of legitimate idealization, however, enables us to reconsider the matter. Space-time "curvature" is an empirically justifiable notion so long as the scale of human perception, together with the inevitable inexactitude of measurement, leave within the field of experience a margin of indeterminacy that does not let us positively decide in favor either of flatness or of small curvature. Here as elsewhere, the principle of legitimate idealization can yield only an ambiguous result. The same empirical evidence justifies both the conception of "curvature" and of flatness. The justification is a question of meaning and not of truth. If the scientist prefers a curved space-time, his reasons are beyond the scope of a philosopher. A philosopher is only concerned with the ontological status of space-time. And if his philosophy prompts him to accept the independent physical existence of space-time (independent of the mind, that is), he need not go beyond the idea of specifiable medium of events, in a state of potentiality or power, into considerations of actual specification.[52]

ANDREW PAUL USHENKO

DEPARTMENT OF PHILOSOPHY
PRINCETON UNIVERSITY

[52] On the other hand, the physicist is not concerned with the distinction between power and actuality, and the contention that space-time is a medium of potentiality is likely to leave him cold. Yet, let us remind him, except for experiments and pointer-readings, which are actual events, physics, as the terminology of physical science clearly demonstrates, is entirely preoccupied with potentialities. For an analysis of the physicist's terminology shows, in addition to such terms as potential energy, an abundance of dispositional adjectives, such as elastic, combustible, compressible, and the like, and of differential equations which, as Russell has observed, must be interpreted in terms of tendencies. And when a physical law is translated from the language of symbols into the language of words, contrary-to-fact conditionals, which are meant to convey that there is something independent of actuality, provide the appropriate linguistic form of translation.

25

Virgil G. Hinshaw, Jr.

EINSTEIN'S SOCIAL PHILOSOPHY

EINSTEIN'S SOCIAL PHILOSOPHY

THE PRESENT sketch is intended as a brief investigation of certain aspects of Albert Einstein's social philosophy. One of the difficulties of such a study is that it is hard to discover, in Einstein's speeches and writings, any systematic position in social ethics. Thus, in most cases, I prefer to speak of his convictions, rather than position, in social philosophy.

SCIENCE AND VALUES

"Concern for man himself and his fate must always form the chief interest of all technical endeavors. . . . Never forget this in the midst of your diagrams and equations."—*Albert Einstein*

Ever since finding this quotation, about ten years ago, in Robert Lynd's *Knowledge for What?*,[1] I have felt that it epitomized Einstein's convictions concerning the place of values in a world of science. I am here using "value" in that familiar sense wherein a value may be defined as "any object of any interest."[2] In this sense I shall distinguish between values as *interests*, in what has (sometimes) been called axiology, and ethical imperatives, in what has sometimes been called deontology.[3] In what follows, I shall be keeping in mind a certain preconception:

Einstein seems to be thinking of values more nearly as interests than as ontologically grounded norms. His ethic is, it seems to me, closer to an empirical, than to an ontological ethic. His

[1] Robert S. Lynd, *Knowledge for What?*, (Princeton, 1939), 114. In most cases, my documentation is supplemented by a conversation I was privileged to have with Professor Einstein at Princeton in May, 1949.

[2] In particular, R. B. Perry's interest theory of value as developed in his *General Theory of Value*, (New York, 1926).

[3] Compare W. Frankena, "Ethics" article (D. Runes (ed.)) *Dictionary of Philosophy*, (New York, 1942), 98-100.

cosmos is more nearly "one-layered," like the monist's, than "two-layered," like the Platonist's.

In the article from which the above quotation was taken, Einstein suggests that we must have this concern for man in order that "the creations of our mind shall be a blessing and not a curse to mankind." Such a statement could be given several interpretations; however, Einstein's meaning is this. For us human beings, our mutual behavior and our conscious striving for our goals is much more important than any factual knowledge. Moreover, Einstein is actually evincing a broader conviction, somewhat like St. Paul's, that charity is of greater value than faith and hope, than the gift of prophecy and the possession of all knowledge. Compare also his statement, in another place, that "only a life lived for others is the life worthwhile."[4]

In recent years, of course, the issues regarding science and values have been sharpened by the atomic bomb, the possibility of atomic energy, and the problem of their control. It is at such a time as this that Einstein, important contributor to the development of the atomic bomb and atomic energy, has reasserted his conviction with increased vigor.

On the one hand, he is a man who has maintained a type of balance, perhaps only possible for one with his scientific background and ethical maturity. "I do not believe," says Einstein, "that civilization will be wiped out in a war fought with the atomic bomb. Perhaps two-thirds of the people of the earth might be killed; but enough men, capable of thinking, and enough books would be left to start again, and civilization could be restored."[5] Likewise, he has tried to outline wisely the rôle of both the scientist and the man of letters in these times of crisis. "The intellectual workers," he says, ". . . cannot successfully intervene directly in the political struggle. They can achieve, however, the spreading of clear ideas about the situation and the possibility of successful action. They can contribute through enlightenment to prevent able statesmen from being hampered in their work by antiquated opinions and prejudices."[6]

[4] *New York Times* (hereafter NYT), 20 June 1932, p. 17, col. 3.
[5] *Ibid.*, 24 February 1946, sect. 6, p. 42, col. 3.
[6] *Ibid.*, 18 November 1946, p. 25, col. 1.

On the other hand, Einstein has shown considerable leadership in showing the way, as he sees it, to the resolution of the "major moral problem of our age." His position concerning the control of atomic energy is too well known to require detailed documentation. Nevertheless, as Chairman of the Emergency Committee of Atomic Scientists, Einstein has said many things worth repeating. For example, his telegram soliciting funds for the Committee: "Our world faces a crisis as yet unperceived by those possessing power to make great decisions for good or evil. The unleashed power of the atom has changed everything save our modes of thinking and we thus drift toward unparalleled catastrophe." In short, "a new type of thinking is essential if mankind is to survive and move toward higher levels."[7]

Mention must here be made, as it will again presently, of Einstein's insistence upon social action on the part of the intellectual of our times. Take his interview entitled "The Real Problem is in the Hearts of Men," which we shall have occasion to cite shortly. Again, remember the fact that Einstein was one of the first members of the Commission for Intellectual Co-operation with the League of Nations. Still again, compare his being asked about the advisability of establishing a "Court of Wisdom,"[8] as was originally suggested at the Harvard Tercentenary Conference. Such a Court, similar to the medieval University of Paris, would be able, it was thought, to bring forth powerful moral judgments. If established, Einstein answered, such a body could represent a "conscience of mankind;" and it could, in the course of time, exert a "highly beneficial and . . . even a standard-setting influence on the development of the social and economic affairs of the world." Affirming that such a Court would necessarily call for concentrated efforts of the best minds, Einstein actually outlines how members of the Court ought to be elected and how vacancies ought to be filled. In short, in this letter of 1939 (as elsewhere, later), Einstein indicates that he is devoting much thought to the question concerning the means of organizing the intellectual and spiritual

[7] *Ibid.*, 25 May 1946, p. 13, col. 5.
[8] The quotations concerning the "Court" are found in NYT, 14 March 1939, p. 1, col. 3.

forces of the world into a unified moral force, which would serve as "a sort of conscience of mankind."

Moreover, the conviction concerning the rôle of the intellectual in social action is, once again, embodied explicitly in his urging the intellectual workers, of the United States and other free countries, to organize and fight for the establishment of a supra-national political force as protection against aggression. Specifically, the aim of such a union of intellectual workers would be to supply, for the majority of people, the clear thinking necessary if international co-operation is to become a fact. "In the organization and promotion of enlightenment on this subject, I see the most important service . . . intellectual workers can perform in this historical moment."[9]

To Einstein's concern with social action I shall revert throughout the remainder of this sketch.

Finally, a word about the "neutrality" of the scientist in the process of valuation. This is the hackneyed, though substantial, problem: How can the scientist (who, insofar as possible, maintains complete objectivity in the laboratory) even be interested in, let alone concerned with, value-judgments—which are, by their very nature, either largely subjective if concerned with *interests* or, if concerned with *ethical norms* or *imperatives*, investigable only by philosophic methods? Though he fails to face squarely in his writings some of the issues involved, Einstein surely envisages the major problem. Moreover, in a letter of February 6, 1939, Einstein, in effect, resolves the problem by distinguishing (essentially) two rôles of the intellectual worker: his rôle as scientist or man of letters, *and* his rôle as citizen.

In this letter (a reply to Lincoln's Birthday Committee), he urged united collective action by scientists in their rôles *as citizens* to protect the freedom of teaching and publication. This, in a word, is his answer to the problem.

But his thinking (in this particular letter, along the lines of academic freedom) does not stop there. He agreed that scientists must stand guard against *any* infringement of the freedom of scientific research and teaching. Moreover, Einstein called on the government to protect teachers against influences brought on by economic pressure.

THE STATE AND THE INDIVIDUAL

"Never do anything against conscience, even if the state demands it."
—*Albert Einstein*

"But Peter and the apostles answered and said, we must obey God rather than men."—*The Acts*, V, 29

In broad strokes, Einstein's convictions concerning the ethical duty of the individual in relation to the state are these. A moral man cannot identify himself with the state. If the state decides upon a certain course of moral action, the individual must always evaluate this decision for himself. Einstein suggests as a maxim: "Never do anything against conscience, even if the state demands it."[10] And the spirit of this maxim is reflected in the answer of Peter and the apostles, "we must obey God rather than men."

In explaining this maxim, Einstein suggests that we consider the recent Nürnberg Trials. He believes the Trials indicate that we do, as a matter of fact, think in terms of the guilt of nations. And, if the term "guilt" is to have genuine meaning here, moral judgment beyond nationalism is implied. In short, Einstein insists that these trials were supra-national. The fact of the trials, therefore, Einstein believes, gives evidence that we all do (more or less) accept the maxim.

Succinctly, Einstein suggests that each man should distinguish law of duty from law of the state. A man's duty often clashes with the will of the state. When this occurs, the moral man will side with the deliverances of his own conscience. Here, as elsewhere, the final arbiter of all ethical decisions is conscience. (To some of these points we must again return shortly.)

But surely a misgiving concerning his interpretation of the Trials arises at this point. For my part, I would want to make the following qualification. I would qualify Einstein's belief that we do think in terms of the guilt of nations, with the clause, "If the Trials have any genuine moral and ethical

[10] From notes of private conversation.

significance whatsoever." It is certainly not obvious that the Trials are necessarily significant either for valuation or for obligation—either for axiology or for deontology. The sense in which the Trials may have been farcical has been too often noted to require repetition or comment. And, of course, if they were a mockery of justice, the Trials are more important for the sociology of morals than for social philosophy proper.

Moreover, if the thesis of Reinhold Niebuhr's *Moral Man and Immoral Society* is accurate at all, a further qualification of Einstein's belief is in order. In short, if a "sharp distinction must be drawn between the moral and social behavior of individuals and of social groups . . . ," then "this distinction justifies and necessitates political policies which a purely individualistic ethic must always find embarrassing."[11] The concept of the guilt of nations surely requires careful scrutiny in the light of Niebuhr's remarks.

PACIFISM, THE BOMB, AND THE OUTLAWRY OF WAR

That Albert Einstein has been pacifist during most of his lifetime, is a well known fact which requires little more than acknowledgment in this sketch. The truth of the matter is that Einstein has always been anti-militaristic. As to pacifism, his conviction is this: the only exception to adherence, in our times, to pacifism is the case of militant fascism, specifically, German Nazism. With Gandhi,[12] he would recommend passive resistance. But, unlike Gandhi, he believes in passive resistance only up to a certain point. He believes that one should resort to violence whenever militant fascism arises; that is, whenever militant fascism, as did Nazism, seeks to wipe out humanity's best. If militant fascism tries to destroy the intellectual class of any given society, then violence is not only fully justified, but actually necessary. The only course of action open to moral man in such times is his resorting to violence. No moral man could do otherwise, while relying wholly upon the dictates of his conscience.

[11] Reinhold Niebuhr, *Moral Man and Immoral Society*, (New York, 1932), xi.
[12] He did contribute (p. 79-80) on "Gandhi's Statesmanship" to a memorial volume: *Mahatma Gandhi*—Essays and reflections on his life and work presented to him on his seventieth birthday, edited by S. Radhakrishnan, (London, 1944).

Here one can see close resemblance of position to the Quakers' convictions. Reliance upon the "inner light" both first and last is germane to both positions. Regarding war and peace, the deliverances of conscience are for Einstein and the Quaker quite similar. As a matter of fact, Einstein feels that, in this respect, the Quakers are the only true Christians.

In the article "The Real Problem is in the Hearts of Men,"[13] Einstein clearly states his position regarding the atomic bomb and its immediate implications for our social conduct. In the light of new knowledge, that is, of atomic science, a world authority and an eventual world state are not only desirable but necessary for survival. "Today we must abandon competition and secure co-operation. . . ." "Past thinking and methods did not prevent world wars (but) future thinking *must* prevent wars." America's present superiority in the way of armaments gives her the responsibility of leading mankind's effort to surmount this crisis.

There is no foreseeable (military or scientific) defense against the bomb. "Our defense," says Einstein, "is not in armaments, nor in science, nor in going underground. Our defense is in law and order." Henceforth foreign policy must be judged by this consideration: Does it lead to law and order or to anarchy and death? Einstein does not believe that we can prepare for war and, at the same time, for world community. Likewise, he does not believe the "bomb secret" should be turned loose but asks, "Are we ardently seeking a world in which there will be no need for bombs or secrets, a world in which science and men will be free?" The whole problem, as Bernard Baruch has said, is not one of physics, but of ethics. There has been, it seems to Einstein, too much emphasis on legalisms and procedure. "It is easier," he says, "to denature plutonium than it is to denature the evil spirit of man."

Once again, Einstein insists on the need for supra-nationalism and the conception of world government which it implies; and, from his many statements, one infers that he has seriously considered the possibility of a world government. His optimism,

[13] NYT, 23 June 1946, sect. 6, p. 7, col. 42-43. All quotations up to footnote 14 are taken from this particular article.

therefore, should be judged accordingly. In working toward supra-nationalism as against nationalism, he avers, it is obvious that national spirit will survive longer in armies than anywhere else. Further, Einstein discusses problems involved in world organization. In mentioning Fremont Rider's book,[14] wherein the representation dilemma of the United Nations might be solved by granting it on the basis of education and literacy, Einstein agrees that backward nations, therefore, ought to be told: " 'to get more votes you must *earn* them.' "

Einstein flatly challenges the wisdom of having used the bomb over Japan. The old type of thinking, he asserts, can, of course, raise thousands of objections about the lack of "realism" in this simplicity of belief—in particular, concerning the proposal that the bomb should not have been used, but should have been demonstrated in some isolated area, where (say) the Japanese could have observed its effects. But the thinking evoked in such objections ignores psychological realities. All men fear atomic war. "Between the realities of man's true desires and the realities of man's danger, what are the obsolete 'realities' of protocol and military protection?" Mere reading about the bomb, claims Einstein, promotes knowledge in mind, but "only talk between men promotes feeling in the heart."

The bomb is a real threat, not only to politicians and generals, but to all mankind. Once more, Einstein says too much faith is placed in legalisms, treaties and mechanisms. In the final analysis, the decisions of the United Nations rest on those made in village squares. It is to village squares that facts of atomic energy must be carried. Public understanding of the dilemma facing mankind today is of the essence. Only then will decisions be the "embodiment of a message to humanity from a nation of human beings." The real problem is in the minds and hearts of men. Such is Albert Einstein's conviction.

Finally, I turn, for a moment, to Einstein's convictions as regards the relations between the USA and the USSR. There has been frequent criticism of the man on this score; but, it seems to me, it is not only more charitable to him, but far wiser

---

[14] *The Great Dilemma of World Organizations.*

for us, to know exactly what his position is before criticism comes.

First, Einstein believes that the Russia of today differs considerably from Nazi Germany, particularly as to basic aims and goals. Whereas Nazi Germany sought to "liquidate" the intellectual and his product, in Russia Einstein sees no similar trend. It is true, however, that the recent surge of nationalism in genetics—of "Russian genetics," if you like—perturbs him. But, it seems to me, he fails sufficiently to integrate this worry with other convictions like freedom for the intellectual worker, toleration of the truth no matter what its consequences, and reliance upon the dictates of conscience.

As far as nationalism is concerned, Einstein deplores it in any form. However, he fears the growth of nationalism in the United States more than in the Soviet Union; and this, because he observes among us a kind of mob hysteria, unbecoming to otherwise so great a nation.

In the same manner, Einstein faces the charge of "fellow traveling with Communist Front organizations." Of course, Einstein's insistence upon freedom of conscience, in and of itself necessarily differentiates his position from that of the Communist. In any case, he feels more nearly like Harold C. Urey, Nobel savant, than like the kindly, yet naïve, old man so many take Einstein to be in this matter. Compare Urey's recent statement: "I can't help it if the Communists fellow travel with me on the Spanish line. I do not fellow travel with them."[15] At times, nevertheless, Einstein seems to justify his membership in so many so-called "Communist Front" organizations simply as a reaction to the hysteria among people in this country. Still, one must not forget that Einstein is fully in sympathy with many minority groups and unpopular causes. Compare, for example, his espousal of liberal doctrines by approval of their liberal authors. Such men as Roosevelt, Willkie and Wallace, he thinks,[16] are in a category of men above the petty bickering of the day and without any selfish interest. One must agree, he

[15] *Chicago Daily Tribune*, 20 May 1949, p. 1, col. 6.
[16] NYT, 30 March 1948, p. 25, col. 4.

continues, with the fundamental premises of Henry Wallace's *Toward World Peace*, if one reads without prejudice. "This book is as clear, honest and unassuming as its author."

Finally, Einstein feels that his reaction to our hysteria is more than justified by the fact of our technological superiority over the Russians. Rightly or not, he believes that we are a nation superior to Russia in sheer productive and military strength. Hence, he argues, the guilt of the United States in the present world situation is greater than that of Russia. Being more powerful, we are actually in control of the situation; and, when crises arise, we are (therefore) more culpable than the Soviet Union.

Moreover, Einstein thinks that with our greater strength, we also have greater responsibility than Russia. The duty of a great nation is to accept its responsibility as a great nation. Likewise, the duty of the greatest nation is to acknowledge its place among nations; and Einstein is suggesting that, with our greatness of power, we should also accept our moral responsibility. If we are the most powerful nation, let us try to be the most moral by accepting, with humility and wisdom, this greatness so recently thrust upon us. And, of course, the only genuine resolution, for Einstein, of the USA-USSR problem is premised upon supra-national grounds. Before cavalierly criticizing Einstein as social thinker, one should remember his statement that there is "no other salvation for civilization and even for the human race than the creation of a world government with security on the basis of law."[17]

JUDAISM AND ZIONISM

It seems to me that Einstein's own religious conviction is not at all unrelated to his social philosophy. Moreover, his belief in Zionism is far from irrelevant to his ethical outlook. In reading certain passages from his essays and speeches, I cannot help but think that one does substantial injustice to Einstein's social philosophy if he neglects Einstein's religious beliefs. To a brief sketch of such of his beliefs I now turn.

[17] *Ibid.*, 15 September 1945, p. 11, col. 6.

"In the philosophical sense," says Einstein, "there is, in my opinion, no specifically Jewish point of view. Judaism seems to me to be concerned almost exclusively with the moral attitude in life and to life."[18] "Judaism is not a creed: the Jewish God is simply a negation of superstition, an imaginary result of its elimination. It is also an attempt to base the moral law on fear, a regrettable and discreditable attempt."[19]

"Judaism is thus," Einstein believes, "no transcendental religion; it is concerned with life as we live it and as we can, to a certain extent, grasp it, and nothing else." ". . . no faith but the sanctification of life in a supra-personal sense is demanded of the Jew."[20] The "sanctity of life" and the "sanctification of life" are, claims Einstein, the fundamental principles of Judaism. " 'When a Jew . . . says that he's going hunting to amuse himself, he lies.'—Walter Rathenau. The Jewish sense of the sanctity of life could not be more simply expressed."[21] In defense of Judaism, Einstein has this to say: ". . . it is time to remind the western world that it owes to the Jewish people (a) its religion and therewith its most valuable moral ideals, and (b) to a large extent, the resurrection of the world of Greek thought."[22]

In another place, Einstein holds that "the insistence on the solidarity of all human beings finds still stronger expression [in Judaism], and it is no mere chance that the demands of Socialism were for the most part first raised by Jews."[23]

Einstein's conception of God has been the subject of considerable conjecture. On more than one occasion, he has made himself quite clear as to his conviction in the matter. "I believe in Spinoza's God who reveals Himself in the orderly harmony of what exists, not in a God who concerns himself with

[18] Albert Einstein, *The World as I See It* (hereafter *World*), (New York, 1934), by Covici Friede, Inc., 143. Originally published as *Mein Weltbild*, 1933, by Querido Verlag, Amsterdam. Translated from the German by Alan Harris; Compare items 361-363 in Bibliography of this Volume.

[19] *Ibid.*, 144.

[20] *Ibid.*, 144-145.

[21] *Ibid.*, 146.

[22] *Ibid.*, xv.

[23] *Ibid.*, 146.

fates and actions of Human beings."[24] Of this cablegram, Rabbi Herbert S. Goldstein drew the following interpretation. He made use of it to substantiate his own belief that Einstein was neither atheist nor agnostic. Says Rabbi Goldstein: "Einstein points to a unity." If carried out to its logical conclusion, his theory "would bring to mankind a scientific formula for monotheism."[25]

In one place, Einstein has explicitly stated his conception of religion in general. There he speaks of three conceptions, each one differing in essential respects. First, he distinguishes the most primitive conception of religion, with its anthropocentric God. Second, ". . . on the higher levels of social life, the religion of morality predominates."[26] Third, there is what Einstein thinks of as "cosmic religious feeling."[27] It is this last conception of religion in which Einstein believes; or, rather, it is this sort of religion which he lives.

For a moment, I turn to Einstein's convictions about Zionism. "The object which the leaders of Zionism have before their eyes," he says, "is not a political but a social and cultural one."[28] "Palestine is not primarily a place of refuge for the Jews of Eastern Europe but the embodiment of the reawakening corporate spirit of the whole Jewish nation."[29] "The first step in that direction [i.e., toward 'mutual toleration and respect'] is that we Jews should once more become conscious of our existence as a nationality and regain the self-respect that is necessary to a healthy existence."[30]

"It is not enough," he continues, "for us to play a part as individuals in the cultural development of the human race, we must also tackle tasks which only nations as a whole can perform. Only so can the Jews regain social health." And, with these words, Einstein concludes: "It is from this point of view that I would have you look at the Zionist movement. Today

[24] NYT, 25 April 1929, p. 60, col. 4.
[25] Ibid.
[26] World, 263.
[27] Ibid., 264-265.
[28] Ibid., 152.
[29] Ibid., 154.
[30] Ibid., 156.

history has assigned to us the task of taking an active part in the economic and cultural reconstruction of our native land."[31]

Such are some of the ethical and religious convictions of Albert Einstein. In this sketch, I have made no attempt to indicate in what specific ways these beliefs comprise a consistent and adequate social ethic. I have, rather, only outlined the main trends of Einstein's thought regarding social issues and social action. Such a catalogue of his convictions serves to document the breadth of thought characteristic of the man. What is so commendable in Einstein is that, as intellectual worker in his rôle as citizen, he has seriously faced so many of the vital social questions of his day. The fact that, in so doing, he follows his own precepts demonstrates, as nothing else could, the sincerity of his concern with issues in social ethics.

VIRGIL G. HINSHAW, JR.

DEPARTMENT OF PHILOSOPHY
THE OHIO STATE UNIVERSITY

---

[31] *Ibid.*, 157. These remarks were made sometime during or before 1933, the publication date of *Mein Weltbild*. Compare footnote 18, above.

Albert Einstein

REPLY TO CRITICISMS

REMARKS CONCERNING THE ESSAYS BROUGHT TOGETHER IN THIS CO-OPERATIVE VOLUME*

BY WAY of introduction I must remark that it was not easy for me to do justice to the task of expressing myself concerning the essays contained in this volume. The reason lies in the fact that the essays refer to entirely too many subjects, which, at the present state of our knowledge, are only loosely connected with each other. I first attempted to discuss the essays individually. However, I abandoned this procedure because nothing even approximately homogeneous resulted, so that the reading of it could hardly have been either useful or enjoyable. I finally decided, therefore, to order these remarks, as far as possible, according to topical considerations.

Furthermore, after some vain efforts, I discovered that the mentality which underlies a few of the essays differs so radically from my own, that I am incapable of saying anything useful about them. This is not to be interpreted that I regard those essays—insofar as their content is at all meaningful to me—less highly than I do those which lie closer to my own ways of thinking, to which [latter] I dedicate the following remarks.

To begin with I refer to the essays of Wolfgang Pauli and Max Born. They describe the content of my work concerning quanta and statistics in general in their inner consistency and in their participation in the evolution of physics during the last half century. It is meritorious that they have done this: For only those who have successfully wrestled with the problematic situations of their own age can have a deep insight into those situations; unlike the later historian, who finds it difficult to make abstractions from those concepts and views which appear to his generation as established, or even as self-evident. Both authors

* Translated (from the German typescript) by Paul Arthur Schilpp.

665

deprecate the fact that I reject the basic idea of contemporary statistical quantum theory, insofar as I do not believe that this fundamental concept will provide a useful basis for the whole of physics. More of this later.

I now come to what is probably the most interesting subject which absolutely must be discussed in connection with the detailed arguments of my highly esteemed colleagues Born, Pauli, Heitler, Bohr, and Margenau. They are all firmly convinced that the riddle of the double nature of all corpuscles (corpuscular and undulatory character) has in essence found its final solution in the statistical quantum theory. On the strength of the successes of this theory they consider it proved that a theoretically complete description of a system can, in essence, involve only statistical assertions concerning the measurable quantities of this system. They are apparently all of the opinion that Heisenberg's indeterminacy-relation (the correctness of which is, from my own point of view, rightfully regarded as finally demonstrated) is essentially prejudicial in favor of the character of all thinkable reasonable physical theories in the mentioned sense. In what follows I wish to adduce reasons which keep me from falling in line with the opinion of almost all contemporary theoretical physicists. I am, in fact, firmly convinced that the essentially statistical character of contemporary quantum theory is solely to be ascribed to the fact that this [theory] operates with an incomplete description of physical systems.

Above all, however, the reader should be convinced that I fully recognize the very important progress which the statistical quantum theory has brought to theoretical physics. In the field of *mechanical* problems—i.e., wherever it is possible to consider the interaction of structures and of their parts with sufficient accuracy by postulating a potential energy between material points—[this theory] even now presents a system which, in its closed character, correctly describes the empirical relations between stable phenomena as they were theoretically to be expected. This theory is until now the only one which unites the corpuscular and undulatory dual character of matter in a logically satisfactory fashion; and the (testable) relations, which are contained in it, are, within the natural limits fixed by the indeterminacy-relation, *complete*. The formal relations which are given in this theory—i.e., its entire mathematical formalism—will probably have to be contained, in the form of logical inferences, in every useful future theory.

What does not satisfy me in that theory, from the standpoint of principle, is its attitude towards that which appears to me to be the programmatic aim of all physics: the complete description of any (individual) real situation (as it supposedly exists irrespective of any act of observation or substantiation). Whenever the positivistically inclined modern physicist hears such a formulation his reaction is that of a pitying smile. He says to himself: "there we have the naked formulation of a metaphysical prejudice, empty of content, a prejudice, moreover, the conquest of which constitutes the major epistemological achievement of physicists within the last quarter-century. Has any man ever perceived a 'real physical situation'? How is it possible that a reasonable person could today still believe that he can refute our essential knowledge and understanding by drawing up such a bloodless ghost?" Patience! The above laconic characterization was not meant to convince anyone; it was merely to indicate the point of view around which the following elementary considerations freely group themselves. In doing this I shall proceed as follows: I shall first of all show in simple special cases what seems essential to me, and then I shall make a few remarks about some more general ideas which are involved.

We consider as a physical system, in the first instance, a radioactive atom of definite average decay time, which is practically exactly localized at a point of the co-ordinate system. The radioactive process consists in the emission of a (comparatively light) particle. For the sake of simplicity we neglect the motion of the residual atom after the disintegration-process. Then it is possible for us, following Gamow, to replace the rest of the atom by a space of atomic order of magnitude, surrounded by a closed potential energy barrier which, at a time $t = 0$, encloses the particle to be emitted. The radioactive process thus schematized is then, as is well known, to be described—in the sense of elementary quantum mechanics—by a ψ-function in three dimensions, which at the time $t = 0$ is different from zero only inside of the barrier, but which, for positive times, expands into the outer space. This ψ-function yields the probability that the particle, at some chosen instant, is actually in a chosen part of space (i.e., is actually found there by a measurement of position). On the other hand, the ψ-function does not imply any assertion *concerning the time instant of the disintegration* of the radioactive atom.

Now we raise the question: Can this theoretical description be taken as the *complete* description of the disintegration of a single individual atom? The immediately plausible answer is: No. For one is, first of all, inclined to assume that the individual atom decays at a definite time; however, such a definite time-value is not implied in the description by the ψ-function. If, therefore, the individual atom has a definite disintegration-time, then as regards the individual atom its description by means of the ψ-function must be interpreted as an incomplete description. In this case the ψ-function is to be taken as the description, not of a singular system, but of an ideal ensemble of systems. In this case one is driven to the conviction that a complete description of a single system should, after all, be possible; but for such complete description there is no room in the conceptual world of statistical quantum theory.

To this the quantum theorist will reply: This consideration stands and falls with the assertion that there actually is such a thing as a definite time of disintegration of the individual atom (an instant of time existing independently of any observation). But this assertion is, from my point of view, not merely arbitrary but actually meaningless. The assertion of the existence of a definite time-instant for the disintegration makes sense only if I can in principle determine this time-instant empirically. Such an assertion, however, (which, finally, leads to the attempt to prove the existence of the particle outside of the force barrier), involves a definite disturbance of the system in which we are interested; so that the result of the determination does not permit a conclusion concerning the status of the undisturbed system. The supposition, therefore, that a radioactive atom has a definite disintegration-time is not justified by anything whatsoever; it is, therefore, not demonstrated either that the ψ-function can not be conceived as a complete description of the individual system. The entire alleged difficulty proceeds from the fact that one postulates something not observable as "real." (This the answer of the quantum theorist.)

What I dislike in this kind of argumentation is the basic positivistic attitude, which from my point of view is untenable, and which seems to me to come to the same thing as Berkeley's principle, *esse est percipi.* "Being" is always something which is mentally constructed by us, that is, something which we freely posit (in the logical sense). The justification of such constructs does not lie in their derivation from what is given by the senses. Such a type of derivation (in the sense of logical deducibility) is nowhere to be had, not even in the domain of pre-scientific thinking. The justification of the constructs, which represent "reality" for us, lies alone in their quality of making intelligible what is sensorily given (the vague character of this expression is here forced upon me by my striving for brevity). Applied to the specifically chosen example this consideration tells us the following:

One may not merely ask: "Does a definite time instant for the transformation of a single atom exist?" but rather: "Is it, within the framework of our theoretical total construction, reasonable to posit the existence of a definite point of time for the transformation of a single atom?" One may not even ask what this assertion *means.* One can only ask whether such a proposition, within the framework of the chosen conceptual system—with a view to its ability to grasp theoretically what is empirically given—is reasonable or not.

Insofar, then, as a quantum-theoretician takes the position that the description by means of a ψ-function refers only to an ideal systematic totality but in no wise to the individual system, he may calmly assume a definite point of time for the transformation. But, if he represents the assumption that his description by way of the ψ-function is to be taken as the *complete* description of the individual system, then he must reject the postulation of a specific decay-time. He can justifiably point to the fact that a determination of the instant of disintegration is not possible on an isolated system, but would require disturbances of such a character that they must not be neglected in the critical examination of the situation. It would, for example, not be possible to conclude from the empirical statement that the transformation has already taken place, that this would have been the case if the disturbances of the system had not taken place.

As far as I know, it was E. Schrödinger who first called attention to a modification of this consideration, which shows an interpretation of this type to be impracticable. Rather than considering a system which comprises only a radioactive atom (and its process of transformation), one considers a system which includes also the means for ascertaining the radioactive transformation—for example, a Geiger-counter with automatic registration-mechanism. Let this latter include a registration-strip, moved by a clockwork, upon which a mark is made by tripping the counter. True, from the point of view of quantum mechanics this total system is very complex and its configuration space is of very high dimension. But there is in principle no objection to treating this entire system from the standpoint of quantum mechanics. Here too the theory determines the probability of each configuration of all its co-ordinates for every time instant. If one considers all configurations of the coordinates, for a time large compared with the average decay-time of the radioactive atom, there will be (at most) *one* such registration-mark on the paper strip. To each co-ordinate-configuration corresponds a definite position of the mark on the paper strip. But, inasmuch as the theory yields only the relative probability of the thinkable co-ordinate-configurations, it also offers only relative probabilities for the positions of the mark on the paperstrip, but no definite location for this mark.

In this consideration the location of the mark on the strip plays the rôle played in the original consideration by the time of the disintegration. The reason for the introduction of the system supplemented by the registration-mechanism lies in the following. The location of the mark on the registration-strip is a fact which belongs entirely within the sphere of macroscopic concepts, in contradistinction to the instant of disintegration of a single atom. If we attempt [to work with] the interpretation that the quantum-theoretical description is to be understood as a complete description of the individual system, we are forced to the interpretation that the location of the mark on the strip is nothing which belongs to the system *per se,* but that the existence of that location is essentially dependent upon the carrying out of an observation made on the registration-strip. Such an interpretation is certainly by no means absurd from a purely logical standpoint; yet there is hardly likely to be anyone who would be inclined to consider it seriously. For, in the macroscopic sphere it simply is considered certain that one must adhere to the program of a realistic description in space and time; whereas in the sphere of microscopic situations one is more readily inclined to give up, or at least to modify, this program.

This discussion was only to bring out the following. One arrives at very implausible theoretical conceptions, if one attempts to maintain the thesis that the statistical quantum theory is in principle capable of producing a complete description of an individual physical system. On the other hand, those difficulties of theoretical interpretation disappear, if one views the quantum-mechanical description as the description of ensembles of systems.

I reached this conclusion as the result of quite different types of considerations. I am convinced that everyone who will take the trouble to carry through such reflections conscientiously will find himself finally driven to this interpretation of quantum-theoretical description (the ψ-function is to be understood as the description not of a single system but of an ensemble of systems).

Roughly stated the conclusion is this: Within the framework of statistical quantum theory there is no such thing as a complete description of the individual system. More cautiously it might be put as follows: The attempt to conceive the quantum-theoretical description as the complete description of the individual systems leads to unnatural theoretical interpretations, which become immediately unnecessary if one accepts the interpretation that the description refers to ensembles of systems and not to individual systems. In that case the whole "egg-walking" performed in order to avoid the "physically real" becomes superfluous. There exists, however, a simple psychological reason for the fact that this most nearly obvious interpretation is being shunned. For if the statistical quantum theory does not pretend to describe the individual system (and its development in time) completely, it appears unavoidable to look elsewhere for a complete description of the individual system; in doing so it would be clear from the very beginning that the elements of such a description are not contained within the conceptual scheme of the statistical quantum theory. With this one would admit that, in principle, this scheme could not serve as the basis of theoretical physics. Assuming the success of efforts to accomplish a complete physical description, the statistical quantum theory would, within the framework of future physics, take an approximately analogous position to the statistical mechanics within the framework of classical mechanics. I am rather firmly convinced that the development of theoretical physics will be of this type; but the path will be lengthy and difficult.

I now imagine a quantum theoretician who may even admit that the quantum-theoretical description refers to ensembles of systems and not to individual systems, but who, nevertheless, clings to the idea that the type of description of the statistical quantum theory will, in its essential features, be retained in the future. He may argue as follows: True, I admit that the quantum-theoretical description is an incomplete description of the individual system. I even admit that a complete theoretical description is, in principle, thinkable. But I consider it proven that the search for such a complete description would be aimless. For the lawfulness of nature is thus constituted that the laws can be completely and suitably formulated within the framework of our incomplete description.

To this I can only reply as follows: Your point of view—taken as theoretical possibility—is incontestable. For me, however, the expectation that the adequate formulation of the universal laws involves the use of *all* conceptual elements which are necessary for a complete description, is more natural. It is furthermore not at all surprising that, by using an incomplete description, (in the main) only statistical statements can be obtained out of such description. If it should be possible to move forward to a complete description, it is likely that the laws would represent relations among all the conceptual elements of this description which, *per se,* have nothing to do with statistics.

A few more remarks of a general nature concerning concepts and [also] concerning the insinuation that a concept—for example that of the real—is something metaphysical (and therefore to be rejected). A basic conceptual distinction, which is a necessary prerequisite of scientific and pre-scientific thinking, is the distinction between "sense-impressions" (and the recollection of such) on the one hand and mere ideas on the other. There is no such thing as a conceptual definition of this distinction (aside from circular definitions, i.e., of such as make a hidden use of the object to be defined). Nor can it be maintained that at the base of this distinction there is a type of evidence, such as underlies, for example, the distinction between red and blue. Yet, one needs this distinction in order to be able to overcome solipsism. Solution: we shall make use of this distinction unconcerned with the reproach that, in doing so, we are guilty of the metaphysical "original sin." We regard the distinction as a category which we use in order that we might the better find our way in the world of immediate sensations. The "sense" and the justification of this distinction lies simply in this achievement. But this is only a first step. We represent the sense-impressions as conditioned by an "objective" and by a "subjective" factor. For this conceptual distinction there also is no logical-philosophical justification. But if we reject it, we cannot escape solipsism. It is also the presupposition of every kind of physical thinking. Here too, the only justification lies in its usefulness. We are here concerned with "categories" or schemes of thought, the selection of which is, in principle, entirely open to us and whose qualification can only be judged by the degree to which its use contributes to making the totality of the contents of consciousness "intelligible." The above mentioned "objective factor" is the totality of such concepts and conceptual relations as are thought of as independent of experience, viz., of perceptions. So long as we move within the thus programmatically fixed sphere of thought we are thinking physically. Insofar as physical thinking justifies itself, in the more than once indicated sense, by its ability to grasp experiences intellectually, we regard it as "knowledge of the real."

After what has been said, the "real" in physics is to be taken as a type of program, to which we are, however, not forced to cling *a priori*. No one is likely to be inclined to attempt to give up this program within the realm of the "macroscopic" (location of the mark on the paperstrip "real"). But the "macroscopic" and the "microscopic" are so inter-related that it appears impracticable to give up this program in the "microscopic" alone. Nor can I see any occasion anywhere within the observable facts of the quantum-field for doing so, unless, indeed, one clings *a priori* to the thesis that the description of nature by the statistical scheme of quantum-mechanics is final.

The theoretical attitude here advocated is distinct from that of Kant only by the fact that we do not conceive of the "categories" as unalterable (conditioned by the nature of the understanding) but as (in the logical sense) free conventions. They appear to be *a priori* only insofar as thinking without the positing of categories and of concepts in general would be as impossible as is breathing in a vacuum.

From these meager remarks one will see that to me it must seem a mistake to permit theoretical description to be directly dependent upon acts of empirical assertions, as it seems to me to be intended [for example] in Bohr's principle of complementarity, the sharp formulation of which, moreover, I have been unable to achieve despite much effort which I have expended on it. From my point of view [such] statements or measurements can occur only as special instances, viz., parts, of physical description, to which I cannot ascribe any exceptional position above the rest.

The above mentioned essays by Bohr and Pauli contain a historical appreciation of my efforts in the area of physical statistics and quanta and, in addition, an accusation which is brought forward in the friendliest of fashion. In briefest formulation this latter runs as follows: "Rigid adherence to classical theory." This accusation demands either a defense or the confession of guilt. The one or the other is, however, being rendered much more difficult because it is by no means immediately clear what is meant by "classical theory." Newton's theory deserves the name of a classical theory. It has nevertheless been abandoned since Maxwell and Hertz have shown that the idea of forces at a distance has to be relinquished and that one cannot manage without the idea of continuous "fields." The opinion that continuous fields are to be viewed as the only acceptable basic concepts, which must also [be assumed to] underlie the theory of the material particles, soon won out. Now this conception became, so to speak, "classical;" but a proper, and in principle complete, *theory* has not grown out of it. Maxwell's theory of the electric field remained a torso, because it was unable to set up laws for the behavior of electric density, without which there can, of course, be no such thing as an electro-magnetic field. Analogously the general theory of relativity furnished then a field theory of gravitation, but no theory of the field-creating masses. (These remarks presuppose it as self-evident that a field-theory may not contain any singularities, i.e., any positions or parts in space in which the field-laws are not valid.)

Consequently there is, strictly speaking, today no such thing as a classical field-theory; one can, therefore, also not rigidly adhere to it. Nevertheless, field-theory does exist as a program: "Continuous functions in the four-dimensional [continuum] as basic concepts of the theory." Rigid adherence to this program can rightfully be asserted of me. The deeper ground for this lies in the following: The theory of gravitation showed me that the non-linearity of these equations results in the fact that this theory yields interactions among structures (localized things) at all. But the theoretical search for non-linear equations is hopeless (because of too great variety of possibilities), if one does not use the general principle of relativity (invariance under general continuous co-ordinate-transformations). In the meantime, however, it does not seem possible to formulate this principle, if one seeks to deviate from the above program. Herein lies a coercion which I cannot evade. This for my justification.

Nevertheless I am forced to weaken this justification by a confession. If one disregards quantum structure, one can justify the introduction of the g_{ik} "operationally" by pointing to the fact that one can hardly doubt the physical reality of the elementary light cone which belongs to a point. In doing so one implicitly makes use of the existence of an arbitrarily sharp optical signal. Such a signal, however, as regards the quantum facts, involves infinitely high frequencies and energies, and therefore a complete destruction of the field to be determined. That kind of a physical justification for the introduction of the g_{ik} falls by the wayside, unless one limits himself to the "macroscopic." The application of the formal basis of the general theory of relativity to the "microscopic" can, therefore, be based only upon the fact that that tensor is the formally simplest covariant structure which can come under consideration. Such argumentation, however, carries no weight with anyone who doubts that we have to adhere to the continuum at all. All honor to his doubt—but where else is there a passable road?

Now I come to the theme of the relation of the theory of relativity to philosophy. Here it is Reichenbach's piece of work which, by the precision of deductions and by the sharpness of his assertions, irresistibly invites a brief commentary. Robertson's lucid discussion also is interesting mainly from the standpoint of general epistemology, although it limits itself to the narrower theme of "the theory of relativity and geometry." To the question: Do you consider true what Reichenbach has here asserted, I can answer only with Pilate's famous question: "What is truth?"

Let us first take a good look at the question: Is a geometry —looked at from the physical point of view—verifiable (viz., falsifiable) or not? Reichenbach, together with Helmholtz, says: Yes, provided that the empirically given solid body realizes the concept of "distance." Poincaré says no and consequently is condemned by Reichenbach. Now the following short conversation takes place:

Poincaré: The empirically given bodies are not rigid, and consequently can not be used for the embodiment of geometric intervals. Therefore, the theorems of geometry are not verifiable.

Reichenbach: I admit that there are no bodies which can be *immediately* adduced for the "real definition" of the interval. Nevertheless, this real definition can be achieved by taking the thermal volume-dependence, elasticity, electro- and magneto-striction, etc., into consideration. That this is really [and] without contradiction possible, classical physics has surely demonstrated.

Poincaré: In gaining the real definition improved by yourself you have made use of physical laws, the formulation of which presupposes (in this case) Euclidean geometry. The verification, of which you have spoken, refers, therefore, not merely to geometry but to the entire system of physical laws which constitute its foundation. An examination of geometry by itself is consequently not thinkable.—Why should it consequently not be entirely up to me to choose geometry according to my own convenience (i.e., Euclidean) and to fit the remaining (in the usual sense "physical") laws to this choice in such manner that there can arise no contradiction of the whole with experience?

(The conversation cannot be continued in this fashion because the respect of the [present] writer for Poincaré's superiority as thinker and author does not permit it; in what follows therefore, an anonymous non-positivist is substituted for Poincaré.—)

Reichenbach: There is something quite attractive in this conception. But, on the other hand, it is noteworthy that the adherence to the objective meaning of length and to the interpretation of the differences of co-ordinates as distances (in prerelativistic physics) has not led to complications. Should we not, on the basis of this astounding fact, be justified in operating further at least tentatively with the concept of the measurable length, as if there were such things as rigid measuring-rods? In any case it would have been impossible for Einstein *de facto* (even if not theoretically) to set up the theory of general relativity, if he had not adhered to the objective meaning of length.

Against Poincaré's suggestion it is to be pointed out that what really matters is not merely the greatest possible simplicity of the geometry alone, but rather the greatest possible simplicity of all of physics (inclusive of geometry). This is what is, in the first instance, involved in the fact that today we must decline as unsuitable the suggestion to adhere to Euclidean geometry.

Non-Positivist: If, under the stated circumstances, you hold distance to be a legitimate concept, how then is it with your basic principle (meaning = verifiability)? Do you not have to reach the point where you must deny the meaning of geometrical concepts and theorems and to acknowledge meaning only within the completely developed theory of relativity (which, however, does not yet exist at all as a finished product)? Do you not have to admit that, in your sense of the word, no "meaning" can be attributed to the individual concepts and assertions of a physical theory at all, and to the entire system only insofar as it makes what is given in experience "intelligible?" Why do the individual concepts which occur in a theory require any specific justification anyway, if they are only indispensable within the framework of the logical structure of the theory, and the theory only in its entirety validates itself?

It seems to me, moreover, that you have not at all done justice to the really significant philosophical achievement of Kant. From Hume Kant had learned that there are concepts (as, for example, that of causal connection), which play a dominating rôle in our thinking, and which, nevertheless, can not be deduced by means of a logical process from the empirically given (a fact which several empiricists recognize, it is true, but seem always again to forget). What justifies the use of such concepts? Suppose he had replied in this sense: Thinking is necessary in order to understand the empirically given, *and concepts and "categories" are necessary as indispensable elements of thinking.* If he had remained satisfied with this type of an answer, he would have avoided scepticism and you would not have been able to find fault with him. He, however, was misled by the erroneous opinion—difficult to avoid in his time —that Euclidean geometry is necessary to thinking and offers *assured* (i.e., not dependent upon sensory experience) knowledge concerning the objects of "external" perception. From this easily understandable error he concluded the existence of synthetic judgments *a priori*, which are produced by the reason alone, and which, consequently, can lay claim to absolute validity. I think your censure is directed less against Kant himself than against those who today still adhere to the errors of "synthetic judgments *a priori*." —

I can hardly think of anything more stimulating as the basis for discussion in an epistemological seminar than this brief essay by Reichenbach (best taken together with Robertson's essay).

What has been discussed thus far is closely related to Bridgman's essay, so that it will be possible for me to express myself quite briefly without having to harbor too much fear that I shall be misunderstood. In order to be able to consider a logical system as physical theory it is not necessary to demand that all of its assertions can be independently interpreted and "tested" "operationally;" *de facto* this has never yet been achieved by any theory and can not at all be achieved. In order to be able to consider a theory as a *physical* theory it is only necessary that it implies empirically testable assertions in general.

This formulation is insofar entirely unprecise as "testability" is a quality which refers not merely to the assertion itself but also to the co-ordination of concepts, contained in it, with experience. But it is probably hardly necessary for me to enter upon a discussion of this ticklish problem, inasmuch as it is not likely that there exist any essential differences of opinion at this point. —

Margenau. This essay contains several original specific remarks, which I must consider separately:

To his Sec. 1: "Einstein's position . . . contains features of rationalism and extreme empiricism. . . ." This remark is entirely correct. From whence comes this fluctuation? A logical conceptual system is physics insofar as its concepts and assertions are necessarily brought into relationship with the world of experiences. Whoever desires to set up such a system will find a dangerous obstacle in arbitrary choice (*embarras de richesse*). This is why he seeks to connect his concepts as directly and necessarily as possible with the world of experience. In this case his attitude is empirical. This path is often fruitful, but it is always open to doubt, because the specific concept and the individual assertion can, after all, assert something confronted by the empirically given only in connection with the entire system. He then recognizes that there exists no logical path from the empirically given to that conceptual world. His attitude becomes then more nearly rationalistic, because he recognizes the logical independence of the system. The danger in this attitude lies in the fact that in the search for the system one can lose every contact with the world of experience. A wavering between these extremes appears to me unavoidable.

To his Sec. 2: I did not grow up in the Kantian tradition, but came to understand the truly valuable which is to be found in his doctrine, alongside of errors which today are quite obvious, only quite late. It is contained in the sentence: "The real is not given to us, but put to us (*aufgegeben*) (by way of a riddle)." This obviously means: There is such a thing as a conceptual construction for the grasping of the inter-personal, the authority of which lies purely in its validation. This conceptual construction refers precisely to the "real" (by definition), and every further question concerning the "nature of the real" appears empty.

To his Sec. 4: This discussion has not convinced me at all. For it is clear *per se* that every magnitude and every assertion of a theory lays claim to "objective meaning" (within the framework of the theory). A problem arises only when we ascribe group-characteristics to a theory, i.e., if we assume or postulate that the same physical situation admits of several ways of description, each of which is to be viewed as equally justified. For in this case we obviously cannot ascribe complete objective meaning (for example the x-component of the velocity of a particle or its x-co-ordinates) to the individual (not eliminable) magnitudes. In this case, which has always existed in physics, we have to limit ourselves to ascribing objective meaning to the general laws of the theory, i.e., we have to demand that these laws are valid for every description of the system which is recognized as justified by the group. It is, therefore, not true that "objectivity" presupposes a group-characteristic, but that the group-characteristic forces a refinement of the concept of objectivity. The positing of group characteristics is heuristically so important for theory, because this characteristic always considerably limits the variety of the mathematically meaningful laws.

Now there follows a claim that the group-characteristics determine that the laws must have the form of differential equations; I can not at all see this. Then Margenau insists that the laws expressed by way of the differential equations (especially the partial ones) are "least specific." Upon what does he base this contention? If they could be proved to be correct, it is true that the attempt to ground physics upon differential equations would then turn out to be hopeless. We are, however, far from being able to judge whether differential laws of the type to be considered have any solutions at all which are everywhere singularity-free; and, if so, whether there are too many such solutions.

And now just a remark concerning the discussions about the Einstein-Podolski-Rosen Paradox. I do not think that Margenau's defense of the "orthodox" ("orthodox" refers to the thesis that the ψ-function characterizes the individual system *exhaustively*) quantum position hits the essential [aspects]. Of the "orthodox" quantum theoreticians whose position I know, Niels Bohr's seems to me to come nearest to doing justice to the problem. Translated into my own way of putting it, he argues as follows:

If the partial systems A and B form a total system which is described by its ψ-function $\psi/(AB)$, there is no reason why any mutually independent existence (state of reality) should be ascribed to the partial systems A and B viewed separately, *not even if the partial systems are spatially separated from each other at the particular time under consideration.* The assertion that, in this latter case, the real situation of B could not be (directly) influenced by any measurement taken on A is, therefore, within the framework of quantum theory, unfounded and (as the paradox shows) unacceptable.

By this way of looking at the matter it becomes evident that the paradox forces us to relinquish one of the following two assertions:

(1) the description by means of the ψ-function is *complete*

(2) the real states of spatially separated objects are independent of each other.

On the other hand, it is possible to adhere to (2), if one regards the ψ-function as the description of a (statistical) ensemble of systems (and therefore relinquishes (1)). However, this view blasts the framework of the "orthodox quantum theory."

One more remark to Margenau's Sec. 7. In the characterization of quantum mechanics the brief little sentence will be found: "on the classical level it corresponds to ordinary dynamics." This is entirely correct—*cum grano salis;* and it is precisely this *granum salis* which is significant for the question of interpretation.

If our concern is with macroscopic masses (billiard balls or stars), we are operating with very short de Broglie-waves, which are determinative for the behavior of the center of gravity of such masses. This is the reason why it is possible to arrange the quantum-theoretical description for a reasonable time in such a manner that for the macroscopic way of viewing things, it becomes sufficiently precise in position as well as in momentum. It is true also that this sharpness remains for a long time and that the quasi-points thus represented behave just like the mass-points of classical mechanics. However, the theory shows also that, after a sufficiently long time, the point-like character of the ψ-function is completely lost to the center of gravity-co-ordinates, so that one can no longer speak of any quasi-localisation of the centers of gravity. The picture then becomes, for example in the case of a single macro-mass-point, quite similar to that involved in a single free electron.

If now, in accordance with the orthodox position, I view the ψ-function as the complete description of a real matter of fact for the individual case, I cannot but consider the essentially unlimited lack of sharpness of the position of the (macroscopic) body as *real*. On the other hand, however, we know that, by illuminating the body by means of a lantern at rest against the system of co-ordinates, we get a (macroscopically judged) sharp determination of position. In order to comprehend this I must assume that that sharply defined position is determined not merely by the real situation of the observed body, but also by the act of illumination. This is again a paradox (similar to the mark on the paperstrip in the above mentioned example). The spook disappears only if one relinquishes the orthodox standpoint, according to which the ψ-function is accepted as a complete description of the single system.

It may appear as if all such considerations were just superfluous learned hairsplitting, which have nothing to do with physics proper. However, it depends precisely upon such considerations in which direction one believes one must look for the future conceptual basis of physics.

I close these expositions, which have grown rather lengthy, concerning the interpretation of quantum theory with the reproduction of a brief conversation which I had with an important theoretical physicist. He: "I am inclined to believe in telepathy." I: "This has probably more to do with physics than with psychology." He: "Yes." —

The essays by Lenzen and Northrop both aim to treat my occasional utterances of epistemological content systematically. From those utterances Lenzen constructs a synoptic total picture, in which what is missing in the utterances is carefully and with delicacy of feeling supplied. Everything said therein appears to me convincing and correct. Northrop uses these utterances as point of departure for a comparative critique of the major epistemological systems. I see in this critique a masterpiece of unbiased thinking and concise discussion, which nowhere permits itself to be diverted from the essential.

The reciprocal relationship of epistemology and science is of noteworthy kind. They are dependent upon each other. Epistemology without contact with science becomes an empty scheme. Science without epistemology is—insofar as it is thinkable at all—primitive and muddled. However, no sooner has the epistemologist, who is seeking a clear system, fought his way through to such a system, than he is inclined to interpret the thought-content of science in the sense of his system and to reject whatever does not fit into his system. The scientist, however, cannot afford to carry his striving for epistemological systematic that far. He accepts gratefully the epistemological conceptual analysis; but the external conditions, which are set for him by the facts of experience, do not permit him to let himself be too much restricted in the construction of his conceptual world by the adherence to an epistemological system. He therefore must appear to the systematic epistemologist as a type of unscrupulous opportunist: he appears as *realist* insofar as he seeks to describe a world independent of the acts of perception; as *idealist* insofar as he looks upon the concepts and theories as the free inventions of the human spirit (not logically derivable from what is empirically given); as *positivist* insofar as he considers his concepts and theories justified *only* to the extent to which they furnish a logical representation of relations among sensory experiences. He may even appear as *Platonist* or *Pythagorean* insofar as he considers the viewpoint of logical simplicity as an indispensable and effective tool of his research.

All of this is splendidly elucidated in Lenzen's and Northrop's essays. —— ——

And now a few remarks concerning the essays by E. A. Milne, G. Lemaître, and L. Infeld as concerns the cosmological problem:

Concerning Milne's ingenious reflections I can only say that I find their theoretical basis too narrow. From my point of view one cannot arrive, by way of theory, at any at least somewhat reliable results in the field of cosmology, if one makes no use of the principle of general relativity.

As concerns Lemaître's arguments in favor of the so-called "cosmological constant" in the equations of gravitation, I must admit that these arguments do not appear to me as sufficiently convincing in view of the present state of our knowledge.

The introduction of such a constant implies a considerable

renunciation of the logical simplicity of theory, a renunciation which appeared to me unavoidable only so long as one had no reason to doubt the essentially static nature of space. After Hubble's discovery of the "expansion" of the stellar system, and since Friedmann's discovery that the unsupplemented equations involve the possibility of the existence of an average (positive) density of matter in an expanding universe, the introduction of such a constant appears to me, from the theoretical standpoint, at present unjustified.

The situation becomes complicated by the fact that the entire duration of the expansion of space to the present, based on the equations in their simplest form, turns out smaller than appears credible in view of the reliably known age of terrestrial minerals. But the introduction of the "cosmological constant" offers absolutely no natural escape from the difficulty. This latter difficulty is given by way of the numerical value of Hubble's expansion-constant and the age-measurement of minerals, completely independent of any cosmological theory, provided that one interprets the Hubble-effect as Doppler-effect.

Everything finally depends upon the question: Can a spectral line be considered as a measure of a "proper time" (*Eigen-Zeit*)*ds* ($ds^2 = g_{ik}dx_i dx_k$), (if one takes into consideration regions of cosmic dimensions)? Is there such a thing as a natural object which incorporates the "natural-measuring-stick" independently of its position in four-dimensional space? The affirmation of this question made the invention of the general theory of relativity *psychologically* possible; however this supposition is logically not necessary. For the construction of the present theory of relativity the following is essential:

(1) Physical things are described by continuous functions, field-variables of four co-ordinates. As long as the topological connection is preserved, these latter can be freely chosen.

(2) The field-variables are tensor-components; among the tensors is a symmetrical tensor g_{ik} for the description of the gravitational field.

(3) There are physical objects, which (in the macroscopic field) measure the invariant ds.

If (1) and (2) are accepted, (3) is plausible, but not necessary. The construction of mathematical theory rests exclusively upon (1) and (2).

A *complete* theory of physics as a totality, in accordance with (1) and (2) does not yet exist. If it did exist, there would be no room for the supposition (3). For the objects used as tools for measurement do not lead an independent existence alongside of the objects implicated by the field-equations. — — It is not necessary that one should permit one's cosmological considerations to be restrained by such a sceptical attitude; but neither should one close one's mind towards them from the very beginning. — — —

These reflections bring me to Karl Menger's essay. For the quantum-facts suggest the suspicion that doubt may also be raised concerning the ultimate usefulness of the program characterized in (1) and (2). There exists the possibility of doubting only (2) and, in doing so, to question the possibility of being able adequately to formulate the laws by means of differential equations, without dropping (1). The more radical effort of surrendering (1) with (2) appears to me—and I believe to Dr. Menger also—to lie more closely at hand. So long as no one has new concepts, which appear to have sufficient constructive power, mere doubt remains; this is, unfortunately, my own situation. Adhering to the continuum originates with me not in a prejudice, but arises out of the fact that I have been unable to think up anything organic to take its place. How is one to conserve four-dimensionality in essence (or in near approximation) and [at the same time] surrender the continuum? —

L. Infeld's essay is an independently understandable, excellent introduction into the so-called "cosmological problem" of the theory of relativity, which critically examines all essential points. — — —

Max von Laue: An historical investigation of the development of the conservation postulates, which, in my opinion, is of lasting value. I think it would be worth while to make this essay easily accessible to students by way of independent publication. — — —

In spite of serious efforts I have not succeeded in quite understanding H. Dingle's essay, not even as concerns its aim. Is the
idea of the special theory of relativity to be expanded in the
sense that new group-characteristics, which are not implied by
the Lorentz-invariance, are to be postulated? Are these postulates empirically founded or only by way of a trial "posited"?
Upon what does the confidence in the existence of such group-
characteristics rest? ― ― ―

Kurt Gödel's essay constitutes, in my opinion, an important
contribution to the general theory of relativity, especially to
the analysis of the concept of time. The problem here involved
disturbed me already at the time of the building up of the general theory of relativity, without my having succeeded in
clarifying it. Entirely aside from the relation of the theory
of relativity to idealistic philosophy or to any philosophical
formulation of questions, the problem presents itself as follows:

If P is a world-point, a "light-cone"
$(ds^2 = 0)$ belongs to it. We draw
a "time-like" world-line through P
and on this line observe the close
world-points B and A, separated by
P. Does it make any sense to provide
the world-line with an arrow, and to
assert that B is *before P, A after P?* Is
what remains of temporal connection
between world-points in the theory
of relativity an asymmetrical relation,

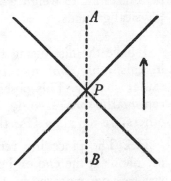

or would one be just as much justified, from the physical point
of view, to indicate the arrow in the opposite direction and to
assert that A is *before P, B after P?*

In the first instance the alternative is decided in the negative,
if we are justified in saying: If it is possible to send (to tele-
graph) a signal (also passing by in the close proximity of P)
from B to A, but not from A to B, then the one-sided (asymmetrical) character of time is secured, i.e., there exists no free
choice for the direction of the arrow. What is essential in this is
the fact that the sending of a signal is, in the sense of thermodynamics, an irreversible process, a process which is connected

with the growth of entropy (whereas, *according to our present knowledge*, all elementary processes are reversible).

If, therefore, *B* and *A* are two, sufficiently neighboring, world-points, which can be connected by a time-like line, then the assertion: "*B* is before *A*," makes physical sense. But does this assertion still make sense, if the points, which are connectable by the time-like line, are arbitrarily far separated from each other? Certainly not, if there exist point-series connectable by time-like lines in such a way that each point precedes temporally the preceding one, *and if the series is closed in itself*. In that case the distinction "earlier – later" is abandoned for world-points which lie far apart in a cosmological sense, and those paradoxes, regarding the *direction* of the causal connection, arise, of which Mr. Gödel has spoken.

Such cosmological solutions of the gravitation-equations (with not vanishing Λ-constant) have been found by Mr. Gödel. It will be interesting to weigh whether these are not to be excluded on physical grounds.

* * * * * *

I have the distressing feeling that I have expressed myself, in this reply, not merely somewhat longwindedly but also rather sharply. This observation may serve as my excuse: one can really quarrel only with his brothers or close friends; others are too alien [for that]. —

P.S. The preceding remarks refer to essays which were in my hands at the end of January 1949. Inasmuch as the volume was to have appeared in March, it was high time to write down these reflections.

After they had been concluded I learned that the publication of the volume would experience a further delay and that some additional important essays had come in. I decided, nevertheless, not to expand my remarks further, which had already become too long, and to desist from taking any position with reference to those essays which came into my hands after the conclusion of my remarks.

INSTITUTE OF ADVANCED STUDY
PRINCETON, NEW JERSEY
FEBRUARY 1, 1949

A. Einstein.

BIBLIOGRAPHY OF THE WRITINGS OF ALBERT EINSTEIN

TO MAY 1951

Compiled by

MARGARET C. SHIELDS

PREFACE TO THE BIBLIOGRAPHY

OVER the fireplace in the professors' lounge of Fine Hall, the home of the Princeton University department of mathematics, are these words of Einstein, *"Raffiniert ist der Herr Gott, aber boshaft ist er nicht,"* ("God is subtle, but he is not malicious") which are said not to have been taken from any writing, but to have been treasured from a conversation. This instance may perhaps be taken as representative of the way in which the thoughts of the man have been sown broadcast over the earth so that any attempt to collect even his printed words with any degree of completeness is beyond attainable possibility.

A fairly complete list of his scientific work may be presumed contained in the following pages, but the published material representing his other interests is much more difficult to garner, and the present record of it is clearly inadequate. Of these widely scattered items, multitudinous and significant even when brief, relatively few could be traced through periodical indexes. Many have been published in minor German weeklies, etc., which are not covered by the *Bibliographie der Deutschen Zeitschriften* and its *Beilage,* and most of these publications, at least for the period 1920-1930, are not available in this country for direct searching. Four items from this *Bibliographie* have been included though the Library of Congress reports they are not in any American library. The several Einstein anthologies, with one exception, fail to indicate the original places of publication of the items in their contents, and the circumstances of the years since the anthologies were issued have made it impossible to obtain this information from either editor or publisher. The editor of this volume will be most grateful to readers who will report to him citations for missing items to be inserted in a second edition; there are at least a score of items of this period of which the compiler knows the existence but which she has failed to locate.

Even for the last few years with free access to the original manuscripts the task is quite as clearly impossible. One finds among these manuscripts a letter to the Jews of Montevideo which was reprinted there in facsimile as a broadside on June 5, 1948, captioned *Fuer unsere Haganah*. One finds a message to the Japanese people on peace and security which was printed in the New Year 1948 issue of a Japanese language paper, *Ahasi*. Neither of these could be included in the bibliography, though both may have been several times reprinted in the far corners of the earth. There are messages to gatherings like the World Federalists Conference at Montreux, August 17, 1947, radio broadcasts, endorsements of worthy persons and worthy causes, which once made public may be printed in an endless variety of places, but which are not to be located by any reasonable process of search, or which, such as letters quoted on book jackets, are not suitable for inclusion.

Some points may be mentioned as to details of the bibliography, particularly certain modifications of the style prevailing in earlier volume of this series which have kindly received the sanction of the editor. The remaining departures from normal library procedure it is hoped will be as kindly overlooked. Mistakes on the part of the compiler there may be which require, not forgiveness, but correction.

The material has been divided into three categories; such division is clearly suggested by the material itself and will increase, it is hoped, the convenience of the bibliography for its users. The first major division is the scientific writings; the second, publications other than those in Part III bearing on his wide humanitarian interests; third, the text of speeches, letters, etc., published in the *New York Times*.

Reprinted items are recorded only under the date of first publication, with a note indicating subsequent reprintings. In case of items not reprintings, textually similar but bibliographically distinct, they have been so listed under the appropriate year.

The dates used in case of periodical articles are the dates appearing on the title pages of completed volumes; when the periodical year does not coincide with the calendar year, this date may follow by one year the actual date of issue of the paper, but for the purpose of seeking out the article in a library the title page date is the more convenient.

Many of the monographs, particularly those in the *Sitzungsberichte* of the Prussian Academy, are listed in dealers' catalogs as separates with the high prices of collectors' items. These are entered here, however, only as are other periodical articles.

Within each year the order is first books, then periodical articles arranged alphabetically by the periodical title, for convenience in locating a particular item when one has only that much information to begin on.

To all the large number of libraries and individuals who have been approached with questions, whether they were able to supply information or not, the compiler again extends her warm thanks, and to those who will turn to the bibliography for service her regret that it is not more perfect.

Margaret C. Shields

Fine Hall Library
Princeton University
June 1, 1948

BIBLIOGRAPHY

I

SCIENTIFIC WRITINGS

1901

1. Folgerungen aus den Kapillaritätserscheinungen. *Annalen der Physik*, ser. 4, vol. 4, pp. 513-523.

1902

2. Thermodynamische Theorie der Potentialdifferenz zwischen Metallen und vollständig dissoziierten Lösungen ihrer Salze, und eine elektrische Methode zur Erforschung der Molekularkräfte. *Annalen der Physik*, ser. 4, vol. 8, pp. 798-814.

3. Kinetische Theorie des Wärmegleichgewichtes und des zweiten Hauptsatzes der Thermodynamik. *Annalen der Physik*, ser. 4, vol. 9, pp. 417-433.

1903

4. Theorie der Grundlagen der Thermodynamik. *Annalen der Physik*, ser. 4, vol. 11, pp. 170-187.

1904

5. Allgemeine molekulare Theorie der Wärme. *Annalen der Physik*, ser. 4, vol. 14, pp. 354-362.

1905

6. EINE NEUE BESTIMMUNG DER MOLEKÜLDIMENSIONEN. Bern, Wyss. 21 pp.

   Inaugural-dissertation, Zürich Universität. Published also in *Annalen der Physik*, (item 11).

7. Über einen die Erzeugung und Verwandlung des Lichtes betreffenden heuristischen Gesichtspunkt. *Annalen der Physik*, ser. 4, vol. 17, pp. 132-148.

   This paper and item 13 present the fundamental photoelectric equation in explicit form though not in current notation. It was nominally for this work that the Nobel prize was awarded Einstein. (See also item 45).

8. Die von der molekularkinetischen Theorie der Wärme geforderte Bewegung von in ruhenden Flüssigkeiten suspendierten Teilchen. *Annalen der Physik*, ser. 4, vol. 17, pp. 549-560.

Included in item 157 and item 198.

9. Elektrodynamik bewegter Körper. *Annalen der Physik*, ser. 4, vol. 17, pp. 891-921.

This is the initial paper on special relativity.

At a war bond rally in Kansas City a manuscript copy was sold for six million dollars and deposited with the Library of Congress. (see *New York Times*, Feb. 5, 1944, p. 5, and Aug. 4, p. 15)

The paper was reprinted in H. A. LORENTZ: *Das Relativitätsprinzip, eine Sammlung von Abhandlungen*, Leipzig, Teubner, 1913, and also in its subsequent editions. This book is also available in an English translation by W. Perrett and G. B. Jeffery, H. A. LORENTZ: *The principle of relativity, a collection of original memoirs* . . . London, Methuen, 1923.

See also item 128 for another English translation, item 189 for a French translation.

Excerpts are included in BUILDERS OF THE UNIVERSE, Los Angeles, 1932 (See item 345).

10. Ist die Trägheit eines Körpers von seinem Energieinhalt abhängig? *Annalen der Physik*, ser. 4, vol. 18, pp. 639-641.

In subject matter this is closely associated with item 9; it is included in the LORENTZ there mentioned, and in its translation. For French translation see item 189.

1906

11. Eine neue Bestimmung der Moleküldimensionen. *Annalen der Physik*, ser. 4, vol. 19, pp. 289-306.

This is his inaugural-dissertation, item 6, with a brief "Nachtrag." It is also included in his *Untersuchungen über die Theorie der Brownschen Bewegungen*, item 157, and its translation, item 198.

12. Zur Theorie der Brownschen Bewegung. *Annalen der Physik*, ser. 4, vol. 19, pp. 371-381.

Included in items 157 and 198.

13. Theorie der Lichterzeugung und Lichtabsorption. *Annalen der Physik*, ser. 4, vol. 20, pp. 199-206.

See note under item 7.

14. Prinzip von der Erhaltung der Schwerpunktsbewegung und die Trägheit der Energie.
    Annalen der Physik, ser. 4, vol. 20, pp. 627-633.

15. Eine Methode zur Bestimmung des Verhältnisses der transversalen und longitudinalen Masse des Elektrons.
    Annalen der Physik, ser. 4, vol. 21, pp. 583-586.

    French translation in *L'Éclairage électrique*, vol. 49, pp. 493-494.

1907

16. Plancksche Theorie der Strahlung und die Theorie der spezifischen Wärme.
    Annalen der Physik, ser. 4, vol. 22, pp. 180-190, and p. 800 (Berichtigung).

17. Gültigkeitsgrenze des Satzes vom thermodynamischen Gleichgewicht und die Möglichkeit einer neuen Bestimmung der Elementarquanta.
    Annalen der Physik, ser. 4, vol. 22, pp. 569-572.

18. Möglichkeit einer neuen Prüfung des Relativitätsprinzips.
    Annalen der Physik, ser. 4, vol. 23, pp. 197-198.

    An analysis of the Doppler effect.

19. Bemerkung zur Notiz des Herrn P. Ehrenfest: Translation deformierbarer Elektronen und der Flächensatz.
    Annalen der Physik, ser. 4, vol. 23, pp. 206-208.

20. Die vom Relativitätsprinzip geforderte Trägheit der Energie
    Annalen der Physik, ser. 4, vol. 23, pp. 371-384.

21. Relativitätsprinzip und die aus demselben gezogenen Folgerungen.
    Jahrbuch der Radioaktivität, vol. 4, pp. 411-462, and vol. 5, pp. 98-99 (Berichtigungen)

    > On page 443 appear probably for the first time explicit statements both of the equivalence of inertial and gravitational mass, and of the equation for mass in terms of energy which has been blazoned since August 1945 on so many graphic presentations of the release of atomic energy.

22. Theoretische Bemerkungen über die Brownsche Bewegung.
    Zeitschrift für Elektrochemie, vol. 13, pp. 41-42.

    Included in items 157 and 198.

1908

23. Electromagnetische Grundgleichungen für bewegte Körper, with J. Laub.
Annalen der Physik, ser. 4, vol. 26, pp. 532-540, and vol. 27, p. 232 (Berichtigungen).

See also Item 27.

24. Die im elektromagnetischen Felde auf ruhende Körper ausgeübten ponderomotorischen Kräfte, with J. Laub.
Annalen der Physik, ser. 4, vol. 26, pp. 541-550.

25. Neue elektrostatische Methode zur Messung kleiner Elektrizitätsmengen.
Physikalische Zeitschrift, vol. 9, pp. 216-217.

26. Elementare Theorie der Brownschen Bewegung.
Zeitschrift für Elektrochemie, vol. 14, pp. 235-239.

Included in items 157 and 198.

1909

27. Bemerkungen zu unserer Arbeit: Elektromagnetische Grundgleichungen für bewegte Körper, with J. Laub.
Annalen der Physik, ser. 4, vol. 28, pp. 445-447.

28. Bemerkung zur Arbeit von Mirimanoff: Die Grundgleichungen.
Annalen der Physik, ser. 4, vol. 28, pp. 885-888.

Points out correspondence of this work with that of Minkowski.

29. Zum gegenwärtigen Stande des Strahlungsproblems.
Physikalische Zeitschrift, vol. 10, pp. 185-193.

Ibid., pp. 323-324, under the same title there appears a clarification of his point of view in this paper vs. that of W. Ritz.

30. Entwicklung unserer Anschauungen über das Wesen und die Konstitution der Strahlung.
Physikalische Zeitschrift, vol. 10, pp. 817-825.

Address before the 81st assembly of the Gesellschaft Deutscher Naturforscher, Salzburg, 1909. It is also published in *Deutsche physikalische Gesellschaft, Verhandlungen*, Jahrg. 11, pp. 482-500.

1910

31. Über einen Satz der Wahrscheinlichkeitsrechnung und seine Anwendung in der Strahlungstheorie, with L. Hopf.
Annalen der Physik, ser. 4, vol. 33, pp. 1096-1104.

See item 79 for further discussion of the topic.

32. Statistische Untersuchung der Bewegung eines Resonators in einem Strahlungsfeld, with L. Hopf.
   Annalen der Physik, ser. 4, vol. 33, pp. 1105-1115.

33. Theorie der Opaleszenz von homogenen Flüssigkeiten und Flüssigkeitsgemischen in der Nähe des kritischen Zustandes.
   Annalen der Physik, ser. 4, vol. 33, pp. 1275-1298.

34. Principe de relativité et ses conséquences dans la physique moderne.
   Archives des sciences physiques et naturelles, ser. 4, vol. 29, pp. 5-28, and 125-244.

   The translation is by E. Guillaume, but it is not of item 21.

35. Théorie des quantités lumineuses et la question de la localisation de l'énergie électromagnétique.
   Archives des sciences physiques et naturelles, ser. 4, vol. 29, pp. 525-528.

36. Forces pondéromotrices qui agissent sur les conducteurs ferromagnétiques disposés dans un champ magnétique et parcourus par un courant.
   Archives des sciences physiques et naturelles, ser. 4, vol. 30, pp. 323-324.

1911

37. Bemerkung zu dem Gesetz von Eötvös.
   Annalen der Physik, ser. 4, vol. 34, pp. 165-169.

38. Beziehung zwischen dem elastischen Verhalten und der spezifischen Wärme bei festen Körpern mit einatomigem Molekül.
   Annalen der Physik, ser. 4, vol. 34, pp. 170-174, and p. 590.

39. Bemerkungen zu den P. Hertzschen Arbeiten: Mechanische Grundlagen der Thermodynamik.
   Annalen der Physik, ser. 4, vol. 34, pp. 175-176.

40. Berichtigung zu meiner Arbeit: Eine neue Bestimmung der Moleküldimensionen.
   Annalen der Physik, ser. 4, vol. 34, pp. 591-592.

   See items 6 and 11.

41. Elementare Betrachtungen über die thermische Molekularbewegung in festen Körpern.
   Annalen der Physik, ser. 4, vol. 35, pp. 679-694.

42. Einfluss der Schwerkraft auf die Ausbreitung des Lichtes.
Annalen der Physik, ser. 4, vol. 35, pp. 898-908.

> This paper returns to the ideas of item 21, and deduces from those ideas for the first time the consequence that star beams must be bent in passing the edge of the sun's disc.
>
> It appears in the third and later editions of H. A. LORENTZ: *Relativitätsprinzip* and in its English Translation (see item 9).

43. Relativitätstheorie.
Naturforschende Gesellschaft, Zürich, Vierteljahresschrift, vol. 56, pp. 1-14.

> Vortrag gehalten in der Sitzung der Gesellschaft.

44. Zum Ehrenfestschen Paradoxon.
Physikalische Zeitschrift, vol. 12, pp. 509-510.

> Corrects a misapprehension of the Lorentz contraction.

1912

45. Thermodynamische Begründung des photochemischen Äquivalentgesetzes.
Annalen der Physik, ser. 4, vol. 37, pp. 832-838, and vol. 38, pp. 881-884.

46. Lichtgeschwindigkeit und Statik des Gravitationsfeldes.
Annalen der Physik, ser. 4, vol. 38, pp. 355-369.

47. Theorie des statischen Gravitationsfeldes.
Annalen der Physik, ser. 4, vol. 38, pp. 443-458.

48. Antwort auf eine Bemerkung von J. Stark: Anwendung des Planckschen Elementargesetzes.
Annalen der Physik, ser. 4, vol. 38, p. 888.

49. Relativität und Gravitation: Erwiderung auf eine Bemerkung von M. Abraham.
Annalen der Physik, ser. 4, vol. 38, pp. 1059-1064.

50. Bemerkung zu Abraham's Auseinandersetzung: Nochmals Relativität und Gravitation.
Annalen der Physik, ser. 4, vol. 39, p. 704.

51. État actuel du problème des chaleurs spécifiques.
pp. 407-435 of INSTITUTS SOLVAY. CONSEIL DE PHYSIQUE, 1er, 1911. *Rapports*. Paris, Gauthier.

> For German text see item 63.

52. Gibt es eine Gravitationswirkung die der elektrodynamischen Induktionswirkung analog ist?
    Vierteljahrsschrift für gerichtliche Medizin, ser. 3, vol. 44, pp. 37-40.

1913

53. ENTWURF EINER VERALLGEMEINERTEN RELATIVITÄTSTHEORIE UND EINE THEORIE DER GRAVITATION. I. Physikalischer Teil von A. Einstein. II. Mathematischer Teil von M. Grossmann. Leipzig, Teubner. 38 pp.
    Sonderdruck aus *Zeitschrift für Mathematik und Physik*, vol. 62, pp. 225-261 (Physikalischer Teil, pp. 225-244).

    This paper may be called a review of the ideas developing in items 21, 42, 46 and 47. For critical comment see item 68.

54. Einige Argumente für die Annahme einer molekular Agitation beim absoluten Nullpunkt, with O. Stern.
    Annalen der Physik, ser. 4, vol. 40, pp. 551-560.

55. Déduction thermodynamique de la loi de l'équivalence photochimique.
    Journal de physique, ser. 5, vol. 3, pp. 277-282.

    Not a translation of item 45, but an address March 27, 1913, before the Société Française de Physique.

56. Physikalische Grundlagen einer Gravitationstheorie.
    Naturforschende Gesellschaft, Zürich, Vierteljahrsschrift, vol. 58, pp. 284-290.

    Address before this Swiss society, Sept. 9, 1913. A résumé is printed in *Schweizerische naturforschende Gesellschaft, Verhandlungen*, 1913, Part 2, pp. 137-138.

57. Max Planck als Forscher.
    Naturwissenschaften, vol. 1, pp. 1077-1079.

58. Zum gegenwärtigen Stande des Gravitationsproblems.
    Physikalische Zeitschrift, vol. 14, pp. 1249-1266.

    Address at 85*th* Versammlung Deutscher Naturforscher, Wien, Sept. 21, 1913. The citation above includes the open discussion of the paper.

    Also published in *Gesellschaft deutscher Naturforscher und Ärzte, Verhandlungen*, 1914, pp. 3-24. A "referat" was published in *Himmel und Erde*, vol. 26, pp. 90-93.

59. Nordströmsche Gravitationstheorie vom Standpunkt des absoluten Differentialkalküls, with A. D. Fokker.
Annalen der Physik, ser. 4, vol. 44, pp. 321-328.

60. Bases physiques d'une théorie de la gravitation. [Translated by E. Guillaume]
Archives des sciences physiques et naturelles, ser. 4, vol. 37, pp. 5-12.

   For German original see item 56.

61. Bemerkung zu P. Harzers Abhandlung: Die Mitführung des Lichtes in Glas und die Aberration.
Astronomische Nachrichten, vol. 199, pp. 8-10.

62. Antwort auf eine Replik P. Harzers.
Astronomische Nachrichten, vol. 199, pp. 47-48.

63. Zum gegenwärtigen Stande des Problems der spezifischen Wärme.
Deutsche Bunsengesellschaft, Abhandlungen, nr. 7, pp. 330-364.

   This volume is the German edition of the proceedings of the first Solvay congress (see item 51). Pages 353-364 of the citation are the questions and answers of the general discussion.

64. Beiträge zur Quantentheorie.
Deutsche physikalische Gesellschaft, Berichte, 1914 (or its *Verhandlungen*, vol. 16), pp. 820-828.

65. Zur Theorie der Gravitation.
Naturforschende Gesellschaft, Zürich, Vierteljahrsschrift, vol. 59, pp. 4-6.

66. [Review of] H. A. LORENTZ: Das Relativitätsprinzip.
Naturwissenschaften, vol. 2, p. 1018.

67. Nachträgliche Antwort auf eine Frage von Reissner.
Physikalische Zeitschrift, vol. 15, pp. 108-110.

   On the question of the mass of a gravitational field.

68. Principielles zur verallgemeinerten Relativitätstheorie und Gravitationstheorie.
Physikalische Zeitschrift, vol. 15, pp. 176-180.

   Reply to comment by G. Mie on the relation of Einstein's work as represented in item 53 to Minkowski's.

69. Antrittsrede.

   Preussische Akademie der Wissenschaften, Sitzungsberichte,
   1914, pt. 2, pp. 739-742.

   On the relative rôles of theoretical and experimental physics. Included
   in *Mein Weltbild* and in its translation (cf. 361 and 362).

70. Formale Grundlage der allgemeinen Relativitätstheorie.

   Preussische Akademie der Wissenschaften, Sitzungsberichte,
   1914, pt. 2, pp. 1030-1085.

71. Zum Relativitätsproblem.

   Scientia (Bologna), vol. 15, pp. 337-348.

   An exposition in reply to two papers of the opposition previously
   issued in this journal.

72. Physikalische Grundlagen und leitende Gedanken für eine Gravitationstheorie.

   Schweizerische naturforschende Gesellschaft, Verhandlungen,
   Vol. 96, pt. 2, p. 146.

   Listed by title only. Lecture delivered at the 96*th* session of the
   Swiss society Sept., 19 1913; item 56 is the same lecture.

73. Gravitationstheorie.

   Schweizerische naturforschende Gesellschaft, Verhandlungen,
   vol. 96, pt. 2, pp. 137-138.

   For full text see item 56.

74. Relativitätsprinzip.

   Vossische Zeitung, 26 April 1914, pp. 33-34.

   A rather full and serious popular presentation, not identifiable with
   any other.

75. Kovarianzeigenschaften der Feldgleichungen der auf die verall-
   gemeinerte Relativitätstheorie gegründeten Gravitationstheorie,
   with M. Grossmann.

   Zeitschrift für Mathematik und Physik, vol. 63, pp. 215-225.

1915

76. Theoretische Atomistik.

   pp. 251-263 of DIE PHYSIK unter Redaktion von E. Lecher.
   Leipzig, Teubner. (Kultur der Gegenwart, teil 3, abt. 3,
   bd. 1.).

   For a revised edition see item 191.

77. Relativitätstheorie.

    pp. 703-713 of DIE PHYSIK.

      See item 76 for bibliographic detail.

      For a revised edition see item 192.

78. Proefondervindelijk bewijs voor het bestaan der moleculaire stroomen van Ampère, with W. J. de Haas.

    Akademie van wetenschappen, Amsterdam, Verslag., ser. 4, vol. 23, pp. 1449-1464.

      A translation into Dutch of item 80.

79. Antwort auf eine Abhandlung M. von Laues: Ein Satz der Wahrscheinlichkeitsrechnung und seine Anwendung auf die Strahlungstheorie.

    Annalen der Physik, ser. 4, vol. 47, pp. 879-885.

      Discussion bearing upon item 31.

80. Experimenteller Nachweis der Ampèreschen Molekularströme, with W. J. de Haas.

    Deutsche physikalische Gesellschaft, Verhandlungen, vol. 17, pp. 152-170, and p. 203 (Berichtigung).

      Notiz zu unserer Arbeit, *ibid.*, p. 420.

      For an English translation see item 88.

81. Experimenteller Nachweis der Ampèreschen Molekularströme, with W. J. de Haas.

    Naturwissenschaften, vol. 3, pp. 237-238.

      A preliminary note covering item 80.

82. Grundgedanken der allgemeinen Relativitätstheorie und Anwendung dieser Theorie in der Astronomie.

    Preussische Akademie der Wissenschaften, Sitzungsberichte, 1915, pt. 1, p. 315.

      This is an abstract; published in full as items 83 and 84.

83. Zur allgemeinen Relativitätstheorie.

    Preussische Akademie der Wissenschaften, Sitzungsberichte, 1915, pt. 2, pp. 778-786, 799-801.

84. Erklärung der Perihelbewegung des Merkur aus der allgemeinen Relativitätstheorie.

    Preussische Akademie der Wissenschaften, Sitzungsberichte, 1915, pt. 2, pp. 831-839.

85. Feldgleichungen der Gravitation.
   Preussische Akademie der Wissenschaften, Sitzungsberichte,
   1915, pt. 2, pp. 844-847.

1916

86. GRUNDLAGE DER ALLGEMEINEN RELATIVITÄTSTHEORIE. Leipzig, Barth. 64 pp.

   "Sonderdruck aus *Annalen der Physik,*" (item 89), with "Inhalt"
   and "Einleitung" added. It has gone through several printings, at
   least up to the "5. unveränderter Abdruck," Barth, 1929.

   For English and French translations see items 128 and 266, respectively.

87. Vorwort.
   ERWIN F. FREUNDLICH: *Grundlagen der Einsteinschen
   Gravitationstheorie.* Berlin, Springer.

   This preface is likewise in all later German editions of the Freundlich and in its two English translations, Cambridge university press,
   1920, and Methuen, 1924; also in the Polish translation, Warsaw,
   about 1923.

88. Experimental proof of the existence of Ampère's molecular currents, with W. J. de Haas.
   Akademie van wetenschappen, Amsterdam, Proceedings, vol.
   18, pp. 696-711.

   An English translation of item 80.

89. Grundlage der allgemeinen Relativitätstheorie.
   Annalen der Physik, ser. 4, vol. 49, pp. 769-822.

   This—the first complete exposition of a penetrating generalization
   of the original theory—was added in the third edition of H. A.
   LORENTZ: *Relativitätsprinzip* Teubner, 1920, and is in its English
   translation. There is another English translation in item 128, and
   a French translation in item 266. It has also been issued as a separate
   (see item 86.)

90. Über Fr. Kottlers Abhandlung: Einsteins Äquivalenzhypothese
   und die Gravitation.
   Annalen der Physik, ser. 4, vol. 51, pp. 639-642.

91. Einfaches Experiment zum Nachweis der Ampèreschen Molekularströme.
   Deutsche physikalische Gesellschaft, Verhandlungen, vol. 18,
   pp. 173-177.

"Vorlesungsexperiment . . . eine Variante der . . . mit de Haas aus-geführten Versuche," (item 88).

92. Strahlungs-emission und -absorption nach der Quantentheorie. *Deutsche physikalische Gesellschaft, Verhandlungen*, vol. 18, pp. 318-323.

93. Quantentheorie der Strahlung. *Physikalische Gesellschaft, Zürich, Mitteilungen*, vol. 16, pp. 47-62.

94. [Review of] H. A. LORENTZ: Théories statistiques en thermodynamique. *Naturwissenschaften*, vol. 4, pp. 480-481.

95. Elementare Theorie der Wasserwellen und des Fluges. *Naturwissenschaften*, vol. 4, pp. 509-510.

96. Ernst Mach. *Physikalische Zeitschrift*, vol. 17, pp. 101-104.

97. Neue formale Deutung der Maxwellschen Feldgleichungen der Elektrodynamik. *Preussische Akademie der Wissenschaften, Sitzungsberichte*, 1916, pt. 1, pp. 184-187.

98. Einige anschauliche Überlegungen aus dem Gebiete der Relativitätstheorie. *Preussische Akademie der Wissenschaften, Sitzungsberichte*, 1916, pt. 1, p. 423.

This is an abstract showing that the paper dealt with the behavior of clocks and the Foucault pendulum; never published in full.

99. Näherungsweise Integration der Feldgleichungen der Gravitation. *Preussische Akademie der Wissenschaften, Sitzungsberichte*, 1916, pt. 1, pp. 688-696.

100. Gedächtnisrede auf Karl Schwarzschild. *Preussische Akademie der Wissenschaften, Sitzungsberichte*, 1916, pt. 1, pp. 768-770.

101. Hamiltonsches Prinzip und allgemeine Relativitätstheorie. *Preussische Akademie der Wissenschaften, Sitzungsberichte*, 1916, pt. 2, pp. 1111-1116.

This is included in the third and later editions of H. A. LORENTZ:

Relativitätsprinzip, and is in the English translation, Methuen, 1923. (See note under item 9 for further bibliographic detail.)

1917

102. ÜBER DIE SPEZIELLE UND DIE ALLGEMEINE RELATIVITÄTS-THEORIE, GEMEINVERSTÄNDLICH. Braunschweig, Vieweg. 70 pp. (Sammlung Vieweg, Heft 38).

> The only comprehensive survey by Einstein of his theory, and his most widely known work.
>
> See items 110, 129, 130, 137-141, 154, 169 and 215 for other editions and translations.

103. Zum Quantensatz von Sommerfeld und Epstein.
Deutsche Physikalische Gesellschaft, Verhandlungen, vol. 19, pp. 82-92.

104. [Review of] H. v. HELMHOLTZ: Zwei Vorträge über Goethe.
Naturwissenschaften, vol. 5, p. 675.

105. Marian von Smoluchowski.
Naturwissenschaften, vol. 5, pp. 737-738.

106. Quantentheorie der Strahlung.
Physikalische Zeitschrift, vol. 18, pp. 121-128.

107. Kosmologische Betrachtungen zur allgemeinen Relativitätstheorie.
Preussische Akademie der Wissenschaften, Sitzungsberichte, 1917, pt. 1, pp. 142-152.

> This is included in the third and later editions of H. A. LORENTZ: *Relativitätsprinzip*, and is in the English translation, Methuen, 1923.

108. Eine Ableitung des Theorems von Jacobi.
Preussische Akademie der Wissenschaften, Sitzungsberichte, 1917, pt. 2, pp. 606-608.

109. Friedrich Adler als Physiker.
Vossische Zeitung, Morgen Ausgabe (no. 259) May 23, p. 2.

1918

110. ÜBER DIE SPEZIELLE UND DIE ALLGEMEINE RELATIVITÄTS-THEORIE, GEMEINVERSTÄNDLICH. 3. aufl. Braunschweig, Vieweg. 83 pp.

> For first edition see item 102. The third to ninth editions (1918-1920) have an appendix: "Einfache Ableitung der Lorentz-transformation. Minkowskis vierdimensionale Welt."

111. Motiv des Forschens.

pp. 29-32 of ZU MAX PLANCKS 60. GEBURTSTAG: AN-
SPRACHEN IN DER DEUTSCHEN PHYSIKALISCHEN GESELL-
SCHAFT. Karlsruhe, Müller.

This was reprinted in *Mein Weldbild*, and is in its translation.

112. Prinzipielles zur allgemeinen Relativitätstheorie.

Annalen der Physik, ser. 4, vol. 55, pp. 241-244.

Impelled by various comments, Einstein here sets himself the goal
"lediglich die Grundgedanken herauszuheben wobei ich die Theorie
als bekannt voraussetze."

113. Lassen sich Brechungsexponenten der Körper für Röntgenstrahlen
experimentell ermitteln?

Deutsche Physikalische Gesellschaft, Verhandlungen, vol. 20,
pp. 86-87.

114. Bemerkung zu Gehrckes Notiz: Über den Äther.

Deutsche physikalische Gesellschaft, Verhandlungen, vol. 20,
p. 261.

115. [Review of] H. WEYL: Raum, Zeit, Materie.

Naturwissenschaften, Vol. 6, p. 373.

116. Dialog über Einwände gegen die Relativitätstheorie.

Naturwissenschaften, vol. 6, pp. 697-702.

117. Notiz zu Schrödingers Arbeit: Energiekomponenten des Gravitationsfeldes.

Physikalische Zeitschrift, vol. 19, pp. 115-116.

118. Bemerkung zu Schrödingers Notiz: Lösungssystem der allgemein
kovarianten Gravitationsgleichungen.

Physikalische Zeitschrift, vol. 19, pp. 165-166.

119. Gravitationswellen.

Preussische Akademie der Wissenschaften, Sitzungsberichte,
1918, pt. 1, pp. 154-167.

120. Kritisches zu einer von Hrn. de Sitter gegebenen Lösung der
Gravitationsgleichungen.

Preussische Akademie der Wissenschaften, Sitzungsberichte,
1918, pt. 1, pp. 270-272.

121. Der Energiesatz in der allgemeinen Relativitätstheorie.

Preussische Akademie der Wissenschaften, Sitzungsberichte,
1918, pt. 1, pp. 448-459.

1919

122. Prüfung der allgemeinen Relativitätstheorie.
     Naturwissenschaften, vol. 7, p. 776.

> A few lines based on a telegraphic report of the May 29, 1919, eclipse.

123. Spielen Gravitationsfelder im Aufbau der materiellen Elementarteilchen eine wesentliche Rolle?
     Preussische Akademie der Wissenschaften, Sitzungsberichte, 1919, pt. 1, pp. 349-356.

> This appears in the third and later editions of H. A. LORENTZ: *Relativitätsprinzip,* and in the English translation, Methuen, 1923. (see item 9 for bibliographic detail).

124. Bemerkungen über periodische Schwankungen der Mondlänge, welche bisher nach der Newtonschen Mechanik nicht erklärbar schienen.
     Preussische Akademie der Wissenschaften, Sitzungsberichte, 1919, pt. 1, pp. 433-436.

> Einstein's reply to comment on this paper is found, *ibid.,* pt. 2, p. 711.

125. Feldgleichungen der allgemeinen Relativitätstheorie vom Standpunkte des kosmologischen Problems und des Problems der Konstitution der Materie.
     Preussische Akademie der Wissenschaften, Sitzungsberichte, 1919, pt. 1, p. 463.

> Title only. "Im wesentlichen ein Referat über "Spielen Gravitationsfelder. . . ?" (See item 123).

126. My theory.
     Times, London, November 28, 1919, p. 13.

> Copied under title "Time, space and gravitation" in *Optician, The British optical journal,* vol. 58, pp. 187-188. Noted, with quotations in *Nature,* vol. 104, p. 360. Reprinted in *Living age,* vol. 304, pp. 41-43. German text is in *Mein Weltbild,* pp. 220-228, under the title "Was ist Relativitätstheorie?" (cf. item 361.)

127. Leo Arons als Physiker.
     Sozialistische Monatshefte, vol. 52, (Jahrgang 25, pt. 2) pp. 1055-1056.

1920

128. THE PRINCIPLE OF RELATIVITY: ORIGINAL PAPERS by A. Einstein and H. Minkowski, translated by M. N. Saha and

S. N. Bose, with an historical introduction by P. C. Mahalanobis. Calcutta, University of Calcutta. xxiii, 186 pp.

Contains translations of items 9 and 89.

129. ÜBER DIE SPEZIELLE UND DIE ALLGEMEINE RELATIVITÄTS-THEORIE, GEMEINVERSTÄNDLICH. 10 aufl. Braunschweig, Vieweg. 91 pp.

For first edition see item 102. Editions up to the fourteenth, 1922, are recorded; this last including the sixty-fifth thousand. Editions 10 to 14 contain a third section in the appendix: "Rotverschiebung der Spektrallinien."

130. RELATIVITY, THE SPECIAL AND THE GENERAL THEORY: A POPULAR EXPOSITION. London, Methuen. xiii, 138 pp., port.

Authorized translation by Robert W. Lawson from the fifth German edition, item 110. It contains a brief biographical sketch by Dr. Lawson, a brief bibliography of other books in English on relativity, and an appendix specially written for this edition: "Experimental confirmation of the general theory of relativity." So-called second and third editions were also issued by Methuen in 1920, up to the tenth in 1931. *Autobiography of science*, ed. by F. R. MOULTON, New York, Doubleday, 1945, quotes portions of this text on pp. 524-536. A "condensation" is included in J. W. Knedler: *Masterworks of science*, Doubleday, 1947, pp. 599-637.

131. ÄTHER UND RELATIVITÄTSTHEORIE: REDE GEHALTEN AM 5. MAI 1920 AN DER REICHS-UNIVERSITÄT ZU LEIDEN. Berlin, Springer. 15 pp.

For an English translation see item 152; for French and Italian translations, items 145 and 153 respectively. A Polish translation by L. Freudenheim, Eter a teorja wzglednosci, was published in Lwow without date.

132. Bemerkung zur Abhandlung von W. R. Hess: Theorie der Viscosität heterogener Systeme.
Kolloidzeitschrift, vol. 27, p. 137.

133. Inwiefern lässt sich die moderne Gravitationstheorie ohne die Relativität begründen?
Naturwissenschaften, vol. 8, pp. 1010-1011.

134. Trägheitsmoment des Wasserstoffmoleküls.
Preussische Akademie der Wissenschaften, Sitzungberichte, 1920, p. 65.

Abstract of a paper never published.

135. Schallausbreitung in teilweise dissoziierten Gasen. *Preussische Akademie der Wissenschaften, Sitzungsberichte,* 1920, pp. 380-385.

136. Meine Antwort über die antirelativitätstheoretische G.m.b.H. [Gesellschaft mit beschränkter Haftung]. *Berliner Tageblatt und Handelszeitung,* 27 August 1920, (no. 402), pp. 1-2.

1921

137. RELATIVITY, THE SPECIAL AND THE GENERAL THEORY: A POPULAR EXPOSITION. New York, Holt. xiii, 168 pp.

This differs from the English edition (item 130) only in page arrangement. The same book appears with the imprint, New York, Smith [1931], and again with the imprint, New York, Hartsdale House, Inc., 1947.

138. TEORIA DE LA RELATIVIDAD ESPECIAL Y GENERAL, Trad. de la 12ª ed. alemana por F. Lorente de Nó. Toledo, Peláez, 1921. 79 pp.

Translation of item 129. There are two later Spanish editions, called 2ª and 3ª, of 127 pp., with imprints respectively Cuenca, Ruiz de Lara, 1923, and Toledo, Medina, 1925.

139. SULLA TEORIA SPECIALE E GENERALE DELLA RELATIVITÀ: VOLGARIZZAZIONE. Trad. di G. L. Calisse. Bologna, Zanichelli. xii, 125 pp.

Italian translation of item 129.

140. TEORIIA OTNOSITEL'NOSTI: OBSHCHEDOSTYPNOE IZLOZHENIE. [Berlin] Slowo. 150 pp., portrait.

Russian translation by G. B. Itel'son of item 129. Also the same with imprint date 1922.

141. LA THÉORIE DE LA RELATIVITÉ RESTREINTE ÈT GÉNERALISÉE, traduit d'après la 10ᵉ éd. allemande par Mlle. J. Rouviere. Paris, Gauthier. xii, 120 pp.

Translation of item 129.

142. THE MEANING OF RELATIVITY: FOUR LECTURES DELIVERED AT PRINCETON UNIVERSITY, May, 1921. Transl. by Edwin P. Adams. Princeton University Press. 123 pp.

Contents:—Space and time in pre-relativity physics.—Theory of special relativity.—General theory of relativity.—General relativity (continued).

Reprinted with dates 1922 and 1923. The same title also with the imprint London, Methuen [1922], and [1924]. See items 166, 167, 179 for other translations; 156 for German text; 297 for a second edition.

143. GEOMETRIE UND ERFAHRUNG, ERWEITERTE FASSUNG DES FESTVORTRAGES GEHALTEN AN DER PREUSSISCHEN AKADEMIE. Berlin, Springer, 20 pp.

The original paper, "zur Feier des Jahrestages König Friedrichs II" is in the academy Sitzungsberichte, 1921, pp. 123-130, (item 148). A Polish translation of this was issued in Lwow without date under title, Geometrja a doswiadczenie. See items 144, 152, 153 for other translations.

144. LA GÉOMÉTRIE ET L'EXPÉRIENCE, traduit par Maurice Solovine. Paris, Gauthier, 20 pp.

Translation of item 143. A second edition also issued by Gauthier in 1934, 24 pp.

145. L'ÉTHER ET LA THÉORIE DE LA RELATIVITÉ, traduit par Maurice Solovine. Paris, Gauthier, 15 pp.

A translation of item 131. Another printing carries the date 1925.

146. Einfache Anwendung des Newtonschen Gravitationsgesetzes auf die kugelförmigen Sternhaufen.

pp. 50-52 of KAISER WILHELM GESELLSCHAFT ZUR FÖR-DERUNG DER WISSENSCHAFT, Festschrift . . . zu ihrem zehnjährigen Jubiläum . . . Berlin, Springer.

147. A brief outline of the development of the theory of relativity, [translated by R. W. Lawson]. Nature, vol. 106, pp. 782-784.

Written for a special issue of Nature devoted to relativity.

148. Geometrie und Erfahrung. Preussische Akademie der Wissenschaften, Sitzungsberichte, 1921, pt. 1, pp. 123- 130.

See item 143.

149. Eine naheliegende Ergänzung des Fundamentes der allgemeinen Relativitätstheorie. Preussische Akademie der Wissenschaften, Sitzungsberichte, 1921, pt. 1, pp. 261-264.

150. Ein den Elementarprozess der Lichtemission betreffendes Experiment.

Preussische Akademie der Wissenschaften, Sitzungsberichte, 1921, pt. 2, pp. 882-883.

On the bearing of quantum theory upon the Doppler phenomenon. The proposed experiment was apparently never carried through. But see the related paper, item 202.

151. [Report of lecture at King's College on the development and present position of relativity, with quotations].

Nation and Athenaeum, vol. 29, pp. 431-432.

The German text is included in *Mein Weltbild,* (item 361) pp. 215-220, and a full translation in *The world as I see it.* It is reported without direct quotation in the *Times, London,* June 14, p. 8, also in *Nature,* vol. 107, p. 504.

1922

152. SIDELIGHTS ON RELATIVITY: I. ETHER AND RELATIVITY. II. GEOMETRY AND EXPERIENCE, transl. by G. B. Jeffery and W. Perrett. London, Methuen. 56 pp.

Translations of items 131 and 143. The same was published with the imprint New York, Dutton, 1923. *Geometry and experience* is reproduced complete as chapter 8 of CHICAGO UNIVERSITY: *Methods of the sciences,* 2nd ed., 1947.

153. PROSPETTIVE RELATIVISTICHE DELL'ETERE E DELLA GEOMETRIA, trad. di R. Cantù e T. Bembo. Milan, Andare. 54 pp.

Translations of items 131 and 143.

154. A KÜLÖNLEGES ÉS AZ ÁLTALÁNOS RELATIVITÁS, ELMÉLETE. Budapest, Patheon irodalmi. 94 pp.

Hungarian translation of item 129.

155. O FIZICHESKOI PRIRODIE PROSTRANSTVA, transl. by G. B. Itel'son. Berlin, Slowo. 52 pp.

The translated Russian title is "Physical nature of space." It comprises translations of items 131 and 143.

156. VIER VORLESUNGEN ÜBER RELATIVITÄTSTHEORIE, GEHALTEN IM MAI, 1921, AN DER UNIVERSITÄT PRINCETON. Braunschweig, Vieweg. 70 pp.

The German text of item 142. There is also a second printing by Vieweg of date 1923.

157. Untersuchungen über die Theorie der Brownschen Bewegungen, hrsg. von R. Fürth. Leipzig, Akademische Verlagsgesellschaft. 72 pp. (Oswalds Klassiker der exakten Wissenschaften, Nr. 199).

> A reissue of items 8, 11, 12, 22, 26, with notes by the editor on the history of specific points, derivation of formulæ, etc. For an English translation see item 198.

158. Theoretische Bemerkungen zur Supraleitung der Metalle. pp. 429-435 of Leyden. Rijksuniversiteit. . . . Natuurkundig Laboratorium, Gedenkboek aangeboden aan H. Kamerlingh Onnes . . . Leiden, Ijdo.

159. Bemerkung zur Seletyschen Arbeit: Beiträge zum kosmologischen Problem. *Annalen der Physik*, ser. 4, vol. 69, pp. 436-438.

160. [Review of] W. Pauli: Relativitätstheorie. *Naturwissenschaften*, vol. 10, pp. 184-185.

161. Emil Warburg als Forscher. *Naturwissenschaften*, vol. 10, pp. 823-828.

162. Theorie der Lichtfortpflanzung in dispergierenden Medien. *Preussische Akademie der Wissenschaften, Phys.-math. Klasse, Sitzungsberichte*, 1922, pp. 18-22.

163. Bemerkung zu der Abhandlung von E. Trefftz: Statische Gravitationsfeld zweier Massenpunkte. . . . *Preussische Akademie der Wissenschaften, Phys.-math. Klasse, Sitzungsberichte*, 1922, pp. 448-449.

164. Quantentheoretische Bemerkungen zum Experiment von Stern und Gerlach, with P. Ehrenfest. *Zeitschrift für Physik*, vol. 11, pp. 31-34.

165. Bemerkung zu der Arbeit von A. Friedmann: Über die Krümmung des Raumes. *Zeitschrift für Physik*, vol. 11, p. 326.

> The criticism was withdrawn in a later note, *ibid.* vol. 16, p. 228.

1923

166. Cztery Odczyty o Teorji Wzglednosci Wygloszone w 1921 na Uniwersytecie w Princeton. Wien, and Stanis-

lawow, Renaissance-Verlag.

> Polish translation by A. Gottfryda of item 156 (142).

167. MATEMATICHESKIJA OSNOVY TEORII OTNOSITEL'NOSTI. Berlin, Slowo, 106 pp.

> Russian translation by G. B. Itel'son of item 156 (142).

168. GRUNDGEDANKEN UND PROBLEME DER RELATIVITÄTSTHEORIE. Stockholm, Imprimerie royale. 10 pp.

> Address in acknowledgement of the Nobel prize, delivered before the Nordische Naturforscherversammlung, Göteborg. Also contained in *Nobelstiftelsen, Les prix Nobel en 1921-22.*

169. [Yiddish translation, printed in Hebrew characters, of item 129] Warsaw, Gitlina. 109 pp.

> E. P. Goldsmith and Co., Ltd., Old Bond St., London, list this in an old catalog. No copy has been located in the United States.

170. Bemerkung zu der Notiz von W. Anderson: Neue Erklärung des kontinuierlichen Koronaspektrums.
> *Astronomische Nachrichten,* vol. 219, p. 19.

171. Experimentelle Bestimmung der Kanalweite von Filtern, with H. Mühsam.
> *Deutsche medizinische Wochenschrift,* vol. 49, pp. 1012-1013.

172. Beweis der Nichtexistenz eines überall regulären zentrisch symmetrischen Feldes nach der Feldtheorie von Kaluza, with J. Grommer.
> *Jerusalem University, Scripta,* vol. 1, no. 7, 5 pp.
>
> Hebrew text also.

173. Theory of the affine field.
> *Nature,* vol. 112, pp. 448-449.
>
> This is a relatively non-mathematical statement on electromagnetic and gravitational fields as generalized Riemannian geometry. Translated by R. W. Lawson, but not from item 175.

174. Zur allgemeinen Relativitätstheorie.
> *Preussische Akademie der Wissenschaften, Phys.-math. Klasse, Sitzungsberichte,* 1923, pp. 32-38, 76-77.

175. Zur affinen Feldtheorie.
> *Preussische Akademie der Wissenschaften, Phys.-math. Klasse, Sitzungsberichte,* 1923, pp. 137-140.

176. Bietet die Feldtheorie Möglichkeiten für die Lösung des quanten-problems?
   Preussische Akademie der Wissenschaften, Phys.-math. Klasse, Sitzungsberichte, 1923, pp. 359-364.

177. Théorie de relativité.
   Société française de philosophie, Bulletin, vol. 22, pp. 97, 98, 101, 107, 111-112.

   A discussion to which Einstein contributes two statements as to the relation of his theory to Kant's and to Mach's. These are quoted in full in *Nature,* vol. 112, p. 253.

178. Quantentheorie des Strahlungsgleichgewichts, with P. Ehrenfest.
   Zeitschrift für Physik, vol. 19, pp. 301-306.

1924

179. QUATRE CONFÉRENCES SUR LA THÉORIE DE LA RELATIVITÉ, FAITES À LA UNIVERSITÉ DE PRINCETON, traduit par Maurice Solovine. Paris, Gauthier, 104 pp.

   French translation of item 156 (142).
   A second printing, Gauthier, 1925. 96 pp.

180. Geleitwort.
   vol. 2, p. vi, a-b, of *Lucretius, De rerum natura,* lateinisch und deutsch, von H. DIELS, Berlin, Weidmann.

181. Antwort auf eine Bemerkung von W. Anderson.
   Astronomische Nachrichten, vol. 221, pp. 329-330.

182. Komptonsche Experiment.
   Berliner Tageblatt, April 20, 1924, 1. Beiblatt.

183. Ideas fundamentales y problemas de la teoria de la relatividad.
   Fénix (or *Phoenix*), Buenos Aires. vol. 4, pp. 103-111.

   Translation of address in acknowledgement of Nobel prize. (See item 168.)

184. Zum hundertjährigen Gedenktag von Lord Kelvins Geburt.
   Naturwissenschaften, vol. 12, pp. 601-602.

185. Quantentheorie des einatomigen idealen Gases.
   Preussische Akademie der Wissenschaften, Phys.-math. Klasse, Sitzungsberichte, 1924, p. 261-267.

   Continued in item 194.

186. Über den Äther.

    Schweizerische naturforschende Gesellschaft, Verhandlungen,
    vol. 105, pt. 2, pp. 85-93.

    An historical survey.

187. Theorie der Radiometerkräfte.

    Zeitschrift für Physik, vol. 27, pp. 1-6.

188. [Note appended to paper by Bose: Wärmegleichgewicht im Strahlungsfeld bei Anwesenheit von Materie].

    Zeitschrift für Physik, vol. 27, pp. 392-393.

1925

189. SUR L'ÉLECTRODYNAMIQUE DES CORPS EN MOUVEMENT, traduit par Maurice Solovine. Paris, Gauthier. 56 pp., port. (Maîtres de la pensée scientifique).

    A translation of items 9 and 10.

190. Anhang: Eddingtons Theorie und Hamiltonsches Prinzip.

    p. 366-371, of A. S. EDDINGTON. *Relativitätstheorie in mathematischer Behandlung.* Berlin, Springer.

    Written especially for this German edition of Eddington.

191. Theoretische Atomistik.

    pp. 281-294 of DIE PHYSIK, 2. Aufl. Leipzig, Teubner.

    A revision of item 76.

192. Relativitätstheorie.

    pp. 783-797 of DIE PHYSIK, 2. Aufl. Leipzig, Teubner.

    A revision of item 77.

193. Elektron und allgemeine Relativitätstheorie.

    Physica, vol. 5, pp. 330-334.

194. Quantentheorie des einatomigen idealen Gases. 2. Abhandlung.

    Preussische Akademie der Wissenschaften, Phys.-math. Klasse, Sitzungsberichte, 1925, pp. 3-14.

    A continuation of item 185.

195. Quantentheorie des idealen Gases.

    Preussische Akademie der Wissenschaften, Phys.-math. Klasse, Sitzungsberichte, 1925, pp. 18-25.

    A general condition is deduced which must be satisfied by every theory of a perfect gas.

196. Einheitliche Feldtheorie von Gravitation und Elektrizität.
Preussische Akademie der Wissenschaften, Phys.-math. Klasse, Sitzungsberichte, 1925, pp. 414-419.

197. Bemerkung zu P. Jordans Abhandlung: Theorie der Quantenstrahlung.
Zeitschrift für Physik, vol. 31, pp. 784-785.

1926

198. INVESTIGATIONS ON THE THEORY OF THE BROWNIAN MOVEMENT, edited with notes by R. Fürth, transl. by A. D. Cowper. London, Methuen. 124 pp.

> Translation of item 157. The same was issued with the imprint New York, Dutton.

199. W. H. Julius, 1860-1925
Astrophysical Journal, vol. 63, pp. 196-198.

200. Ursache der Mäanderbildung der Flussläufe und des sogenannten Baerschen Gesetzes.
Naturwissenchaften, vol. 14, pp. 223-224.

> Read before the Prussian Academy, January 7, 1926. Included in *Mein Weltbild* and in its translation (items 361 and 362).

201. Vorschlag zu einem die Natur des elementaren Strahlungs-emissions-prozesses betreffenden Experiment.
Naturwissenschaften, vol. 14, pp. 300-301.

> A preliminary note covering item 202.

202. Interferenzeigenschaften des durch Kanalstrahlen emittierten Lichtes.
Preussische Akademie der Wissenschaften, Phys.-math. Klasse, Sitzungsberichte, 1926, pp. 334-340.

> The prediction here made that canal rays radiate as do classical Hertz oscillators was experimentally verified by Rupp (*Ibid.,* pp. 341-351).

203. Geometría no euclídea y física.
Revista matemática hispano-americana, ser. 2, vol. 1, pp. 72-76.

1927

204. [Introduction]
to T. SHALIT: *Di spetsyele relativitets-teorye.* Berlin, [privately printed] 240 pp.

> Both Yiddish and German texts are given.

205. Einfluss der Erdbewegung auf die Lichtgeschwindigkeit relativ zur Erde.
Forschungen und Fortschritte, vol. 3, pp. 36-37.

206. Formale Beziehung des Riemannschen Krümmungstensors zu den Feldgleichungen der Gravitation.
Mathematische Annalen, vol. 97, pp. 99-103.

Read before Prussian Academy, 1926, under title: Anwendungen einer von Rainich gefundenen Spaltung des Riemannschen Krümmungstensors.

207. Isaac Newton.
Manchester Guardian weekly, vol. 16, pp. 234-235.

Also in the *Manchester Guardian* of March 19, 1927; reprinted in *Observatory*, vol. 50, pp. 146-153, and in *Smithsonian Institution, Report* for 1927, pp. 201-207.

208. Newtons Mechanik und ihr Einfluss auf die Gestaltung der theoretischen Physik.
Naturwissenschaften, vol. 15, pp. 273-276.

Included in *Mein Weltbild*, and in its translation (items 361 and 362).

209. Zu Newtons 200. Todestage.
Nord und Süd, Jahrg. 50, pp. 36-40.

210. [Letter to Royal Society on the occasion of the Newton bicentenary]
Nature, vol. 119, p. 467; *Science*, new ser., vol. 65, pp. 347-348.

211. Establishment of an international bureau of meteorology.
Science, new ser., vol. 65, pp. 415-417.

Report of a subcommitttee of the International Committee on Intellectual Cooperation, signed also by M. Curie and H. A. Lorentz.

212. Kaluzas Theorie des Zusammenhanges von Gravitation und Elektrizität.
Preussische Akademie der Wissenschaften, Phys.-math. Klasse, Sitzungsberichte, 1927, pp. 23-30.

213. Allgemeine Relativitätstheorie und Bewegungsgesetz. (First part with J. Grommer.)
Preussische Akademie der Wissenschaften, Phys.-math. Klasse, Sitzungsberichte, 1927, pp. 2-13, 235-245.

214. Theoretisches und Experimentelles zur Frage der Lichtentstehung.

Zeitschrift für angewandte Chemie, vol. 40, p. 546.

Editorial report of a lecture before the Mathematische-physikalische Arbeitsgemeinschaft, Universität Berlin, 23 Feb.

1928

215. AL TORATH HA-YAHASIUTH HA-PERATITH WEHA-KELALITH (HARZAAH POPULARITH). Tel-Aviv, Dvir. 102 pp.

Hebrew translation by Jacob Greenberg of item 129.

216. H. A. Lorentz.

Mathematisch-naturwissenschaftliche Blätter, vol. 22, pp. 24-25.

Extract from an address at the Leyden University memorial service. In *Mein Weltbild*, p. 25 (item 361).

217. Riemanngeometrie mit Aufrechterhaltung des Begriffes des Fern-Parallelismus.

Preussische Akademie der Wissenschaften, Phys.-math. Klasse, Sitzungsberichte, 1928, pp. 217-221.

218. Neue Möglichkeit für eine einheitliche Feldtheorie von Gravitation und Elektrizität.

Preussische Akademie der Wissenschaften, Phys.-math. Klasse, Sitzungsberichte, 1928, pp. 224-227.

219. A propos de "La déduction relativiste" de M. E. Meyerson.

Revue philosophique de la France, vol. 105, pp. 161-166.

1929

220. Space-time.

Encyclopedia Britannica, 14th ed., vol. 21, pp. 105-108.

This is reprinted without revision in the 1942 edition.

221. Über den gegenwärtigen Stand der Feldtheorie.

pp. 126-132 of FESTSCHRIFT PROF. DR. A. STODOLA ÜBERREICHT. Zürich, Füssli.

A survey much less technical than that in item 235, with emphasis on the antecedents of the theory.

222. Ansprache an Prof. Planck [bei Entgegennahme der Planckmedaille].

Forschungen und Fortschritte, vol. 5, pp. 248-249.

223. [Quotation from interview with (London) *Daily Chronicle* of Jan. 26, on the unitary field theory, in advance of publication of his paper on the subject, item 226].
     Nature, vol. 123, p. 175.

224. [Note appended to a reprinting of Arago's Memorial address on Thomas Young before the French Academy.]
     Naturwissenschaften, vol. 17, p. 363.

225. The new field theory.
     Times, London, of 4 Feb., 1929.

     Translated by L. L. Whyte. Quoted in full in *Observatory*, vol. 52, pp. 82-87 and 114-118, 1930.

226. Einheitliche Feldtheorie.
     Preussische Akademie der Wissenschaften, Phys.-math. Klasse, Sitzungsberichte, 1929, pp. 2-7.

     This paper represents a new development which was immediate news. (See *New York Times* item for Feb. 3rd.) A trustee of Wesleyan University purchased the manuscript directly, for desposit in the Olin Library at Wesleyan. (See *New York Times*, April 8, p. 4, col. 3.) *Scientific monthly*, vol. 28, p. 480, published a facsimile of one page. The critical note by Eddington in *Nature* of Feb. 23 (vol. 123, pp. 280-281) is also of interest in connection with the paper.

227. Einheitliche Feldtheorie und Hamiltonsches Prinzip.
     Preussische Akademie der Wissenschaften, Phys.-math. Klasse, Sitzungsberichte, 1929, pp. 156-159.

228. Sur la théorie synthéthique des champs, with Th. de Donder.
     Revue générale de l'électricité, vol. 25, pp. 35-39.

229. Appreciation of Simon Newcomb.
     Science, new ser., vol. 69, p. 249.

     Translation of a letter to Newcomb's daughter dated July 15, 1926.

230. Sesión especial de la Academia, 16 abril 1925.
     Sociedad científica Argentina, Anales, vol. 107, pp. 337-347.

     Debate with R. G. Loyarte on the equivalence of mass and energy, and discussion with H. Damianovich on the bearing of relativity on a possible "chemical field."

1930

231. Begleitwort.
     D. REICHINSTEIN: *Grenzflächenvorgänge in der unbelebten und belebten Natur*. Leipzig, Barth.

232. Über Kepler.
  Frankfurter Zeitung, 9 Nov. 1930, p. 16, col. 3-4.

  German text is reprinted in *Mein Weltbild*, and a translation in
  The World as I see it (items 361 and 362).

233. Raum-, Feld- und Äther-problem in der Physik.
  World power conference, 2nd, Berlin, 1930. Transactions,
  vol. 19, pp. 1-5.

  An invitation address, widely reported; a rather full account, for
  example, in *Dinglers polytechnisches journal*, vol. 345, p. 122.

234. Raum, Äther und Feld in der Physik.
  Forum Philosophicum, vol. 1, pp. 173-180.

  This is followed by an English translation by E. S. Brightman,
  pp. 180-184. The subject matter of this exposition is similar to that
  of item 233, but the phraseology distinctly different. Both items, in
  turn, are different from "Das Raum-, Äther-, und Feld-problem der
  Physik" contained in *Mein Weltbild*, p. 229-248. See item 415.

235. Théorie unitaire du champ physique.
  Institut H. Poincaré, Annales, vol. I, pp. 1-24.

  A comprehensive survey of the problem.

236. Auf die Riemann-Metrik und den Fern-Parallelismus gegründete
  einheitliche Feldtheorie.
  Mathematische Annalen, vol. 102, pp. 685-697.

237. Das Raum-Zeit Problem.
  Koralle, vol. 5, pp. 486-488.

  A much simplified and abbreviated form of the materal of item 220.

238. [Review of] S. WEINBERG: *Erkenntnistheorie*.
  Naturwissenschaften, vol. 18, pp. 536.

239. Kompatibilität der Feldgleichungen in der einheitlichen Feld-
  theorie.
  *Preussische Akademie der Wissenschaften, Phys.-math. Klasse,
  Sitzungsberichte*, 1930, pp. 18-23.

240. Zwei strenge statische Lösungen der Feldgleichungen der einheit-
  lichen Feldtheorie, with W. Mayer.
  *Preussische Akademie der Wissenschaften, Phys.-math. Klasse,
  Sitzungsberichte*, 1930, pp. 110-120.

241. Theorie der Räume mit Riemannmetrik und Fernparallelismus
     Preussische Akademie der Wissenschaften, Phys.-math. Klasse,
     Sitzungsberichte, 1930, pp. 401-402.

242. Address at University of Nottingham, [transl. by Dr. I. H.
     Brose].
     Science, new ser., vol. 71, pp. 608-610.

     A brief survey of special and general relativity and field theory. A
     summary is published in *Nature,* vol. 125, pp. 897-898, under the
     title "Concept of space."

243. Über den gegenwärtigen stand der allgemeinen Relativitätstheorie.
     Yale University. Library. Gazette. vol. 6, pp. 3-6.

     Followed on pp. 7-10 by a translation by Prof. Leigh Page. Yale
     University possesses the autographed manuscript. As Prof. Page re-
     calls, " a Yale graduate persuaded Dr. Einstein to write this state-
     ment in his own hand;" it was not a lecture.

                                1931
244. Foreword.
     p.v of R. De Villamil: *Newton, the man.* London, Knox.

245. Maxwell's influence on the development of the conception of
     physical reality.
     pp. 66-73 of James Clerk Maxwell: A Commemoration
     Volume. Cambridge, University press.

     German original is in *Mein Weltbild,* and a different English version
     in its translation (items 361 and 362).

246. Foreword.
     p. vii-viii of Sir Isaac Newton: *Optiks* . . . reprinted from
     the 4*th* ed., [London, 1730] New York, McGraw.

     Written expressly for this volume.

247. Theory of Relativity: Its Formal Content and Its Pres-
     ent Problems.

     Rhodes lectures at Oxford University, May, 1931. These dealt in
     Prof. Einstein's opinion with questions "in too fluid a state" for
     publication, and they have consequently never been published. Their
     content is briefly described in *Nature,* vol. 127, pp. 765, 790, 826-
     827.

248. Knowledge of past and future in quantum mechanics, with R. C.
     Tolman and B. Podolsky.
     Physical Review, ser. 2, vol. 37, pp. 780-781.

249. Zum kosmologischen Problem der allgemeinen Relativitätstheorie.
Preussische Akademie der Wissenschaften, Phys.-math. Klasse, Sitzungsberichte, 1931, pp. 235-237.

250. Systematische Untersuchung über kompatible Feldgleichungen welche in einem Riemannschen Raume mit Fern-Parallelismus gesetzt werden können, with W. Mayer.
Preussische Akademie der Wissenschaften, Phys.-math. Klasse, Sitzungsberichte, 1931, pp. 257-265.

251. Einheitliche Theorie von Gravitation und Elektrizität, with W. Mayer.
Preussische Akademie der Wissenschaften, Phys.-math. Klasse, Sitzungsberichte, 1931, pp. 541-557.

A French translation is contained in item 266. Continued in item 261.

252. Thomas Alva Edison, 1847-1931.
Science, new ser., vol. 74, pp. 404-405.

253. Gravitational and electrical fields. [Translation of preliminary report for the Josiah Macy, Jr. foundation.]
Science, new ser., vol. 74, pp. 438-439.

254. [Reply to congratulatory addresses at a dinner given by the California Institute of Technology, January 15, 1931.]
Science, new ser., vol. 73, p. 379.

Stresses the support given his work by experimental physicists. The text of the other addresses is given in the same article.

255. Gedenkworte auf Albert A. Michelson.
Zeitschrift für angewandte Chemie, vol. 44, p. 658.

1932

256. Prologue,
pp. 7-12 of M. PLANCK: *Where is science going?* New York, Norton.

A characterization of the work of Planck and of theoretical physicists generally.

257. Epilogue: a socratic dialogue, interlocutors, Einstein and Murphy.
pp. 201-213 of MAX PLANCK: *Where is science going?* New York, Norton.

"An abridgment of stenographic reports made . . . during various conversations." Essentially on the scientific basis for a philosophy of determinism.

258. On the relation between the expansion and the mean density of the universe, with W. de Sitter.

> *National academy of sciences, Proceedings,* vol. 18, pp. 213-214.

259. Zu Dr. Berliners siebzigstem Geburtstag.

> *Naturwissenschaften,* vol. 20, p. 913.

> Reprinted in *Mein Weltbild,* pp. 29-32 (item 361).

260. Gegenwärtiger Stand der Relativitätstheorie.

> *Paedagogischer Führer* (then called *Die Quelle*), vol. 82, pp. 440-442.

261. Einheitliche Theorie von Gravitation und Elektrizität, 2. Abhandlung, with W. Mayer.

> *Preussische Akademie der Wissenschaften. Phys.-math. Klasse, Sitzungsberichte,* 1932, pp. 130-137.

> A continuation of item 251.

262. Semi-Vektoren und Spinoren, with W. Mayer.

> *Preussiche Akademie der Wissenschaften, Phys.-math. Klasse. Sitzungsberichte,* 1932, pp. 522-550.

263. Unbestimmtheitsrelation.

> *Zeitschrift für angewandte Chemie,* vol. 45, p. 23.

> Abstract of a Colloquium, University of Berlin, Nov. 4, 1931.

1933

264. ON THE METHOD OF THEORETICAL PHYSICS. The Herbert Spencer lecture delivered at Oxford, June 10, 1933. Oxford, Clarendon press. 15 pp.

> The same text was published with the imprint New York, Oxford university press, 1933. 20 pp. It was also reprinted in *Philosophy of science,* vol. 1, pp. 162-169 in 1934. The German text is published in *Mein Weltbild,* pp. 176-187, and a more colloquial translation in *The world as I see it* (items 361 and 362). Selections from it are included (pp. 391-397) in *New worlds in science,* ed. by H. WARD, New York, McBride, 1941.

265. ORIGINS OF THE GENERAL THEORY OF RELATIVITY. Lecture on the George A. Gibson foundation in the University of Glasgow, June 20th, 1933. Glasgow, Jackson. 11 pp. (Glasgow university publications, no. 30.)

> German text is contained in *Mein Weltbild* pp. 248-256. A different

English version is published in *The world as I see it* (item 362). An abstract, with quotations, is in *Nature*, vol. 132, p. 21.

266. LES FONDEMENTS DE LA THÉORIE DE LA RELATIVITÉ GÉNÉRALE. . . . traduit par Maurice Solovine. Paris, Hermann. 109 pp.

> Three essays: translations of items 89 and 251, and "Sur la structure cosmologique de l'espace" (pp. 99-109) which was specially written for this volume. This last is an amplified treatment of the expanding universe (compare items 249 and 258), including the historical setting of the topic. The volume is reputed rare.

267. Dirac Gleichungen für Semi-Vektoren, with W. Mayer.
Akademie van wetenschappen, Amsterdam, Proceedings, vol. 36, pt. 2, pp. 615-619. 1934

268. Spaltung der natürlichsten Feldgleichungen für Semi-Vektoren in Spinor-Gleichungen vom Diracschen Typus, with W. Mayer.
Akademie van wetenschappen, Amsterdam, Proceedings, vol. 36, pt. 2, pp. 615-619.

1934

269. Introduction.
pp. 5-6, of L. INFELD: THE WORLD IN MODERN SCIENCE. London, Gollancz.

> Written especially for this English translation. German original on p. 275.

270. Darstellung der Semi-Vektoren als gewöhnliche Vektoren von besonderem Differentiations Charakter, with W. Mayer.
Annals of mathematics, ser. 2, vol. 35, pp. 104-110.

271. [Review of] R. TOLMAN: Relativity, thermodynamics and cosmology.
Science, new ser., vol. 80, p. 358.

1935

272. Elementary derivation of the equivalence of mass and energy.
American mathematical society, Bulletin, vol. 41, pp. 223-230.

> Josiah Willard Gibbs lecture, before the American Association for the Advancement of Science, Dec. 28, 1934.

273. Can quantum-mechanical description of physical reality be considered complete? with B. Podolsky and N. Rosen.
Physical Review, ser. 2, vol. 47, pp. 777-780.

> An abstract of this paper by H. T. Flint appears in *Nature*, vol. 135,

pp. 1025-1026. For a news story on the paper see *New York Times*, May 4, 1935, p. 11, col. 4, and May 7, p. 21, col. 5.

274. The particle problem in the general theory of relativity, with N. Rosen.

Physical Review, ser. 2, vol. 48, pp. 73-77.

1936

275. Physik und Realität.

Franklin Institute, Journal, vol. 221, pp. 313-347.

A translation by J. Piccard follows, pp. 349-382. The German text is reprinted in *Zeitschrift für freie deutsche Forschung*, Paris, vol. 1, no. 1, pp. 5-19; no. 2, pp. 1-14, (1938).

276. Two-body problem in general relativity theory, with N. Rosen.

Physical Review, ser. 2, vol. 49, pp. 404-405.

277. Lens-like action of a star by deviation of light in the gravitational field.

Science, vol. 84, pp. 506-507.

1937

278. On gravitational waves, with N. Rosen.

Franklin Institute, Journal, vol. 223, pp. 43-54.

1938

279. THE EVOLUTION OF PHYSICS: THE GROWTH OF IDEAS FROM EARLY CONCEPTS TO RELATIVITY AND QUANTA, with L. Infeld. New York, Simon and Schuster. x, 319 pp.

As explained in the preface, this is "not a systematic course in elementary facts and theories," but is aimed "to give some idea of the eternal struggle of the inventive human mind for a fuller understanding of the laws governing physical phenomena." Contents cover the rise and decline of the mechanical view; field and relativity; quanta.

280. DIE PHYSIK ALS ABENTEUER DER ERKENNTNIS. Leiden, Sijthoff. viii, 222 pp.

German edition of item 279.

281. DREI EEUWEN PHYSICA VAN GALILEI TOT RELATIVITEITS-THEORIE EN QUANTUMTHEORIE. Amsterdam, Centen. viii, 319 pp.

A translation into Dutch by M. C. Geerling of item 279.

282. L'ÉVOLUTION DES IDÉES EN PHYSIQUE DES PREMIERS CONCEPTS AUX THÉORIES DE LA RELATIVITÉ ET DES QUANTA. Traduit par Maurice Solovine. Paris, Flammarion. vii, 298 pp.

French translation of item 279.

283. Gravitational equations and the problems of motion, with L. Infeld and B. Hoffmann.
Annals of mathematics, ser. 2. vol. 39, pp. 65-100.

For continuation see item 286.

284. Generalization of Kaluza's theory of electricity, with P. Bergmann.
Annals of mathematics, ser. 2, vol. 39, pp. 683-701.

1939

285. Stationary system with spherical symmetry consisting of many gravitating masses.
Annals of mathematics, ser. 2, vol. 40, pp. 922-936.

1940

286. Gravitational equations and the problems of motion. II, with L. Infeld.
Annals of mathematics, ser. 2, vol. 41, pp. 455-464.

Continuation of item 283.

287. Considerations concerning the fundamentals of theoretical physics.
Science, new ser., vol. 91, pp. 487-492.

Address at the 8th *American scientific congress*, Washington, May, 1940. Published also in the *Proceedings* of the Congress, vol. 7, pp. 19-27 (1942), and in slightly abridged form in *Nature*, vol. 145, pp. 920-924 (1940).

1941

288. Five-dimensional representation of gravitation and electricity, with V. Bargmann and P. G. Bergmann.
pp. 212-225 of THEODORE VON KARMAN ANNIVERSARY VOLUME. Pasadena, California Institute of Technology.

289. Science and religion.
pp. 209-214 of CONFERENCE ON SCIENCE, PHILOSOPHY, AND RELIGION, 1st, New York, 1940.

Reported in *New York Times* Sept. 11, 1940, p. 30, col. 2, and also in *Nature*, vol. 146, pp. 605-607.

290. Demonstration of the non-existence of gravitational fields with a non-vanishing total mass free of singularities.
Tucumán universidad nac., Revista, ser. A, vol. 2, pp. 11-16.

> Same in Spanish, *ibid.* pp. 5-10. This represents an address before a joint meeting of the American Physical Society and the American Association of Physics Teachers in Princeton, Dec. 29, 1941, under the title "Solutions of finite mass of the gravitational equations."

1942

291. Foreword.
> p. v of PETER G. BERGMANN: *Introduction to the theory of relativity.* New York, Prentice-Hall.

292. The work and personality of Walter Nernst.
Scientific monthly, vol. 54, pp. 195-196.

1943

293. Non-existence of regular stationary solutions of relativistic field equations, with W. Pauli.
Annals of mathematics, ser. 2, vol. 44, pp. 131-137.

1944

294. Remarks on Bertrand Russell's theory of knowledge.
> pp. 277-291 of *The philosophy of Bertrand Russell,* edited by PAUL A. SCHILPP. Evanston, Northwestern University. (Library of living philosophers, vol. 5)

295. Bivector fields, I, with V. Bargmann.
Annals of mathematics, ser. 2, vol. 45, pp. 1-14.

296. Bivector fields, II.
Annals of mathematics, ser. 2, vol. 45, pp. 15-23.

> Just before its publication the manuscript of this paper was sold at a Kansas City bond auction for $5,500,000 (*New York Times,* 5 February 1944, p. 5, col. 3). It was presented to the Library of Congress (*New York Times,* 4 August 1944, p. 15, col. 5).

1945

297. THE MEANING OF RELATIVITY. Princeton, Princeton University press, 135 pp.

> This is a second edition of item 142. An appendix has been added covering The cosmological problem, Four-dimensional space which is isotropic with respect to three dimensions, Field equations, Spatial

curvature, Generalization with respect to ponderable matter. This appendix was translated by Ernst G. Straus. A so-called third edition with the imprint London, Methuen, 1946, is the same as the American edition except for a change of pagination to 130 pp.

298. On the cosmological problem.
American scholar, vol. 14, pp. 137-156; correction, p. 269.

This is a preprinting of part of the appendix to item 297.

299. Generalization of the relativistic theory of gravitation.
Annals of mathematics, ser. 2, vol. 46, pp. 578-584.

300. Influence of the expansion of space on the gravitation fields surrounding the individual stars, with E. G. Straus.
Reviews of modern physics, vol. 17, pp. 120-124; corrections and addition, *ibid.*, vol. 18, pp. 148-149.

1946

301. Generalization of the relativistic theory of gravitation, II, with E. G. Straus.
Annals of mathematics, ser. 2, vol. 47, pp. 731-741.

302. Elementary derivation of the equivalence of mass and energy.
Technion journal, (Yearbook of American Society for Advancement of the Hebrew Institute of Technology in Haifa.) vol. 5, pp. 16-17.

A derivation not published before, which uses the principle of special relativity but not its formal machinery.
Published also in Hebrew in vol. 2 (1947) of Hebrew Technical College (Institute of Technology), Haifa, *Scientific publications*.

1947

303. The problem of space, ether and the field in physics.
pp. 471-482 of Saxe, Commins, and R. N. Linscott, ed., *Man and the universe*. Random House.

Reprinted from *The world as I see it*, pp. 82-100 (item 362). The original has not been identified (see note attached to item 234).

1948

304. El Significado de la Relatividad, trad. por Dr. Carlos E. Prélat. Buenos Aires, Espasa-Calpe. 165 pp.

Spanish translation of item 297.

305. Einstein's theory of relativity.
vol. 9, p. 19 of Grolier Encyclopedia, New York, Grolier

society, 1947. (Actual date of issue is 1948.)

> Einstein wrote only this portion of the article *Relativity: time, space and matter.*

306. Relativity: essence of the theory of relativity.
Vol. 16, col. 604-608, of AMERICAN PEOPLES ENCYCLOPEDIA. Chicago, Spencer press [1948]

307. Quantenmechanik und Wirklichkeit.
Dialectica, vol. 2, pp. 320-324.

308. Generalized theory of gravitation.
Reviews of modern physics, vol. 20, pp. 35-39.

> "A new presentation . . . which constitutes a certain progress in clarity as compared with previous presentations," prepared for the Robert A. Millikan commemorative issue.

1949

309. Motion of particles in general relativity theory, with Leopold Infeld.
Canadian journal of mathematics, vol. 3, pp. 209-241.

II
NON-SCIENTIFIC WRITINGS
Starred titles are not available in the United States.

1920

311. Interview on interplanetary communication.
Daily Mail, London, Jan. 31, 1920.

> Indirect quotation in *New York Times*, Feb. 2, p. 24, col. 2.

1921

312. [Interview for Nieuwe Rotterdamsche Courant on impressions of the United States.]
Berliner Tageblatt, 7 July 1921, p. 2.

> Partly quoted in *Mein Weltbild* (item 361), pp. 54-60, and partly presented in the *New York Times*, 31 July 1921, sect. 2, p. 4, col. 3.

313. Einstein on education.
Nation and Athenaeum, vol. 30, pp. 378-379.

> Contains Quotations, but fails to indicate their source.

1922

314. In Memoriam Walther Rathenau.
Neue Rundschau, vol. 33, pt. 2, pp. 815-816.

315. Conditions in Germany.
New Republic, vol. 32, p. 197.

> Letter to H. N. Brailsford.

1923

316. My impressions of Palestine.
New Palestine, vol. 4, p. 341.

> Included in item 328, pp. 57-60.

1924

317. Une interview [on the League of Nations].
Journal des debats politiques et littéraires, édition hebdomadaire.
vol. 31, pt. 2, p. 184.

318. An die polnische Judenheit.
* *Leipziger jüdische Zeitung*, vol. 3, nr. 46.

1925

319. Botschaft.
Jüdische Rundschau, vol. 30, p. 129 (no. 14, Feb. 17).

> Copied from *La Revue juive*.
> On nationalism as an enemy of peace and as opposed by Zionism.

320. Ein Wort auf den Weg.
Juedische Rundschau, vol. 30, p. 245. (No. 27/28, Mar. 4).

> On the opening of the Hebrew University in Jerusalem.

321. Pan-Europa.
*Das junge Japan, vol. 1, pp. 369-372.

322. Mission of our university.
New Palestine, vol. 8, p. 294.

> Included in item 328, pp. 63-66.

1926

323. Interview urging extension of the Jewish telegraphic agency and support of Dr. Weizmann in his leadership of United Palestine appeal.
New Palestine, vol. 11, p. 334.

1927

324. Soll Deutschland Kolonial-politik treiben? Eine Umfrage. [Einstein's reply].
Europäische Gespräche, vol. 5, p. 626.

1929

325. GELEGENTLICHES . . . ZUM FÜNFZIGSTEN GEBURTSTAG . . .
DARGEBRACHT VON DER SONCINO-GESELLSCHAFT DER FREUNDE
DES JÜDISCHEN BUCHES ZU BERLIN. 32 pp.

Published in a limited edition.

Consists of small fragments: Über Wissenschaft und Politik, (including "Motive des Forschens" and Internationalität der Wissenschaft"),
Judenfrage (various fragments), Vorrede zur hebräischen Übersetzung
der Relativitätstheorie, a poem to Alexander Moszkowski, etc. The
choicest portions are perhaps "Neun Fragen über das eigene Schaffen"
—concise questions and answers, and "Antwort auf neun Fragen über
das Erfinderwesen"—more expansive statements. These have not been
found elsewhere.

326. Palestine troubles.
Manchester Guardian weekly, vol. 21, p. 314.

A letter first published in the *Manchester Guardian* of Oct. 12. Reprinted in item 328, pp. 71-85.

327. G. Stresemanns Mission.
Nord und Süd, Jahrgang 52, pp. 953-954.

Included as a "Foreword," pp. v-vii, to A. VALLENTIN, *Strese-
mann.* New York, Smith; London, Constable, 1931, but not to the
German edition.

1930

328. ABOUT ZIONISM: SPEECHES AND LETTERS, transl. and edited
by Sir Leon Simon. London, Soncino press. 68 pp.

Published also with the imprint New York, Macmillan, 1931. 94 pp.

Passages from *Manchester Guardian, Jüdische Rundschau* (Berlin),
New Palestine (New York), *Jewish Chronicle* (London), *Jüdischer
Almanach* (Prague), etc., which are dated but not identified as to
precise location of original. Selections are arranged under the cap-
tions "Assimilation and nationalism," "Jews in Palestine," "Jew and
Arab."

329. Wissenschaft und Diktatur.
p. 108 of O. FORST-BATTAGLIA, *Prozess der Diktatur.* Zürich,
Amathea-verlag.

A three-line statement, the source of which is not indicated.

An English translation occurs on p. 107 of both English and American
editions of the book, 1930 and 1931 respectively, which are entitled
Dictatorship on trial.

330. Science and God: a dialog.
Forum and Century, vol. 83, pp. 373-379.

> With J. Murphy and J. W. N. Sullivan.
> The conversation touches also the relation of science to other aspects of life, the question of Jewish racial characteristics, etc. It is entirely distinct from item 257.

331. What I believe.
Forum and Century, vol. 84, pp. 193-194.

> The thirteenth of the Forum series "Living philosophies," republished as pp. 3-7 of LIVING PHILOSOPHIES, New York, Simon and Schuster, 1931. It was reprinted in the *Forum* vol. 95, pp. 174-176, 1936. It also appears under the title "Meeting-place of science and religion" on pp. 91-102 of *Has science discovered God?*, edited by E. H. COTTON, New York, Crowell, 1931. The original text is in *Mein Weltbild*, pp. 11-17 (item 361).

332. Judentum im Kampfe für den Frieden, with O. Wassermann.
*Leipziger jüdische Zeitung (or *Allgemeines jüdisches Familien-Blatt*), vol. 11, nr. 3, p. 3.

333. Religion and science.
New York Times, 9 November 1930, sect. 5, pp. 1-4.

> Written expressly for the *New York Times Magazine*.
> Reprinted as the title essay in *Cosmic religion* (item 335).
> German text was published in *Berliner Tageblatt*, 11 November 1930, 1. Beiblatt, p. 1, and reproduced in *Mein Weltbild*, pp. 36-45 (item 361).

334. [Welcome to World power conference]
Vossische Zeitung, 8 June 1930, p. 4.

> A short paragraph included with greetings from other Berlin scientists.

1931

335. COSMIC RELIGION, WITH OTHER OPINIONS AND APHORISMS.
New York, Covici-Friede, 109 pp.

> Contains a biographical note "prepared by the publishers," and an appreciation by George Bernard Shaw. The title essay is item 333; the section captioned "Pacifism" contains item 343 and other fragments; two other sections are headed "The Jews," and "Opinions and Aphorisms." "The Jewish homeland," pp. 71-83, is a composite of quotations also found in item 328.

336. Tagore talks with Einstein.
Asia, vol. 31, pp. 138-142, with special portrait.

Republished in abbreviated form, *ibid*, vol. 37, pp. 151-152, 1937. This conversation is on Eastern music, in a lighter vein than item 340, and reported by Tagore himself.

337. A day with Albert Einstein: interview by Prof. Chaim Tscherno-witz.
Jewish sentinel, vol. 1, no. 1 (September), pp. 19, 44, 50.

Conversation on Jewish philosophy, leading up to Zionism.

338. Mitarbeit am Palästina-Werk.
* Leipziger jüdische Zeitung, vol. 12, no. 13, p. 3.

339. Abrüstungskonferenz, 1932.
Luxemburg Zeitung, 9 November 1931.

This is a letter dated Berlin, Sept. 4, 1931.

340. The nature of reality.
Modern review, Calcutta, vol. 49, pp. 42-43. Also *Living age*, vol. 340, pp. 262-265.

Authorized version of a conversation with Tagore, largely on the nature of truth and beauty.

341. The 1932 Disarmament conference.
Nation, vol. 133, p. 300.

Original German text is included in *Mein Weltbild*, p. 89-92 (cf. 361).

342. Wehrpflicht und Abrüstung.
Neue freie Presse, Wien. 22 Nov. 1931, pp. 1-2.

This is reprinted in *Mein Weltbild*. pp. 83-89 (item 361).

343. Militant pacifism.
World tomorrow, vol. 14, p. 9.

Address before the New History Society, New York City, 14 December 1930, translated by Mme. Rosika Schwimmer. Quoted in part in *New York Times*, 21 December 1930, sect. 9, p. 4, col. 1. Reprinted in items 335 and 353. It was also issued by the NEW HISTORY FOUNDATION in a pamphlet entitled *Torchbearers* (pp. 26-28), which contains as well the other addresses on the same occasion.

1932
344. Message of felicitation to Justice Brandeis.

p. 3, AVUKAH ANNUAL of 1932. New York, American student Zionist federation.

345. Introduction
pp. 9-10 of BUILDERS OF THE UNIVERSE. Los Angeles, U. S. library association.

346. Address to students of the University of California at Los Angeles, February, 1932.
pp. 91-96 of BUILDERS OF THE UNIVERSE, U. S. library association.

Text in both German and English; on science as coordination of observed facts, exemplified in the progression from special relativity to unified field theory.

347. To American Negroes.
Crisis, vol. 39, p. 45.

348. Is there a Jewish view of life?
Opinion, vol. 2, issue of 26 September 1932, p. 7.

1933

349. WARUM KRIEG? EIN BRIEFWECHSEL, Albert Einstein und Sigmund Freud. Paris, Internationales Institut für geistige Zusammenarbeit, Völkerbund. 62 pp. (Nummerierte Aufl. von nur 2000 Exemplaren).

Einstein's letter is pp. 11-21.

350. WHY WAR? Paris, International institute of intellectual cooperation, League of nations, 56 pp. (Open letters, no. 2.)

Einstein's letter is pp. 11-20.
English translation by Stuart Gilbert of item 349.
Reprinted in London, 1934, as New Commonwealth [pamphlet], series A, no. 6. Also reprinted in *Free World,* vol. 11, March issue, pp. 23-25, 1946; and in LEAGUE OF NATIONS, INTELLECTUAL COOPERATION ORGANISATION, *Bulletin,* vol. 1, pp. 239-245.

351. POURQUOT LA GUERRE? Paris, Institut international de coopération intellectuelle, Société des nations. 62 pp. (Limited ed. of 3,000 copies).

Translation into French by B. Briod of item 349.

352. WAAROM OORLOG Amsterdam, Seyffardt. 61 pp.

Translation into Dutch by E. Straat of item 349.

353. THE FIGHT AGAINST WAR, ed. by Alfred Lief. New York, John Day. 64 pp. (John Day pamphlets, no. 20).

Selections from Einstein's writings and speeches covering the period 1914-1932. The historical setting is given for each, and where possible a specific reference. Among the items not readily available elsewhere is the "Counter-manifesto" drawn up by Einstein, Georg F. Nicolai and Wilhelm Foerster in October, 1914, as a protest against the manifesto signed by ninety-three German intellectuals. This is otherwise published only in Nicolai's *Biologie des Krieges*. Zürich, Fussli, 1919, and its translation, New York, Century, 1918. Another is a speech before an Opponents of War International Conference at Lyons, August 1, 1931, under the caption "Now is the time," which was quoted in part in *New York Times*, 2 August 1931, sect. 1, p. 3, col. 5.

354. A declaration.

p. 5 of LES JUIFS. Paris, Société anonyme 'Les Illustrés Français.'

355. On peace, a letter to the editor [Dr. Frederick Kettner].

Biosophical review, vol. 3, p. 27.

356. Zur Deutsch-Amerikanischen Verständigung.

pp. 4-8 of *California Institute of Technology, Bulletin*, vol. 42, no. 138.

An English translation follows, pp. 9-12.

This was part of a symposium on America and the world situation broadcast January 23, 1933. (See *New York Times*, 24 Jan. 1933, p. 2, col. 2.)

357. Address [at a dinner under the auspices of American friends of the Hebrew University in Palestine in New York, March 15]

Science, new ser., vol. 77, pp. 274-275.

358. [Open letter to the Prussian Academy on the matter of his resignation from that body]

Science, new ser., vol. 77, p. 444.

All the correspondence on this occasion is included in *Mein Weltbild*, pp. 120-128, and in *The world as I see it*, pp. 174-182 (items 361 and 362).

359. Victim of misunderstanding.

Times, London. 25 September 1933, p. 12, col. d.

Letter on his position as to Communism.

360. Albert Hall speech: Civilization and science.

Times, London. 4 October 1933, p. 14, col. e.

This was also published as "Europe's danger, Europe's hope," see item 365.

A French translation appeared in 1934 in *Revue bleu* (Item 368).

1934

361. MEIN WELTBILD. Amsterdam, Querido. 269 pp.

> Permission was given "to one of his intimates, J. H." to make "a selection to give a picture of the man"—his writings in the fields of science, Judaism, politics, and pacifism. Some of the contents are noted under the separate items of this bibliography. The book itself gives no clue as to where items were originally published; some may never have appeared in print previously.
> There is also a "2. Aufl." with the same imprint.

362. THE WORLD AS I SEE IT. New York, Covici-Friede. 290 pp.

> A translation by Alan Harris of item 361, though the order of arrangement is different. The same text is also published with the imprint London, Lane, 1935. 214 pp. These editions carry a "Foreword" by Einstein which is not in the German edition. The Philosophical Library, New York, has announced an abridged edition for publication in the fall of 1949.

363. COMMENT JE VOIS LE MONDE. Paris, Flammarion. 258 pp.

> A translation by Col. Cros of item 361.

364. Sauvons la liberté.
    Annales politiques et littéraires, vol. 102, pp. 377-378.

365. Europe's danger; Europe's hope.
    Friends of Europe. Publications. no. 4, 6 pp.

> Address at a meeting in Royal Albert Hall, Oct. 4, 1933, organized by Refugee Assistance Fund. Reprinted under the caption "Personal liberty" by the *New York Herald-Tribune*, 4 February 1934. On the inter-relation of personal freedom and collective security, ending with the words "Only through peril and upheaval can nations be brought to further development."

366. An opinion of H. W. Krutch's article: Was Europe a success?
    Nation, vol. 139, p. 373.

367. Education and world peace.
    Progressive education, vol. 11, p. 440.

> A message read at a New York regional conference of the Progressive Education Association. Quoted in full in the *New York Times*, 24 November 1934, p. 17, col. 4.

368. La science et la civilisation, trad. par L.Baillon de Wailly.
    Revue bleu, littéraire et politique, vol. 72, pp. 641-642.

> Albert Hall speech of October 4, 1933. See items 360 and 365.

1935

369. D'Muth Olami. Tel-Aviv, Stybel publ. co. 224 pp.

> Hebrew translation by S. Ettinger of *Mein Weltbild*, item 361.

370. Lamah Milhamah? Tel-Aviv, 1935? 16 pp.

> Hebrew translation of item 349.

371. Appeal for Jewish unity: address before Women's division of the American Jewish Congress.

> *New Palestine*, vol. 25, issue of 1 March (no. 9), p. 1.

372. Statement on Prof. Hugo Bergmann, newly appointed Rector of the Hebrew University in Jerusalem.

> *New Palestine*, vol. 25, issue of 22 November (no. 36), p. 2.

373. Peace must be waged, an interview by R. M. Bartlett.

> *Survey graphic*, vol. 24, p. 384, with portrait.

1936

374. Some thoughts concerning education.

> *School and society*, vol. 44, pp. 589-592.

> Address for a convocation of the University of the State of New York, Albany. Translated by Lina Arronet.

375. Freedom of learning.

> *Science*, new ser., vol. 83, pp. 372-373.

> Reprint of a letter to the *Times, London*, signed also by E. Schroedinger and V. Tchernavin. (Mar. 25, p. 17, col. e.)

1938

376. Why do they hate the Jews?

> *Collier's weekly*, vol. 102, Nov. 26, pp. 9-10, '38, with portrait.

> Translated by Ruth Norden.

1939

377. Humanity on trial.

> A radio address in support of the United Jewish Appeal, printed as a four-page leaflet by this organization for wider circulation. The text is quoted in the *New York Times*, 22 March 1939, p. 10, col. 2. Also published under the title "Europe will become a barren waste," in *New Palestine*, vol. 29, issue of March 24, pp. 1-2.

378. The Goal.

> Lecture at a summer conference at Princeton Theological Seminary. Circulated in mimeographed form only.

379. Spirit of faith: comment on a British White Book on Palestine.

> *Aufbau*, vol. 5, issue of 1 June (no. 10), p. 7.

380. Message to United Palestine Appeal convened in Washington.

> *New Palestine*, vol. 29, issue of Jan. 20, box on p. 3.

381. On Zionism.

> *New Palestine* vol. 29, issue of March 17, p. 3.

> A special issue in honor of Einstein's sixtieth birthday presents a page of quotations from his writings (cf. item 328).

382. Statement issued on sixtieth birthday, on the American scientific spirit.

> *Science*, new ser., vol. 89, p. 242.

1940

383. Freedom and science.

> pp. 381-383 of *Freedom: its meaning*, edited by RUTH N. ANSHEN, New York, Harcourt, Brace, and Co.

> Translated by Prof. James Gutmann from a manuscript prepared for this volume. There is also an edition of this book with the imprint London, Allen, 1942.

384. Neuer Bund der Nationen.

> *Aufbau*, vol. 6, issue of June 28 (no. 26), pp. 1-2.

> Based on interview at the time he received American citizenship.

385. Meine Stellung zur jüdischen Frage.

> *Aufbau*, vol. 6, issue of December 27 (no. 52), box on p. 9.

386. The hour of decision.

> *Saturday review of literature*, vol. 22, issue of October 19, p. 7.

1941

387. Credo as a Jew.

> Vol. 4, pp. 32-33 of UNIVERSAL JEWISH ENCYCLOPEDIA, edited by I. Landman.

> Quoted in translation, with facsimile of German manuscript; no other source credited.

388. [Statement on significance of American citizenship]
pp. 43-47 of I AM AN AMERICAN, edited by R. S. Benjamin.
New York, Alliance Book Corp.

> This volume had its origin in a series of broadcasts under the auspices of the U.S. Immigration and Naturalization Service. (Also in *New York Times*, 23 June 1940, p. 6, col. 2.)

1942

389. The common language of science.
Advancement of science, vol. 2, (no. 5), p. 109.

> An address radioed to the meeting of the British Association for the Advancement of Science, Sept., 1941.

1943

390. [Address before student body, California Institute of Technology, 16 February 1931, on the misuse of scientific discovery].
pp. 43-44 of *Treasury of science*, ed. by H. SHAPLEY, et al.
New York, Harper.

> The date given in the anthology is incorrect; the text is to be found in the *New York Times*, 17 February 1931, p. 6, col. 3.

1944

391. LETTERA A B. CROCE E RISPOSTA DEL CROCE. Bari, Laterza. 7 pp.

> Einstein's letter is pp. 1-2; there is no clue as to publication elsewhere.

392. Gandhi's statesmanship.
pp. 79-80 of MAHATMA GHANDHI: ESSAYS AND REFLECTIONS ON HIS LIFE AND WORK, presented to him on his seventieth birthday, 1939, edited by S. Radhakrishnan. London, Allen and Unwin, [1944].

393. TEST CASE FOR HUMANITY. London, Jewish agency for Palestine. 7 pp.

> This is a pamphlet reprint of item 399, accompanied by quotations from *About Zionism*, item 328.

394. THE ARABS AND PALESTINE, with E. Kahler. New York, Christian Council on Palestine and American Palestine Committee. 16 pp.

> Two articles originally published in the *Princeton Herald* of 14 April and 28 April 1944 (items 399 and 400).

395. The problem of today and tomorrow.
> *Aufbau*, vol. 10, no. 11 (March 17), box on p. 1.

> A brief birthday message from London.

396. Grüsse zum "I am an American" Day.
> *Aufbau*, vol. 10, no. 20 (May 19), p. 1.

397. Our goal unity, but the Germans are unfit: an interview.
> *Free world*, vol. 8, pp. 370-371.

398. The ethical imperative.
> *Opinion*, vol. 14, March issue, p. 10.

> In tribute to Rabbi Stephen S. Wise.

399. Palestine setting of sacred history of Jewish race, with Eric Kahler.
> *Princeton Herald*, April 14, 1944, pp. 1, 6.

> This and the following item constitute a reply to a letter by Prof. Hitti on the Palestinian question in *Princeton Herald* April 7, p. 1.

> Reprinted as part of item 394.

400. Arabs fare better in Palestine than in Arab countries, with Eric Kahler.
> *Princeton Herald*, April 28, 1944, pp. 1, 6.

> Reprinted as part of item 394.

1945

401. A testimonial from Prof. Einstein.
> pp. 142-143 of JACQUES S. HADAMARD, *An essay on the psychology of invention in the mathematical field*. Princeton University Press.

> This same testimonial is included in the second printing of the book, 1949.

402. Einstein on the atomic bomb, edited by Raymond Gram Swing.
> *Atlantic monthly*, vol. 176, November issue, pp. 43-45.

> Quoted in *New York Times*, Oct. 27, p. 17, col. 6. He clarified his meaning in a statement issued in *New York Times*, October 29, p. 4, col. 3.

> A reprint was distributed November 1947 with an appeal for financial support by the Emergency Committee of Atomic Scientists, and again January 1948 with a letter signed only by Einstein.

403. Gedenkworte für F.D.R.
    Aufbau, vol. 11, no. 17 (April 27), p. 7.

404. Message für Town Hall.
    Aufbau, vol. 11, no. 46 (November 16), p. 17.

405. Einstein verdammt Lessing Rosenwald.
    Aufbau, vol. 11, no. 50 (Dec. 14), p. 11.

406. Interview with Einstein, by Alfred Stern.
    Contemporary Jewish record, vol. 8, pp. 245-249.

    On American science and general scientific questions.

1946

407. ONLY THEN SHALL WE FIND COURAGE.

    An eight-page pamphlet, consisting of reprints of the interview with
    M. Amrine in the *New York Times Magazine* (June 23, sect. 6, p. 7)
    and a supporting article by Dean Christian Gauss entitled "Is Ein-
    stein right?" from *The American Scholar* (vol. 15, pp. 469-476),
    which was published by the Emergency Committee of Atomic
    Scientists for wide circulation in its campaign for funds. As evidence
    of its extensive dissemination one may cite an editorial in *Étude* for
    May, 1947, vol. 65, p. 243, which is based upon it.

408. Social obligation of the scientist.
    pp. 318-319 of *Treasury for the free world*, edited by R.
    RAEBURN. New York, Arco Publ. Co.

    In the form of questions and answers; not found elsewhere, though
    most other items in the anthology are from the *Free world*.

409. The way out.
    pp. 76-77 of *One world or none*, ed. by D. MASTERS and
    K. WAY. New York, McGraw.

410. Introduction.
    pp. ix-xi of RUDOLF KAYSER, *Spinoza: portrait of a spiritual
    hero*. New York, Philosophical Library.

    Not in the German edition.

411. [Quotations from letters on uranium fission research of Aug. 2,
    1939, Mar. 7 and Apr. 25, 1940, as read by Dr. Alexander
    Sachs.]
    pp. 10, 16-17, 19-20 of U.S. SENATE. SUBCOMMITTEE ON
    ATOMIC ENERGY. *Hearings pursuant to Senate Resolution 179.*

Quoted in *New York Times*, Nov. 28, 1945, p. 2, col. 2. See also item 412.

412. [Letter to President Roosevelt, Aug. 2, 1939]

This is published in full in "A statement of purpose" by the Emergency Committee of Atomic Scientists, an eight-page pamphlet distributed in December 1946 as part of its campaign for funds.

413. An die jüdischen Studenten.
   Aufbau, vol. 12, no. 1 (Jan. 4), p. 16.

A telegram to the world conference meeting in Paris.

414. Die Welt muss neu denken lernen.
   Aufbau, vol. 12, no. 38, pp. 1-2 and no. 39, p. 5, (Sept. 20 and 27).

This is the German text of the interview by M. Amrine published in the *New York Times* of June 23, 1946 (q.v., and also item 407).

415. Why war?
   Free world, vol. 11, March issue, pp. 23-25.

A reprint of item 350.

416. Year one—Atomic age. A message.
   Survey graphic, vol. 34, issue for January, box on p. 23.

Included with speeches at a New York meeting of Americans United for World Organization.

417. E = mc²: the most urgent problem of our time.
   Science illustrated, vol. 1, no. 1, April issue, pp. 16-17.

An explanation of the formula for the general reader by analogy.

1947

418. The military mentality.
   American scholar, vol. 16, pp. 353-354

Reprinted in *Bulletin of the atomic scientists*, vol. 3, pp. 223-224.

419. Atomic war or peace, as told to Raymond Swing.
   Atlantic monthly, vol. 180, pp. 29-33 of November issue.

Distributed as a separate by the Emergency Committee of Atomic Scientists with a plea for financial support. The German text, "Atomkrieg oder Frieden?", was published in *Aufbau*, vol. 13, no. 50 (December 12), pp. 1-2, 27.

420. Dear friends in the Mid-West: a Christmas greeting.
   Chicago daily tribune, 24 December, p. 9.

Presented by Marshall Field Co.

421. World unity demanded.
    Cleveland news, 11 November (vol. 106, no. 266). Home final
    ed., p. 1, col. 7 and p. 4, col. 5.

    Address radioed from Princeton to convocations of World Security
    Workers at Western Reserve University, Case Institute of Technology,
    Fenn College, John Carroll University and Cleveland School of
    Art.

422. Musical visit with Einstein: interview by Lili Foldes.
    Étude, vol. 65, issue of January, p. 5.

423. Paul Langevin.
    La Pensée: revue du rationalisme moderne, new ser., no. 12
    (mai-juin), pp. 13-14.

424. Telegraphic response to the editor on Walter White's article:
    Why I remain a negro.
    Saturday review of literature, vol. 30, issue of November 1,
    p. 21.

425. An open letter to the General Assembly of the United Nations,
    on "the way to break the vicious circle."
    United Nations world, vol. 1, issue of October, pp. 13-14.

    Quotations from it and comment in *New York Times,* Sept. 23, p. 16,
    col. 2.

426. Science "gag" can even crimp military use.
    Washington post, August 3, p. 1 of special Atomic energy sup-
    plement.

1948

427. Introduction
    p. 1 of DANIEL Q. POSIN: *I have been to the village.* Ann
    Arbor, Edwards.

428. Foreword.
    pp. 1-2 of LINCOLN BARNETT: *The universe and Dr. Einstein.*
    New York, Sloane.

    This volume is an expansion of articles appearing under this title
    in Harper's during April, May and June 1948, very carefully pre-
    pared.

429. [Letter on universal military training addressed to the Chairman
    of the Senate Committee]

p. 267 of U.S. CONGRESS. SENATE. COMMITTEE ON ARMED SERVICES. *Universal military training.* Hearings. . . .

Read at hearing of March 24.

430. A plea for international understanding.
Bulletin of the atomic scientists, vol. 4, p. 1.

Addressed to the Foreign Press Association of the United Nations, Nov. 11, 1947, in accepting the Association's award. First published in *New York Times,* 12 November 1947, p. 1, col. 7.

431. Reply to Soviet scientists.
Bulletin of the atomic scientists, vol. 4, pp. 33-34.

A statement prepared for the *Bulletin* in reply to a letter published in the *New Times* of Moscow, Nov. 26, 1947, "About certain fallacies of Albert Einstein." This is largely quoted in *New York Times,* 30 January 1948, p. 1, col. 2-3 and p. 12, col. 6.

432. Message to the World Congress of Intellectuals, Warsaw.
Bulletin of the atomic scientists, vol. 4, pp. 295, 299.

Dissimilar version released in Poland appears on p. 320. Both documents appeared first in the *New York Times,* 29 August 1948, sect. 1, p. 1 and 18.

433. Letter [on new financial arrangements for this Bulletin].
Bulletin of the atomic scientists, vol. 4, p. 354.

Later distributed as a circular letter.

434. Religion and science: irreconcilable?
Christian register, vol. 127, June issue, p. 19.

Message addressed to a national Unitarian conference.

435. Atomic science reading list.
Magazine of the year, January 1948 issue, pp. 60-61.

Einstein's choice of six titles with his annotations.

436. Looking ahead.
Rotarian, issue for June, p. 8-10.

This includes a reprinting of items 430 and 431, his message to a citizens' meeting for world government in Portland, Maine, December 11, 1946, and a report of an interview with the editor of the *Rotarian* on the feasibility of world government now.

437. [Letter urging support of a supra-national organization, addressed to the General Conference of the Methodist Church].
Zion's herald, vol. 126, p. 453.

438. Epoche des Friedens?

UNESCO, Monatsschrift für Erziehung, Wissenschaft und Kultur der Österreichischen Liga für die Vereinigten Nationen, Jahrg. 1, pp. 435-436 (Heft 10).

> An interview with Dr. Helmut Leitner, Consul General of Austria in New York.

1949

439. [Letter to Prof. Archibald Henderson on the occasion of the publication of his *Bernard Shaw: playboy and prophet.* Appleton, 1932. 872 pp.]

p. 92 of ARCHIBALD HENDERSON: THE NEW CRICHTON, ed. by Samuel S. Hood. New York, Beechhurst press.

440 [Article by A. Werner in token of Einstein's seventieth birthday, containing questions and answers of an interview.]
Liberal Judaism, vol. 16, issue for April-May, pp. 4-12.

> Also quotes his Credo (item 387).

441. Why socialism.
Monthly review: an independent socialist magazine. vol. 1, issue for May (no. 1), pp. 9-15.

442. A true prophet: greeting to Rabbi Stephen Wise on his seventy-fifth birthday.
Opinion, vol. 19, issue for March (no. 5), p. 12.

443. Facsimile of greeting to ORT convention.
ORT *Bulletin,* vol. 2, issue for May (no. 9), p. 7.

444. Most fateful decision in recorded history.
Southern Patriot, May.

> Reprinted in *Motive,* November (Vol. X, No. 2, p. 36).

445. Notes for an autobiography.
Saturday Review of Literature, Nov. 26 (Vol. XXXII, No. 46), 9ff.

> Excerpts from "Autobiographical Notes," pp. 1-95 of *Albert Einstein: Philosopher-Scientist,* edited by Paul A. Schilpp, Evanston (Library of living philosophers, vol. 7).

III

INTERVIEWS, LETTERS AND SPEECHES
QUOTED IN *NEW YORK TIMES**

(Omitting items more completely published elsewhere)

Letter to Dr. Haenisch on his affection for Berlin. 21 Nov. 1920, sect. 2, p. 10, col. 5.

Reply to tribute paid him at meeting of National Academy of Sciences. placing joy of discovery above personal renown. 27 April 1921, p. 21, col. 2.

Statement on the Edison test for college men. 18 May 1921, p. 18, col. 2.

Speech in Berlin on anti-German attitude in America. 2 July 1921, p. 3, col. 5.

Statement on scientific life in the United States. 31 July 1921, sect. 2, p. 4, col. 3.

Interview in Berlin by Cecil Brown on the theory connecting gravitation and electricity. 27 March 1923, p. 18, col. 8.

Letter resigning from the League of Nations Committee on Intellectual Cooperation, in protest at inadequacy of the League. 28 June 1923, p. 15, col. 4.

Quotation in a special article by H. Bernstein on Europe's craving for peace. 17 May 1925, sect. 9, p. 4, col. 5.

On greatness, from an interview. 18 April 1926, sect. 9, p. 12, col. 4.

Interview on the 200-inch telescope, etc., while an important new discovery is pending. 4 November 1928, p. 1, col. 3, and p. 15, col. 5.

Field theories, old and new, written expressly for the *New York Times*. 3 February 1929, sect. 9, p. 1, col. 1-8.
A simplified presentation of item 225.

Letter to a thirteen-year Los Angeles boy who had written on relativity for a Los Angeles paper. 10 February 1929, p. 26, col. 3.

* These titles have been in almost every case supplied by the editor of this bibliography, since the newspaper captions were either entirely lacking or not specific enough.

Poem acknowledging a birthday greeting. 21 April 1929, sect. 10, p. 7, col. 4-5.

Belief in the God of Spinoza. 25 April 1929, p. 60, col. 4.

Interview, with portrait, by S. J. Woolf; several direct quotations on the philosophy of life, etc. 18 August 1929, sect. 5, p. 1-2.

Text of a broadcast in connection with Edison semicentennial of incandescent lighting. 23 October 1929, p. 3, col. 2.

Cable to *New York Times* on the possibility of disarmament by a single nation. 21 January 1930, p. 5, col. 3.

Lecture at Kroll Opera House, Berlin, on development of physical theories. 17 June 1930, p. 3, col. 1-3.

Address on the marvel and the social significance of radio at opening of radio exhibit, Berlin. 23 August 1930, p. 1, col. 6.
    German original in *Berliner Tageblatt*, Abend Ausgabe, August 22, 1. Beiblatt.

Interview on philosophy of science and art, by Emil Lengyel. 14 September 1930, sect. 5, p. 9, col. 1-4.

Quotations from paper read before International Congress of Palestine Workers in Berlin, Sept. 27. 28 September 1930, sect. 2, p. 5, col. 1.

Reply to George Bernard Shaw at Ort and Oze Society dinner, London, on his attitude toward Jews. 29 October 1930, p. 12, col. 2, and 2 November 1930, sect. 9, p. 2, col. 1.

Religion and science, written expressly for the *New York Times*. 9 November 1930, sect. 5, p. 1, col. 1-4. (see also item 333)

Statement given to Zionist Organization of America criticizing British Zionist policy. 3 December 1930, p. 15, col. 1.

New Year's greeting to America, on its joy in work, and other points. 1 January 1931, p. 13, col. 1.

Letter to A. Geller on his determinist views. 28 January 1931, p. 2, col. 2.

An interview on several subjects, quoted from the *Yale News*. 3 February 1931, p. 8, col. 1.

Science and Happiness. 22 February 1931, sect. 9, p. 2, col. 1. This is his speech at California Institute of Technology reprinted from the issue of 17 February 1931, p. 6, col. 3.

Appreciation of his American reception. Radio address and cable. 15 March 1931, p. 1, col. 2.

Letter read at meeting of International Philosophical Society at Barbizon Plaza, New York, answering questions on theories of art, etc. 17 April 1931, p. 25, col. 7.

Statement to International Conference of Opponents of War, Lyons, August 1, 1931. 2 August 1931, sect. 1, p. 3, col. 5. Quoted in item 353.

Lecture at Berlin planetarium on aim of physicists. 5 October 1931, p. 11, col. 4.

Address on current economic questions at California Institute of Technology dinner. 26 January 1932, p. 13, col. 2.

Talk to university representatives in Pasadena advocating economic boycott in war. 28 February 1932, sect. 2, p. 4, col. 4.

A one-sentence rule for success, quoted from *Youth* published by Young Israel of Williamsburg. 20 June 1932, p. 17, col. 3.

Letter read at Spinoza tercentenary, City College, New York. 24 November 1932, p. 27, col. 8.

Speech at dinner of American Friends of the Hebrew University in Palestine on the significance of the university. 16 March 1933, p. 10, col. 2. Also in *Science* vol. 77, pp. 274-275. (Item 357)

Letter to Prussian Academy to deny his spreading of propaganda on anti-semitic atrocities. 12 April 1933, p. 16, col. 5.

Letter to A. Nahon on application of pacifist principles to the problems of Belgium. 10 September 1933, p. 14, col. 4. Previously published in *La Patrie Humaine*.

Address at Albert Hall, London: a plea for the freedom and integrity of scholarship. 4 October 1933, p. 17, col. 3-4. See item 360.

Address at Nobel centenary, Hotel Roosevelt, New York. 19 December 1933, p. 18, col. 2.

Excerpt from essay on U.S. high school system and importance of education, written for celebration at Weequahic High School, Newark, N.J. 18 March 1934, sect. 4, p. 4, col. 7.

Message on Brotherhood Day stating need of churches to mobilize good will. 30 April 1934, p. 17, col. 6.

Praises P. H. Phenix, Princeton 1934, for senior thesis, "The absolute significance of rotation." 26 July 1934, p. 21, col. 7.

Speech at American Jewish physicians' meeting praising Hebrew University. 28 October 1934, p. 31, col. 2.

Tribute to Dr. W. de Sitter as an astronomer. 22 November 1934, p. 21, col. 1.

Tribute to Madame Curie. 24 January 1935, p. 21, col. 5.

Article quoted from *Daily Princetonian* approving student anti-war movement. 13 April 1935, p. 1, col. 5.

Interview with Henry Rosso, Princeton High School senior, originally printed in special issue of High School paper, *Tower.* 14 April 1935, sect. 2, p. 1, col. 6.

Speech on Maimonides at celebration of the 800*th* anniversary of his birth, Hotel Pennsylvania. 15 April 1935, p. 15, col. 5.

Speech on Palestine urging Jewish-Arab amity, at Passover celebration at the Manhattan Opera House. 21 April 1935, sec. 2, p. 4, col. 7.

The late Emmy Noether: Letter in appreciation. 4 May 1935, p. 12, col. 5-6.

Speech on perils which Judaism faces, to United Jewish Appeal meeting. 27 June 1935, p. 13, col. 5.

Speech at luncheon honoring Max Reinhardt. 29 June 1935, p. 16, col 1.

Message sent for unveiling of a cairn in honor of Simon Newcomb's centenary. 31 August 1935, p. 28, col. 6.

Address at meeting sponsored by American Christian Committee for German Refugees and the Emergency Committee in Aid of Polish Refugees from Nazism. 23 Ocober 1935, p. 22, col. 5.

Comments on extension of relativity theory by Prof. Page, and Dr. L. Silberstein's criticism of theory. 8 February 1936, p. 13, col. 8.

Address at dedication of Museum of Science and Industry. 12 February 1936, p. 1, col. 4.

Comment on ignoring of the ether in relativity theory. 1 March 1936, sect. 10, p. 6, col. 2.

Speech at Jewish Forum dinner, on Jews in Germany. 9 March 1936, p. 21, col. 2.

Letter refuting L. Silberstein's attack on relativity in the *Physical Review* (vol. 49, pp. 268-270). 7 March 1936, p. 10, col. 1.

On games, particularly chess. 28 March 1936, p. 17, col. 2.

Message read at dinner of National Labor Committee, opposing a legislative council for Palestine. 12 April 1936, p. 34, col. 2.

Letter on Hightstown, New Jersey, model farm community. 18 May 1936, p. 6, col. 2.

Message at the 18*th* anniversary of the Jewish Seminary, warning against the menace of materialism. 8 June 1936, p. 22, col. 2.

Address at the convocation of the University of the State of New York on economic struggle for survival. 16 October 1936, p. 11, col. 1.

Appreciative letter to Independent Order of B'rith Abraham for naming lodge after him. Urges cooperation in Jewish cause. 23 January 1937, p. 12, col. 3.

Message to National Labor Committe for Jewish Workers in Palestine. 29 March 1937, p. 6, col. 3.

Telegram to New York City mass meeting on Spanish Civil War, warning of the danger in Spanish loss of political freedom. 19 April 1937, p. 4, col. 5.

Message to Y.M.C.A. on world conditions, urges war on tyranny and preservation of truth. 11 October 1937, p. 19, col. 3.

Message to National Council for Jewish Women, urging Jewish unity. 28 January 1938, p. 22, col. 5.

Tribute at a special stage performance of Jewish stars. Praises work of United Palestine Appeal. 7 April 1938, p. 19, col. 4.

Speech on anti-semitism at a New York dinner of the National Labor Commission for Palestine. 18 April 1938, p. 15, col. 3.
> Published in *New Palestine*, vol. 28, issue of April 29, under the title "Our debt to Zionism."

Interview praising Dr. H. E. Ives' new proof of relativity theory. 27 April 1938, p. 25, col. 2.

Address at Swarthmore College commencement, criticizes barbarity abroad and aloofness here. 7 June 1938, p. 16, col. 1.

Letter put in New York World's Fair time capsule, describes fear and terror in the life of today, with hope for a better world. 16 September 1938, p. 22, col. 1.

Address at American Jewish Congress dedication of refugee home, urging aid for refugees. 30 October 1938, p. 19, col. 2.

Message to New York City Zionist meeting begs England to support Balfour declaration in Palestine. 3 November 1938, p. 16, col. 2.

Speech on presentation of A. Einstein medal to Dr. Thomas Mann. 29 January 1939, p. 23, col. 1.

Letter replying to Lincoln's Birthday Committee for democracy and intellectual freedom. 6 February 1939, p. 19, col. 4.

Letter replying to questionnaire on law linking all physical phenomena and on world science association. 14 March 1939, p. 1, col. 3.

Explanation of radio altimeter at visit to Newark airport. 23 March 1939, p. 25, col. 6.

Speech on cosmic rays on the occasion of the first illumination of the World's Fair when cosmic rays were demonstrated to 200,000 persons. 1 May 1939, p. 6, col. 5.

Speech by radio to Town Hall assembly of Jewish National Workers Alliance on importance of British friendship in Palestine. 28 May 1939, p. 13, col. 1.

Address at dedication of Palestine Pavilion at World's Fair. 29 May 1939, p. 7, col. 1.

In symposium of five Nobel Prize winners, "World Leaders on Peace and Democracy," at World's Fair, Einstein urges an international superior court. 2 July 1939, p. 13, col. 1.

Warning to World Student Association convention on spread of fascism. 17 August 1939, p. 15, col. 8.

Address to New Jersey Education Association on education in democracy. 11 November 1939, p. 34, col. 2.

Defense of Bertrand Russell's appointment as Professor of Philosophy at City College of New York. 19 March 1940, p. 22, col. 4.

At Testimonial dinner asks fund for Hebrew Institute of Technology in Haifa. 9 May 1940, p. 15, col. 2.

Telegram urging Roosevelt to aid allies, heads list of 17 members of Princeton University to sign it. 21 May 1940, p. 12, col. 5.

International broadcast, predicts armed League of Nations needed to preserve peace. 23 June 1940, p. 6, col. 2.

Message sent to United Palestine Appeal rally for war fund. 25 February 1941, p. 46, col. 2.

Speech at Hechalitz Organization dedication of Hightstown, New Jersey, farm. 16 June 1941, p. 9, col. 1.

Interview on change in his pacifist attiude. 30 December 1941, p. 9, col. 4.

Adddress at Russian war relief Jewish council dinner on USSR rôle in the peace. 26 October 1942, p. 17, col. 2.

"Einstein's theory of living", interview by D. Schwarz. 12 March 1944, sect. 6, p. 16, col. 38-39.

Tribute to war-time heroism of British public. 14 March 1944, p. 20, col. 3.

Statement sent to National Wartime Conference urging a union of thinkers. 29 May 1944, p. 17, col. 8.

Message sent to a meeting of American Fund for Palestinian Industry. 6 June 1944, p. 18, col. 2.

Statement repudiating biography of himself by Dr. Marianoff, former son-in-law, and P. Wayne as unreliable and un-authorized. 5 August 1944, p. 13, col. 6. German text in *Aufbau*, 1944, no. 32, p. 14.

Statement urging Roosevelt reelection, as important to securing lasting peace. 10 October 1944, p. 15, col. 3.

Statement on acceptance of honorary chairmanship of New York City Fund drive for Institute of Religion. 22 July 1945, p. 39, col. 1.

Explanation of solar and nuclear energy in interview. 12 August 1945, p. 29, col. 3.

On harnessing solar energy. (Quoted from a 1920 interview in the *Manchester Guardian*.) 14 August 1945, p. 18, col. 3.

Interview, asserts world government is prerequisite to lasting peace. 15 September 1945, p. 11, col. 6.

Letter thanking *New York Times* for articles of October 27, and recommending Emery Reves' book, *The anatomy of peace*. 1 November 1945, p. 22, col. 7.
     See item 402.

Address at the American Nobel Anniversary Commission dinner. Message on peace, transcribed. 11 December 1945, p. 15, col. 1.

Testifies against British policy in Palestine before Anglo-American Committee of Inquiry on Palestine. 12 January 1946, p. 7, col. 1.

Letter sent to meeting of Progressive Palestine Association, Washington, D.C., urging that UNO run Palestine. 15 February 1946, p. 2, col. 2.

Statement on civilization's capacity to survive atomic warfare. 24 February 1946, sect. 6, p. 42, col. 3.

Letter sent to Jewish Council for Russian Relief urging American Jews to continue relief shipments to USSR. 17 April 1946, p. 27, col. 4.

Address at Lincoln University upon receipt of doctorate. Sees future for Negro. 4 May 1946, p. 7, col. 4.

Message sent to National Council of Organization for Yeshiva University stating its importance to Jewish tradition. 6 May 1946, p. 6, col. 3.

Telegram asking prominent persons for funds for Atomic Scientists' Emergency Committee. 25 May 1946, p. 13, col. 5.

Radio speech to Students for Federal World Government at Chicago rally; on international peace and the need for United States-Soviet accord. 30 May 1946, p. 18, col. 5. (National radio broadcast on ABC.)

INTERVIEWS, LETTERS, SPEECHES 755

"The real problem is in the hearts of men," interview with M. Amrine. 23 June 1946, sec. 6, p. 7, col. 42-43. (See items 407 and 414.)

Statement on atomic bomb for *France-Soir*. 22 June 1946, p. 6, col. 8.

Statement on atomic bomb for *Sunday Express*, London. 19 August 1946, p. 1, col. 7.

Letter to Pres. Truman on lynching. [partially quoted] 23 September 1946, p. 16, col. 4.

Letter to Urban League for Service among Negroes. [partially quoted] 25 September 1946, p. 38, col. 2.

Nation-wide radio address opening the campaign for a million dollar educational fund for the Emergency Committee of Atomic Scientists. 18 November 1946, p. 25, col. 1

Einstein backs Lilienthal for Atomic Energy Commission [partially quoted] 22 February 1947, p. 4, col. 3-4.

Plea made in concert with the Federation of American Scientists for United Nations control of atomic energy. 16 July 1947, p. 2, col. 4. and 20 July 1947, sect. IV, p. 8, col. 4.

Conference with H. C. Usborne on world government. 29 September 1947, p. 7, col. 1.

Message on the occasion of the dedication of Riverside Drive Memorial to six million martyred Jews of Europe. 16 October 1947, p. 30, col. 4.

Message to United World Federalists, testifying to their support by the Emergency Committee of Atomic Scientists. 2 November 1947, p. 50, col. 3.

Message read at dinner of the American committee for the Weizmann Institute. 26 November 1947, p. 6, col. 4.

Commendation of Henry Wallace's *Toward World Peace* 30 March 1948, p. 25, col. 4.
This letter was also quoted on the dust jacket of the book.

Letter to the Editor. Palestine cooperation: appeal made to Jews to work for the goal of the common welfare. 18 April 1948, sect. IV, p. 8. col. 6.
Letter is signed jointly with Leo Baeck.

Speech read in Carnegie Hall at presentation of "One World Award," decrying U.S. rearmament. 28 April 1948, p. 2, col. 2.

Assails education today. 13 March 1949, sect. 1, p. 34, col. 1.
Forms part of an article assembled by William Laurence in honor of Einstein's seventieth birthday. Einstein's part is a quotation from the autobiographical chapter of the book *Albert Einstein: Philosopher-Scientist, ed.* by PAUL ARTHUR SCHILPP, Library of living philosophers, volume VII, Evanston, Ill.

Proposes international society of social studies to break the spell of nationalism. 11 August 1949, p. 8, col. 6.
Full text is included in a report to be submitted by Secretary-General Trygve Lie to the UN Committee for the establishment of a research laboratory.

ADDENDA TO THE WRITINGS OF ALBERT EINSTEIN

WRITINGS

1950

446. Out of My Later Years, New York, Philosophical Library.
A collection of articles and essays written since 1934.

447. Introduction to *Relativity - a Richer Truth,* by Philipp Frank, Beacon Press, Boston.

448. Generalized Theory of Gravitation.
Published as appendix II to *The Meaning of Relativity,* Princeton University Press, Princeton 1950.

449. Preface to *Explaining the Atom,* by Selig Hecht, Lindsay Drummond Ltd., London 1950.

Interviews, Letters, Speeches

Statement on occasion of receiving Honorary Degree from Hebrew University, 16 March, 1949, p. 29, col. 4.

Message of congratulations to Hebrew University on 25th Anniversary, 23 October, 1949.

Statement for Symposium, Morris R. Cohen Memorial Fund, City College of New York, 17 November, 1949.

Broadcast for United Jewish Appeal Conference in Atlantic City, 29 November, 1949.

Message for Manilal Gandhi, editor of *Indian Opinion*, Phoenix, Natal, So. Africa, on the occasion of Indian Independence, December, 1949.

Sixteen, including A. Einstein and T. Mann sign statement protesting censure of attorneys who defend minority and labor groups, 1 February, 1950, p. 19, col. 5.

Broadcast on Mrs. Eleanor Roosevelt's television program concerning the dangers of atomic warfare, etc., 13 February, 1950, p. 3, col. 2.

Message to the Southern Conference for the Fight Against Racial Discrimination, Atlanta University, 8 April, 1950.

Message for the 25th Anniversary of the Hebrew University of Jerusalem, May, 1950.

Einstein urges Jewry support cultural institutions to provide openings for youth, 11 May, 1950, p. 27, col. 4.

Statement in interview for documentary program on atomic energy, "Year of Decision" in UN radio series entitled "The Pursuit of Peace," June, 1950.

Einstein urges international control of A-bomb stock piles, 19 June, 1950, p. 10, col. 3.

Message to 42nd meeting of Societa Italiana par il Progresse de la Scienze in Lucca, Italy, published in issue 3-4, Vol. 1, 1950 of *Impact*, periodical of UNESCO, Paris.

Letter to Viscount Samuel, published in the latter's *Essay in Physics*, Basil Blackwell, Oxford, November, 1950.

Address (tape recording) to the convention of the International College of Surgeons on the occasion of being named an Honorary Fellow, Cleveland, Ohio, 3 November, 1950.

Article by Gertrude Samuels "Where Einstein Surveys the Cosmos," November, 1950, Sec. VI, p. 14.

Message for U.I.T. (University of Jerusalem, Weizmann-Institute Rechovoth and Technion, Haifa) Dinner, Waldorf-Astoria, New York, 30 November, 1950, p. 15, col. 2.

Statement to the Society for Social Responsibility in Science, 22 December, 1950, in *Science*, Vol. CXII, p. 160.

Dr. Einstein's secretary, Miss Helen Dukas, quotes briefly Einstein's comment on Gertrude Samuels' article, 24 December, 1950, Sec. VI, p. 2, col. 3.

Dr. Einstein holds UN can become world government only if Assembly representatives are elected directly by the people, 27 December, 1950, p. 2, col. 6.

Statment to Fyke Farmer on the necessity of world government, for the Geneva Convention, December, 1950.

Message for the 75th Anniversary of the Ethical Cultural Society, New York, 6 January, 1951, p. 16, col. 6.

Message of congratulations for the Israel Symphony Orchestra, January, 1951.

Message for 400th Anniversary of University of San Marcos on receiving honorary doctor's degree, Lima, Peru, May 1951.

Letter of recommendation for Meyer Levin's book, *In Search*, Horizon Publishers, New York, 1950.

CHRONOLOGICAL LIST OF PRINCIPAL WORKS

The figures in brackets after each title refer to the number in the Bibliography

1905—Über einen die Erzeugung und Verwandlung des Lichtes betreffenden heuristischen Gesichtspunkt. [7]

1905—Die von der molekularkinetischen Theorie der Wärme geforderte Bewegung von in ruhenden Flüssigkeiten suspendierten Teilchen. [8]

1905—Elektrodynamik bewegter Körper. [9]

1905—Ist die Trägheit eines Körpers von seinem Energieinhalt abhängig? [10]

1906—Zur Theorie der Brownschen Bewegung. [12]

1906—Theorie der Lichterzeugung und Lichtabsorption. [13]

1907—Plancksche Theorie der Strahlung und die Theorie der spezifischen Wärme. [16]

1907—Relativitätsprinzip und die aus demselben gezogenen Folgerungen. [21]

1910—Theorie der Opaleszenz von homogenen Flüssigkeiten und Flüssigkeitsgemischen in der Nähe des kritischen Zustandes. [33]

1911—Beziehung zwischen dem elastischen Verhalten und der spezifischen Wärme bei festen Körpern mit einatomigem Molekül. [38]

1911—Einfluss der Schwerkraft auf die Ausbreitung des Lichtes. [42]

1913—Entwurf einer verallgemeinerten Relativitätstheorie und eine Theorie der Gravitation. [53]

1915—Experimenteller Nachweis der Ampèreschen Molekularströme. [80]

1915—Erklärung der Perihelbewegung des Merkur aus der allgemeinen Relativitätstheorie. [84]

1916—Experimental proof of the existence of Ampère's molecular currents. [88]

1916—Grundlage der allgemeinen Relativitätstheorie. [89]

1916—Strahlungs-Emission und -Absorption nach der Quantentheorie. [92]

INDEX

Arranged by

SURINDAR SURI AND KENNETH G. HALVORSEN

ments of mathematics, 15; studies elements of natural sciences, 15; support of world government, 655; theory of knowledge, 131; three conceptions of religion, 660; turning point in his development, 7; universe, 481, 484, 490, 496; on the verifiability of the theorems of geometry, 676ff
Einstein's reply to: Niels Bohr, 666ff; Max Born, 665ff; P. W. Bridgman, 679; Herbert Dingle, 687; Kurt Gödel, 687f; Walter Heitler, 666ff; Leopold Infeld, 684, 686; Max von Laue, 686; Georges Lemaître, 684ff; Victor F. Lenzen, 683f; H. Margenau, 666ff, 679ff; Karl Menger, 686; E. A. Milne, 684; F. S. C. Northrop, 683f; Wolfgang Pauli, 665ff; Hans Reichenbach, 676ff; H. P. Robertson, 676ff
Einstein, His Life and Times (Philipp Frank), 281
Eisenhart, L. P., 321n
Élan vital, 604
Eleatics, 585
Eleatic world, 587
Electric(ity), charges, 377; (and) magnetism (Maxwell's theory), 518; masses, 25; resistance of the pure metallic conductors, 549
Electrodynamics, 517; classical theory of, 204; of Faraday and Maxwell, 25
Electromagnetic, energy inertia of, 521, 523; field, 378, 411, 518; momentum, 519; waves, 517
Electromagnetism, incorporation of optics into the theory of, 33
Electron, diffraction, 174, 188; deflection, 521; model (Abraham's), 522; recoil, 207, 216; unit of charge, 239; wave, 187f
Electrostatics, 383
Elementary light cone, 676
Elementary terms, 275
Elliptical universe, 482, 496
Ellis, C. D., 124
Elsasser, 174
Emergency Committee of Atomic Scientists, 651
Emission in a spherical wave, 154
Empirical, concepts, 13, 360; ethics, 649; knowledge, 359; meanings, 407
Empiricism, 565; logical—, 275
Empiricists, 678
Empty space, 338

Encyclopædia Brittanica, 317n
Encyclopedia of Unified Science, 276
Energeia, 592
Energy, 350; of cosmic rays, 451, 454; density, 75; inertia of, 521ff, 529; invariant, 434; kinetic, 510; law of, 510, 515; equivalence of mass and, 104, 225, 443; matter, 454; origin of, 510; potential, 514; principle of, 515f; radiation, 518; -time, 551; transfer, control of, 225; zero-level, 443
Enlightened rationalism, 573
Enquiry Into Meaning and Truth (B. Russell), 641n
Entropy, 43, 45, 105, 136, 153, 166, 168, 171, 350, 376, 527n, 545, 551, 688; net loss of, 547
Eötvös, Roland, 65, 100, 118
Epistemological, mystery, 358; question, 99; analysis of theoretical physics, 358
Epistemology, 135, 137, 357, 387, 583; of atomic physics, 157, 231, 235, 237; of classical physics, 267; and laws of physics, 413; and Lorentz formulae, 416; positivistic critique of Einstein's, 667; and quantum mechanics, 223, 267; and science, 683f
Epoch, 429ff; of creation, 434
Equal length, 294
Equations, field, 37, 100, 145
Equilibrium, 447; state of matter going through, 448ff; statistical, 445, 454
Equivalence, collinear observers form, 417; description of, 295; fundamental particles of, 419; mass and energy, 585; observers and, 433
Erkenntnistheorie, 359
Essay on the Psychology of Invention in the Mathematical Field, An (S. Hadamard), 279, 280n
Eternal objects, 642
Ether, 25, 111, 139, 538, 585, 589
Ethics, and classical mechanics, 196; relative, 99
Ethics (Spinoza) 471
Euclid(ean), 332, 391, 459, 461, 467, 472, 474; analytic geometry, geodesics, 439; concept of an extensionless point, 644; geometry, 251, 328, 369, 573, 633, 677f; manifold, 548; plane, 320; reference system, 67; space, 101, 118, 322, 414, 422, 433, 439, 464, 471, 477, 594
Euler, Leonhard, 19, 460, 508, 511
Event, 340n, 341, 344, 632